Theory of ORDINARY DIFFERENTIAL EQUATIONS

The Appleton-Century Mathematics Series

Raymond W. Brink and John M. H. Olmsted, *Editors*

A First Year of College Mathematics, 2nd ed., by Raymond W. Brink
Algebra—College Course, 2nd ed., by Raymond W. Brink
Analytic Geometry, rev. ed., by Raymond W. Brink
College Algebra, 2nd ed., by Raymond W. Brink
Plane Trigonometry, 3rd ed., by Raymond W. Brink
Spherical Trigonometry by Raymond W. Brink
An Introduction to Matrices, Vectors, and Linear Programming by Hugh G. Campbell
Matrices With Applications by Hugh G. Campbell
Modern Basic Mathematics by Hobart C. Carter
Elementary Concepts of Modern Mathematics by Flora Dinkines
Parts also available individually under the following titles:
Part I, *Elementary Theory of Sets*
Part II, *Introduction to Mathematical Logic*
Part III, *Abstract Mathematical Systems*
Introduction to the Laplace Transform by Dio L. Holl, Clair G. Maple, and Bernard Vinograde
Introductory Analysis by V. O. McBrien
College Geometry by Leslie H. Miller
A Second Course in Calculus by John M. H. Olmsted
Advanced Calculus by John M. H. Olmsted
Basic Concepts of Calculus by John M. H. Olmsted
Calculus with Analytic Geometry (2 volumes) by John M. H. Olmsted
Intermediate Analysis by John M. H. Olmsted
Prelude to Calculus and Linear Algebra by John M. H. Olmsted
Real Variables by John M. H. Olmsted
Solid Analytic Geometry by John M. H. Olmsted
The Real Number System by John M. H. Olmsted
Analytic Geometry by Edwin J. Purcell
Calculus with Analytic Geometry by Edwin J. Purcell
Analytic Geometry and Calculus by Lloyd L. Smail
Calculus by Lloyd L. Smail
The Mathematics of Finance by Franklin C. Smith

RANDAL H. COLE
The University of Western Ontario

Theory of ORDINARY DIFFERENTIAL EQUATIONS

New York

APPLETON-CENTURY-CROFTS
Division of Meredith Corporation

668–1

Library of Congress Card Number: 68–13433
PRINTED IN THE UNITED STATES OF AMERICA

E 20235

TO

SABINA

Preface

This book is designed to serve as a text for an advanced undergraduate or a first- or second-year graduate course. It is assumed that the reader has a certain amount of mathematical maturity and that he has had a course in linear algebra and one in advanced calculus or elementary analysis. No preliminary course in differential equations is assumed, but some previous practice in manipulating and solving elementary differential equations is desirable. No attempt has been made to include all the significant topics in the field. However, those which have been included are thought to form a natural sequence and to make a contribution to a general education in mathematics.

The traditional elementary courses in differential equations have been criticized for their lack of mathematical content. Because of this deficiency, some recently proposed programs in mathematics make no provision for a course in differential equations. The criticism may be justified, but the omission is unfortunate. The contributions of differential equations to the development of mathematics have earned a place for this subject in any mathematics program. Moreover, some of the topics of differential equations provide a natural bond between algebra and analysis. A notable example of this is the theory of eigenfunction expansions, of which the theory of Fourier series forms a special instance. By approaching expansion theory through spectral analysis, the results are seen as a generalization of spectral theory for a finite dimensional vector space.

A course designed on the material of this book provides a good foundation for advanced work in classical and functional analysis. The subject matter of the book is differential equations, but the point of view and the vocabulary serve to introduce the student to basic concepts in analysis. For example, a natural introduction to the concept of a function space is provided by specifying the domains of the various operators that are defined. Also, the discussion at the end of the chapter on the self-adjoint eigenvalue problem introduces the concept of the Lebesgue integral. It is not assumed that the reader is familiar with this integral, but the reasons for its introduction are clearly set forth. At the same time the fundamental properties of a Hilbert space are introduced. Finally, the method of treating the eigenvalue problem prepares the way for a course on linear operator theory. The latter topic occupies a prominent position in many graduate programs. In the preface to his book *Spectral Theory* E. R. Lorch (*see reference 34 of Bibliography beginning on page 266*) conjectures that "the theory of linear operators will be in the future the central trunk around which the fundamental graduate course in analysis will be built."

Some of the special features of the book are listed below:

(1) The introductory material contains a proof of the fixed point theorem for a contraction mapping on a complete metric space. The basic existence and uniqueness theorem follows easily from the fixed point theorem.

(2) Results for an *n*th-order equation and for a first-order system of *n* equations are developed in parallel throughout the book. In many cases, an economy of effort is achieved by inferring the results for an *n*th-order equation from those for a system.

(3) A thorough treatment of the two-point boundary problem is given. This includes the derivation of Green's function and of the adjoint boundary problem. A parametric representation of boundary conditions is introduced and used to advantage in the discussion of the properties of Green's function.

(4) The expansion theory associated with a self-adjoint boundary problem is developed through the spectral analysis of the corresponding integral operator. The concepts of inner product, orthogonality, and projection operators are introduced as natural generalizations of the corresponding concepts for a finite-dimensional vector space.

(5) The expansion theory for the non-self-adjoint boundary problem is treated by classical methods. This treatment stands in sharp contrast to the spectral analysis approach used for the self-adjoint problem. However, it serves to round out the discussion and has the added virtue of providing some applications of the tools of classical analysis.

It is a pleasure to acknowledge my indebtedness to Professor R. E. Langer for a stimulating introduction to the theory of differential equations. I wish to thank Professor R. W. Brink for many helpful suggestions during the preparation of the manuscript. Miss Carolyn Hill contributed skillful and painstaking effort in typing and retyping the manuscript. Finally, I am grateful to the many students who have been subjected to preliminary versions of the material in this book. Their comments and reactions have influenced both the content and the manner of its presentation.

London, Canada R. H. C.

Contents

4 LINEAR EQUATIONS WITH CONSTANT COEFFICIENTS

5 SERIES SOLUTIONS

6 THE TWO-POINT BOUNDARY PROBLEM

7 INTRODUCTION TO EIGENVALUE PROBLEMS AND EXPANSION THEORY

8 SELF-ADJOINT EIGENVALUE PROBLEMS

9 STURMIAN THEORY

10 NON-SELF-ADJOINT EIGENVALUE PROBLEMS

Theory of ORDINARY DIFFERENTIAL EQUATIONS

1

Preliminary Concepts

1-1. FUNCTIONS

Functions are fundamental to the study of differential equations. It is appropriate, therefore, to begin our discussion with a definition of this basic concept. Let X and Y be any two nonempty sets. The *Cartesian product of X and Y*, denoted by $X \times Y$, is the set of all ordered pairs (x, y), where x is any element of X and y is any element of Y. A subset f of this Cartesian product is called a *function* with *domain X* provided that each element x of X occurs in one and only one member of f. This definition does not require that each element of Y occur in some ordered pair of f. The set of elements of Y which do occur in at least one ordered pair is called the *range of f*. If (x, y) is an element of f, then y is called the *functional value at x* and may be represented by the symbol $f(x)$. Thus, for a specific x, (x, y) and $(x, f(x))$ designate the same ordered pair.

It should be noted that the sets X and Y are not restricted to sets of numbers. If they were so restricted, the above definition would specify the same mathematical entity that is familiar to any student of elementary calculus. The definition of a function as a "set" is preferred here to definitions given in many calculus texts. Some texts define a function as a "rule," or a "correspondence," while others merely specify the meaning of the statement "y is a function of x."

A function is usually represented by a single symbol such as f, g, or x. This notation is particularly appropriate for the development of an algebra of functions. However, from time to time we use functional value symbols, $f(t)$, $g(t, s)$, or $x(t)$, to represent functions. Besides being a concession to custom, this latter notation provides a convenient manner of indicating the independent variable (or variables). The fundamental differential equation

$$y' = f(t, y)$$

is an example of a mixed usage of notations. This equation poses the problem of finding a function y on some interval I such that

$$y'(t) = f(t, y(t))$$

for each t in I. Since it is usually clear from the context whether the symbol represents a function or a functional value, there is little danger of confusion.

1-2. VECTOR SPACES

It is assumed that the reader has had an introductory course in linear algebra, including the algebra of matrices. Nevertheless, it is convenient to outline certain salient features of this subject and to establish certain notational conventions.

Let S be a set with elements $a, b, \ldots$. Let F be a field with elements α, $\beta, \ldots$, called *scalars*. Let an *operation of addition* be defined for S such that if a and b are any two elements of S then their sum $a+b$ must be an element of S. Also, if a is any element of S and α is any element of F, then a *scalar product* is defined and represented by αa.

Definition 1-2.1. *The set S is called a* **vector space** *over the field F, if the operations of addition and scalar multiplication satisfy the following postulates.*

(i) *For every a and b in S*

$$a+b = b+a \ .$$

(ii) *For every a, b, and c in S*

$$(a+b)+c = a+(b+c) \ .$$

(iii) *For every a in S there is a unique element* 0 *in S such that*

$$a+0 = a \ .$$

(iv) *For every a in S there is a unique inverse, represented by* $-a$, *such that*

$$a+(-a) = 0 \ .$$

(v) *For any a in S and any two scalars* α *and* β,

$$\alpha(\beta a) = (\alpha\beta)a \ .$$

(vi) *If* 1 *is the unit element of F, then*

$$1a = a \ .$$

(vii) *If a and b are any two elements in S and* α *and* β *are any two scalars, then*

(a) $$(\alpha+\beta)a = \alpha a+\beta a \ ,$$

(b) $$\alpha(a+b) = \alpha a+\alpha b \ .$$

Example 1. Let S consist of n-tuples of elements in F written as one-row (or one-column) matrices with addition and scalar multiplication defined in the familiar manner. This example, with the field F being the real or complex numbers, is extensively treated in most introductions to linear algebra. The symbol $V_n(F)$ represents this space and the elements are referred to as n-vectors, row (or column) vectors, or simply as vectors when from the context confusion is not possible.

Example 2. A generalization of the previous example may be achieved by letting S consist of all m by n matrices with components in F. Again the standard definitions of addition and scalar multiplication are used.

Example 3. Let S consist of all continuous real-valued functions on the interval $[0, 1]$ and be represented by $C[0, 1]$. If f and g are any two elements of $C[0, 1]$, then their sum $f+g$ is the function whose functional value at t is given by $f(t)+g(t)$. The scalar product αf, f an element in $C[0, 1]$ and α any scalar, is the function whose functional value at t is $\alpha f(t)$. It is easily verified that this system is a vector space.

Many subsets of this space are themselves vector spaces and, hence, can be referred to as *subspaces*. One example is the set $C^n[0, 1]$ of all functions on $[0, 1]$ with n continuous derivatives. Another subspace of $C[0, 1]$ consists of all functions which have a functional value of zero at a specified point a in $[0, 1]$ or

$$\{f : f \in C[0, 1], f(a) = 0\} .$$

A third subspace is defined by

$$\{f : f \in C[0, 1], \sum_{h=1}^{m} \alpha_h f(a_h) = 0\} ,$$

where $a_1, a_2, \ldots, a_m$ is any finite set of points in $[0, 1]$, and $\alpha_1, \alpha_2, \ldots, \alpha_m$ is a set of scalars. A fourth subspace is defined by

$$\{f : f \in C[0, 1], \int_0^1 k(t) f(t)\, dt = 0\} ,$$

where $k(t)$ is any bounded integrable function on $[0, 1]$. The verification that all these subspaces are in fact vector spaces is left to the reader.

Example 4. It was pointed out in Example 1 that the set of all n-tuples of field elements is a vector space. A generalization of this space can be achieved by considering, for the set S, the set of all n-vectors of functions which are themselves members of a vector space V. Thus, let V be a set of functions which form a vector space over the field R of real numbers. Let S consist of elements $\mathbf{u}, \mathbf{v}, \ldots$, where

$$\mathbf{u} = \begin{pmatrix} u_1 \\ u_2 \\ \cdot \\ \cdot \\ \cdot \\ u_n \end{pmatrix}, \quad \mathbf{v} = \begin{pmatrix} v_1 \\ v_2 \\ \cdot \\ \cdot \\ \cdot \\ v_n \end{pmatrix}, \ldots$$

and u_i and v_i, $i = 1, 2, \ldots, n$, are elements of V.
Addition is defined by

$$\mathbf{u}+\mathbf{v} = \begin{pmatrix} u_1+v_1 \\ u_2+v_2 \\ \cdot \\ \cdot \\ \cdot \\ u_n+v_n \end{pmatrix},$$

and scalar multiplication by

$$\alpha\mathbf{u} = \begin{pmatrix} \alpha u_1 \\ \alpha u_2 \\ \cdot \\ \cdot \\ \cdot \\ \alpha u_n \end{pmatrix} .$$

The identity element $\mathbf{o}$ of S is the n-vector, each of whose components is the zero function. It is easily verified that this space inherits its vector space properties from the original space V. This space and its counterpart, the space obtained by replacing R by the field of complex numbers, are of prime importance for later developments in this text.

1-3. NOTATION

Matrix algebra is used extensively. Matrices are generally represented by boldface capital letters, and their components are represented by the corresponding lower-case italic letters, for example,

$$\mathbf{A} = \begin{pmatrix} a_{11} & a_{12} & \cdots & a_{1n} \\ a_{21} & a_{22} & \cdots & a_{2n} \\ \cdot & \cdot & \cdot & \cdot \\ \cdot & \cdot & \cdot & \cdot \\ \cdot & \cdot & \cdot & \cdot \\ a_{m1} & a_{m2} & \cdots & a_{mn} \end{pmatrix} .$$

From the context it should be clear whether the components of a matrix are functions or scalars. To eliminate confusion, as indicated in Section 1-1, the matrix can be represented by $\mathbf{A}(t)$ and its general component by $a_{ij}(t)$, where the components are functions of a variable t.

Matrices of one column are represented by lower-case boldface letters and are called column vectors. The transpose of a matrix $\mathbf{A}$ is represented by $\tilde{\mathbf{A}}$. Hence, a row vector can be represented as the transpose of a column vector. Both row and column vectors will be called n-vectors or simply vectors, if their nature is clear from the context.

The zero matrix is represented by $\mathbf{0}$, the zero vector by $\mathbf{o}$, and the multiplicative identity matrix by $\mathbf{I}$. For the latter we have

$$\mathbf{I} = (\delta_{ij}) ,$$

where δ_{ij} is Kronecker's delta, defined by $\delta_{ij} = 1$ if $i = j$ and $\delta_{ij} = 0$ if $i \neq j$. It is convenient to define the vectors $\mathbf{d}_1, \mathbf{d}_2, \ldots, \mathbf{d}_n$ as

$$\mathbf{d}_1 = \begin{pmatrix} 1 \\ 0 \\ \cdot \\ \cdot \\ \cdot \\ 0 \end{pmatrix}, \quad \mathbf{d}_2 = \begin{pmatrix} 0 \\ 1 \\ \cdot \\ \cdot \\ \cdot \\ 0 \end{pmatrix}, \quad \ldots, \quad \mathbf{d}_n = \begin{pmatrix} 0 \\ 0 \\ \cdot \\ \cdot \\ \cdot \\ 1 \end{pmatrix}.$$

The derivative of a matrix $\mathbf{A}$ is the matrix obtained by differentiating each component of $\mathbf{A}$, that is, $\mathbf{A}' = (a_{ij}')$. Higher derivatives are indicated by bracketed superscripts, for example, the kth derivative of $\mathbf{A}$ is

$$\mathbf{A}^{[k]} = (a_{ij}^{[k]}) .$$

When $k = 2$ or 3, we may sometimes use $\mathbf{A}''$ and $\mathbf{A}'''$ instead of $\mathbf{A}^{[2]}$ and $\mathbf{A}^{[3]}$.

If u is any function with $n-1$ derivatives, the vector

$$\mathbf{k}(u) = \begin{pmatrix} u \\ u' \\ \cdot \\ \cdot \\ \cdot \\ u^{[n-1]} \end{pmatrix},$$

is called the *Wronskian vector* of u. If $u_1, u_2, \ldots, u_n$ is any set of n functions with $n-1$ derivatives, and $\mathbf{u}$ is the vector with these functions as components, then the matrix

$$\mathbf{K}(\mathbf{u}) = \begin{pmatrix} u_1 & u_2 & \cdots & u_n \\ u_1' & u_2' & \cdots & u_n' \\ \cdot & \cdot & \cdot & \cdot \\ \cdot & \cdot & \cdot & \cdot \\ \cdot & \cdot & \cdot & \cdot \\ u_1^{[n-1]} & u_2^{[n-1]} & \cdots & u_n^{[n-1]} \end{pmatrix},$$

is called the *Wronskian matrix* of $\mathbf{u}$ (or of the components of $\mathbf{u}$). Clearly, the jth column of the Wronskian matrix $\mathbf{K}(\mathbf{u})$ is the Wronskian vector of u_j so that $\mathbf{K}(\mathbf{u}) = (\mathbf{k}(u_1), \mathbf{k}(u_2) \ldots \mathbf{k}(u_n))$.

If the components of a matrix $\mathbf{A}$ are integrable functions on an interval $[a, b]$, the integral of the matrix is defined by

$$\int_a^b \mathbf{A}(t)\, dt = \left(\int_a^b a_{ij}(t)\, dt \right) .$$

1-4. LINEAR DEPENDENCE

The concepts of linear dependence and linear independence are basic to the consideration of any linear space. A set of n elements $u_1, u_2, \ldots, u_n$ in a vector space S is *linearly dependent* if a set of scalars $\alpha_1, \alpha_2, \ldots, \alpha_n$, not all zero, exists such that

$$\alpha_1 u_1 + \alpha_2 u_2 + \cdots + \alpha_n u_n = 0 \ .$$

It should be noted that the right-hand member is the zero element of the vector space. A set of elements which is not linearly dependent is *linearly independent*. It follows that if the set $u_1, u_2, \ldots, u_n$ is linearly independent and if

$$\alpha_1 u_1 + \alpha_2 u_2 + \cdots + \alpha_n u_n = 0 \ ,$$

then each of the scalar coefficients must be zero.

Since n-tuples of functions appear frequently, the following observation is pertinent. Let $\mathbf{u}$, $\mathbf{v}$, and $\mathbf{w}$ be n-vectors with components in $C[0, 1]$. If this set of vectors is linearly dependent, then

$$\alpha\mathbf{u} + \beta\mathbf{v} + \gamma\mathbf{w} = \mathbf{o}$$

for some set of three scalars α, β, and γ, not all zero. For any value of the variable t in [0, 1] it must follow that

$$\alpha\mathbf{u}(t) + \beta\mathbf{v}(t) + \gamma\mathbf{w}(t) = \mathbf{o} \ .$$

That is to say, the set of vectors of functional values is linearly dependent. The converse is not true since the set $\mathbf{u}(t)$, $\mathbf{v}(t)$, $\mathbf{w}(t)$ may be linearly dependent at each point t whereas the set $\mathbf{u}$, $\mathbf{v}$, $\mathbf{w}$ could be in fact linearly independent. A simple example is

$$\mathbf{u}(t) = \begin{pmatrix} 1 \\ 1 \end{pmatrix}, \quad \mathbf{v}(t) = \begin{pmatrix} t \\ 1 \end{pmatrix}, \quad \mathbf{w}(t) = \begin{pmatrix} t^2 \\ 1 \end{pmatrix} .$$

When the components are interpreted as functions on [0, 1], this set of vectors is obviously linearly independent. However, for any specified value of t, these vectors are column vectors of dimension 2 and must be linearly dependent because there are three of them.

The definition of linear independence has been made for a finite set. To extend this definition to an infinite set U, we define the set to be linearly independent if every finite subset of U is linearly independent.

It is convenient to follow common practice and to speak of "a set of linearly independent vectors" when according to the definition we should say "a linearly independent set of vectors."

If a vector x in a vector space S can be expressed as

$$x = \sum_{i=1}^{n} \alpha_i x_i \ ,$$

where $\{x_i\}$ is a set of n elements of S then we say that x is a *linear combination* of the elements of $\{x_i\}$. It can easily be verified that all the elements x which can be expressed as a linear combination of $\{x_i\}$ form a subspace of S. This subspace is the subspace *spanned* by $\{x_i\}$. If X is a set of linearly independent elements which span S, we say X is a *basis* for S. A vector space can have many different bases, but each of them has the same number of elements. This number is the *dimension* of the space.

1-5. LINEAR TRANSFORMATIONS

Let S and T be any two vector spaces over a common field F, and let A be a function mapping S into T. If x is any element in S, it is customary in the case under discussion to represent the functional value at x by Ax instead of $A(x)$. The function is a *linear transformation* if for any two elements x_1 and x_2 in S and any two scalars α_1 and α_2 in F

$$A(\alpha_1 x_1 + \alpha_2 x_2) = \alpha_1 A x_1 + \alpha_2 A x_2 \ .$$

Example 1. Let $\mathbf{A}$ be an m by n matrix of real numbers. The relation

(1-5.1) $$\mathbf{y} = \mathbf{A}\mathbf{x} \ ,$$

where $\mathbf{x}$ is any n-vector in $V_n(R)$, defines $\mathbf{y}$ as an m-vector in $V_m(R)$. The relation therefore maps $V_n(R)$ into $V_m(R)$. The properties of matrix multiplication insure that the function is a linear transformation. If $m = n$ and if $\mathbf{A}$ is nonsingular then the transformation maps $V_n(R)$ onto $V_n(R)$ and the inverse transformation exists.

The *composition* of linear transformations is also facilitated by the properties of matrix multiplication. Let $\mathbf{B}$ be an n by k matrix, and let the relation

(1-5.2) $$\mathbf{x} = \mathbf{B}\mathbf{v}$$

map the k-vector $\mathbf{v}$ in $V_k(R)$ into $V_n(R)$. Then the relation

$$\mathbf{y} = \mathbf{C}\mathbf{v} \ ,$$

where $\mathbf{C} = \mathbf{AB}$, is a linear transformation mapping $V_k(R)$ into $V_m(R)$. This transformation is clearly equivalent to the successive application of the transformations defined by (1-5.2) and (1-5.1).

Example 2. Let f be a function in $C[0, 1]$. The relation

$$g(t) = \int_0^t f(s)\, ds$$

maps $C[0, 1]$ into $C[0, 1]$. Since

$$\int_0^t (\alpha_1 f_1(s) + \alpha_2 f_2(s))\, ds = \alpha_1 \int_0^t f_1(s)\, ds + \alpha_2 \int_0^t f_2(s)\, ds \ ,$$

the transformation is obviously linear.

Example 3. If $u \in C^2[0, 1]$, consider the transformation $v = Lu$, where $p_1, p_2 \in C[0, 1]$ and

$$Lu = u'' + p_1 u' + p_2 u \ .$$

Because of the linear properties of differentiation, Lu is readily seen to be a linear transformation of $C^2[0, 1]$ into $C[0, 1]$.

Example 4. Let **y** be an n-vector with components in $C^1[0, 1]$, and let **A** be an n by n matrix with components in $C[0, 1]$. The relation

$$\mathbf{v} = \mathbf{y}' - \mathbf{A}\mathbf{y}$$

defines a linear transformation that may be represented by $\mathbf{v} = M\mathbf{y}$.

1-6. LINEAR FUNCTIONALS

If in the definition of a linear transformation the image space T is restricted to be the scalar space F, then the transformation is called a *linear functional.* For example, if

$$\mathbf{v} = \begin{pmatrix} v_1 \\ v_2 \\ \cdot \\ \cdot \\ \cdot \\ v_n \end{pmatrix}$$

is a variable in $V_n(R)$, then it is clear that

$$y = \sum_{i=1}^{n} \alpha_i v_i$$

is a linear functional. It can be shown that every linear functional on $V_n(R)$ can be represented in this form. Since the set α_i of coefficients are definitive for the functional, it is readily appreciated that the set of all linear functionals forms a vector space when the natural definitions for addition and scalar multiplication are made.

In general, if S is any vector space, the set of all linear functionals (when addition and scalar multiplication are appropriately defined) is a vector space and is called the *dual space* associated with S.[1]

Exercises

1. Prove that any linear functional $y = f(\mathbf{x})$ on $V_n(R)$ can be expressed in the form

$$y = \sum_{i=1}^{n} \alpha_i x_i \ .$$

2. Prove that the set of all linear functionals on a given vector space V (with the natural definition of addition and scalar multiplication for linear functionals) is a vector space.

3. Prove that the space of linear functionals on $V_n(R)$ has dimension n.

4. Let **v** be a specific point in $V_n(R)$, and let S be the set of all linear functionals which map **v** into zero. Show that S is a vector space.

---

[1] Halmos [21], Section 31.

1-7. NORMS FOR VECTOR SPACES

It is possible to extend the geometric notions of angle and length associated with either $V_2(R)$ or $V_3(R)$ to higher dimensional spaces by using the concept of the inner product. It is also convenient, however, to define distance functions other than the one associated with the inner product. For this reason, the general definitions of a *norm* and a *metric* (or distance function) are given before introducing the special inner product norm.

Definition 1-7.1. *A* ***norm*** *for a vector space S (over the real or complex number field) is a real-valued function whose functional value at any point x in S is represented by* $\| x \|$. *It has the following properties for any x, y in S and any scalar* α*:*

$$\text{(i)} \quad \| x \| \geqq 0 \, , \quad \text{and } \| x \| = 0 \textit{ if and only if } x = 0 \, .$$

$$(1\text{-}7.1) \qquad \text{(ii)} \quad \| \alpha x \| = | \alpha | \, \| x \| \, .$$

$$\text{(iii)} \quad \| x + y \| \leqq \| x \| + \| y \| \, .$$

Example 1. If $\mathbf{v} \in V_n(R)$ (or $V_n(C)$), then it is a familiar fact that

$$\| \mathbf{v} \| = \left\{ \sum_{i=1}^{n} | v_i |^2 \right\}^{1/2}$$

is a suitable norm for the space. An equally suitable norm is

$$\| \mathbf{v} \| = \sum_{i=1}^{n} | v_i | \, .$$

A third possibility for the same space is

$$\| \mathbf{v} \| = \max_i | v_i | \, .$$

Example 2. If $x \in C[0, 1]$, we may define $\| x \|$ by

$$\| x \| = \left\{ \int_0^1 | x^2(t) | \, dt \right\}^{1/2} .$$

A distinctly different, but equally suitable, definition of a norm for this space is

$$\| x \| = \max_{t \in [0, 1]} | x(t) | \, .$$

A modification of the preceding norm is

$$\| x \| = \sup_{t \in [0, 1]} | x(t) | \, .$$

For the space under consideration the last two norms are equivalent. The latter one, however, is more general than the former and is a natural norm to use for a space of bounded functions.

When a norm has been defined for a space, it is natural to introduce a *metric* or a measure of the distance between any two elements of the space. This is done in the following definition.

Definition 1-7.2. *A metric (or distance function) ρ for a normed vector space S is given by*

$$\rho(x, y) = \| x - y \| ,$$

where x and y are any two elements of S.

The distance function, defined above, has the following properties, where x, y, and z are any three elements of S:

$$\text{(1-7.2)}\qquad \begin{aligned} &\text{(i)}\quad \rho(x, y) \geqq 0 \ , \text{ and } \rho(x, y) = 0 \text{ if and only if } x = y \ . \\ &\text{(ii)}\quad \rho(x, y) = \rho(y, x) \ . \\ &\text{(iii)}\quad \rho(x, y) \leqq \rho(x, z) + \rho(z, y) \ . \end{aligned}$$

Each of these properties follows readily from the corresponding properties of a norm. For example, to establish property (ii), we have

$$\begin{aligned} \rho(x, y) &= \| x - y \| \\ &= \| (-1)(y - x) \| \\ &= | -1 | \, \| y - x \| \\ &= \rho(y, x) \ . \end{aligned}$$

Property (iii), which is known as the *triangle inequality*, is obtained from the third property of relations (1-7.1) by replacing x by $x - z$ and y by $z - y$.

The distance function is designed so that whenever $\rho(x, y)$ is small, the two vectors x and y are in some sense close to each other. It, therefore, plays a fundamental role in the definitions of continuity and convergence.

Exercises

1. Show that each of the norms given in the examples has the properties listed in relations (1-7.1).

2. If S is a normed vector space and x, y, and z are any three vectors in S, show that

(a) $\| x - y \| \geqq | \, \| x \| - \| y \| \, |$;

(b) $\rho(x, y) \geqq | \rho(x, z) - \rho(z, y) |$.

1-8. INNER PRODUCT

An *inner product*, associated with a vector space S over the real field R, is a real-valued function of the ordered pair of vectors x and y. The functional value at the pair x, y is represented by (x, y) and is such that:

$$\text{(i)}\quad (x,y) = (y,x)\ .$$

$$\text{(1-8.1)}\qquad \text{(ii)}\quad (\alpha_1 x_1+\alpha_2 x_2, y) = \alpha_1(x_1, y)+\alpha_2(x_2, y)\ .$$

$$\text{(iii)}\quad (x,x) \geqq 0 \quad \text{and} \quad (x,x) = 0 \text{ if and only if } x = 0\ .$$

A vector space for which an inner product has been defined is called an *inner product space.*

If the scalar field is the complex instead of the real field, the inner product is a complex-valued function and property (i) in relations (1-8.1) is replaced by

$$\text{(i)}\quad (x,y) = \overline{(y,x)}\ ,$$

where $\overline{(y, x)}$ is the complex conjugate of (y, x).

Example 1. The most familiar example of an inner product space is $V_n(R)$ with the inner product defined by

$$(\mathbf{u}, \mathbf{v}) = \sum_{i=1}^{n} u_i v_i\ .$$

In view of the definitions of matrix multiplication and of the transpose of a matrix, the above relation can be expressed as

$$(\mathbf{u}, \mathbf{v}) = \tilde{\mathbf{v}}\mathbf{u}\ .$$

It is a routine matter to check that this function has the three properties required for an inner product.

For the space $V_n(C)$ the definition of an inner product function is given by

$$\begin{aligned}(\mathbf{u}, \mathbf{v}) &= \tilde{\bar{\mathbf{v}}}\mathbf{u} \\ &= \sum_{i=1}^{n} u_i\bar{v}_i\ .\end{aligned}$$

Example 2. If x and y are members of the space $C[0, 1]$ we may define their inner product by

$$(x,y) = \int_0^1 x(t)y(t)\,dt\ .$$

If the functions are assumed to be complex-valued instead of real-valued, the definition is modified by replacing $y(t)$ in the integrand by its complex conjugate $\bar{y}(t)$.

Whenever an inner product is defined for a vector space, the space can easily be made a normed space by means of the definition

$$\| x \| = \{(x,x)\}^{1/2}\ .$$

When a norm is so defined, it is easily verified that $\| x \| \geqq 0$, $\| x \| = 0$ if and only if $x = 0$, and $\| \alpha x \| = |\alpha|\ \| x \|$. The triangle inequality for this norm is established in Section 1-9 after the derivation of the Schwarz inequality.

1-9. ORTHOGONALITY

The vectors of $V_3(R)$ can be interpreted as directed line segments, and when this is done the inner product of **u** and **v** is

$$(\mathbf{u}, \mathbf{v}) = \| \mathbf{u} \| \; \| \mathbf{v} \| \cos\theta \ ,$$

where θ is the angle between the two segments. In particular the two segments are orthogonal to each other if $(\mathbf{u}, \mathbf{v}) = 0$. In general, then, we can make the following definition.

Definition 1-9.1. *Any two vectors in an inner product space are said to be* ***orthogonal*** *to each other if their inner product is zero. A set of vectors is called an* ***orthonormal*** *set, if each member of the set has unit norm and is orthogonal to every other member of the set. Two subspaces are said to be* ***orthogonal to each other*** *if every vector in each is orthogonal to every vector in the other. An orthonormal set is said to be* ***complete*** *if it is not contained in any larger orthonormal set.*

Any orthonormal set is a linearly independent set. If $\{x_1, x_2, \ldots, x_n\}$ is an orthonormal set, let $\{\alpha_i\}$ be a set of scalars such that

$$\alpha_1 x_1 + \alpha_2 x_2 + \cdots + \alpha_n x_n = 0 \ .$$

By taking the inner product of each side of this relation with x_j, we get

$$\alpha_j = 0 \ , \quad j = 1, 2, \ldots, n \ .$$

Hence, $\{x_1, x_2, \ldots, x_n\}$ is a linearly independent set.

It follows that a vector space of dimension n cannot contain an orthonormal set of more than n vectors. Conversely, application of the *Gram-Schmidt orthogonalization process*[2] to any set of n linearly independent vectors produces an orthonormal set of n vectors. This implies that every n-dimensional inner product space contains a complete orthonormal set of n vectors, this set is called an *orthonormal basis.*

Inner product spaces have notable properties, some of which are outlined now. We first note that if $\{x_1, x_2, \ldots, x_n\}$ is a complete orthonormal set for the vector space S, it is a basis for S. This implies that any x in S can be uniquely expressed as

$$x = \sum_{i=1}^{n} \alpha_i x_i \ .$$

Taking the inner product of both sides of this relation with x_j, we infer that

$$\alpha_j = (x, x_j) \ , \quad j = 1, 2, \ldots, n \ .$$

Hence

$$x = \sum_{i=1}^{n} (x, x_i) x_i \ .$$

[2] Halmos [21], page 127.

Theorem 1-9.1. Bessel's Inequality. *If $\{x_1, x_2, \ldots, x_n\}$ is an orthonormal set and if x is any vector in S, then*

$$\sum_{i=1}^{n} |\alpha_i|^2 \leqq \|x\|^2, \quad \alpha_i = (x, x_i).$$

PROOF.

$$\left\| x - \sum_{i=1}^{n} \alpha_i x_i \right\|^2 = \left(x - \sum_{i=1}^{n} \alpha_i x_i, x - \sum_{i=1}^{n} \alpha_i x_i \right)$$

$$= (x, x) - 2 \sum_{i=1}^{n} \alpha_i (x, x_i) + \sum_{i=1}^{n} \sum_{j=1}^{n} \alpha_i \alpha_j (x_i, x_j)$$

$$= \|x\|^2 - 2 \sum_{i=1}^{n} \alpha_i^2 + \sum_{i=1}^{n} \alpha_i^2$$

$$= \|x\|^2 - \sum_{i=1}^{n} |\alpha_i|^2.$$

Since the left-hand side is nonnegative, the desired result follows. The proof has been made under the assumption that the scalar field is real. The theorem also holds if the scalars are complex (this is the reason for writing $|\alpha_i|^2$ rather than α_i^2).

Corollary 1-9.2. *If the orthonormal set is complete, then:*

(i) $\sum_{i=1}^{n} |\alpha_i|^2 = \|x\|^2$.

(ii) *For any two vectors x and y,* $(x, y) = \sum_{i=1}^{n} (x, x_i)(y, x_i)$.

The first relation (i) *is the* ***Parseval identity***.

Theorem 1-9.2. Schwarz's Inequality. *If x and y are vectors in an inner product space, then*

$$|(x, y)| \leqq \|x\| \, \|y\|.$$

PROOF. If $y = 0$, then the validity of the result is obvious. For y not equal to zero, we may regard $\{y/\|y\|\}$ as an orthonormal set containing a single vector. Using Bessel's inequality

$$|(x, y/\|y\|)|^2 \leqq \|x\|^2.$$

Multiplication of both sides by $\|y\|^2$ yields the desired result.

The Schwarz inequality may be written as

$$\frac{|(x, y)|}{\|x\| \, \|y\|} \leqq 1.$$

This is consistent with the definition of the angle θ between two vectors x and y in n-dimensional Euclidean space by means of the relation

$$\cos\theta = \frac{(x, y)}{\| x \| \, \| y \|} .$$

The triangle inequality can now be established for an inner product norm. Thus, let x and y be any two vectors.

$$\begin{aligned} \| x+y \|^2 &= (x+y, x+y) \\ &= (x, x)+(x, y)+(y, x)+(y, y) \\ &= \| x \|^2+2(x, y)+\| y \|^2 . \end{aligned}$$

From the Schwarz inequality, we infer that the middle term on the right-hand side is no larger than $2\| x \| \, \| y \|$. Hence,

$$\| x+y \|^2 \leqq \{\| x \| + \| y \|\}^2 .$$

That is,

$$\| x+y \| \leqq \| x \| + \| y \| .$$

In the complex case, the middle term mentioned above is $2 \operatorname{Re}\{(x, y)\}$ so that the same result follows.

1-10. ELEMENTARY TOPOLOGY FOR METRIC SPACES

Definition 1-10.1. *A **metric space** is any nonempty set of elements for which a metric (or distance function) is defined.*

The postulates for a distance function ρ are given in relations (1-7.2). It should be noted that the set on which ρ is defined need not be a vector space nor, in fact, have any algebraic properties. However, all the spaces that are introduced in subsequent chapters are vector spaces and their distance functions are frequently defined in terms of a norm.

The following definitions are obvious generalizations of definitions in point set theory for Euclidean one-space.

Definition 1-10.2. *If S is a metric space, $\bar{x} \in S$, and r is any positive real number, then the set of all points x in S such that*

$$\rho(\bar{x}, x) < r ,$$

*is called a **spherical neighborhood** of $\bar{x}$ and is represented by $K(\bar{x}, r)$. The term **neighborhood** is commonly used as an abbreviation for "spherical neighborhood."*

If M is any subset of S, we indicate this by writing $M \subset S$, and we use the symbol $S-M$ to represent the *complement* of M with respect to S.

Definition 1-10.3 *If $M \subset S$, a point x is called an* ***interior point*** *or an* ***inner point*** *of M if there exists a positive real number ε such that $K(x, \varepsilon) \subset M$.*

Definition 1-10.4. *A set M in a metric space S is called an* ***open set*** *if every point of M is an interior point of M. A set M is called a* ***closed set*** *if $S - M$ is open.*

It should be noted that the set S itself, as a subset of the metric space S, is open. The empty set $\varnothing$ is defined to be open. It can be inferred immediately that these two sets, being complements of each other, are also closed.

Definition 1-10.5. *A set M is* ***bounded*** *if there is a point x in S and a positive real number r such that $M \subset K(x, r)$.*

Definition 1-10.6. *If $M \subset S$, a point x in S is a* ***boundary point*** *of M if every neighborhood of x contains at least one point of M and at least one point of $S - M$. The set of all boundary points of M is called the* ***boundary of*** *M, designated by M_b.*

Definition 1-10.7. *If the single point x is removed from the neighborhood $K(x, r)$ the resulting set is called a* ***deleted neighborhood*** *of x.*

Definition 1-10.8. *If $M \subset S$, a point x is called a* ***limit point of*** *M, if every deleted neighborhood of x contains at least one point of M. The set of all limit points of M is represented by M', and the set $M \cup M'$ is called the* ***closure of*** *M and is represented by $\overline{M}$.*

The following three theorems provide alternative definitions of a closed set and reveal the relationship between limit points and boundary points.

Theorem 1-10.1. *In a metric space S, a necessary and sufficient condition that a set M be closed is that it contain all its limit points.*

PROOF. (i) Suppose M is closed. Let x be any point of S which does not belong to M. It must therefore belong to $S - M$ which, by hypothesis, is open. It follows that some neighborhood of x contains only points of $S - M$, so that x cannot be a limit point of M. This implies that every limit point of M belongs to M.

(ii) Suppose M contains all its limit points. By hypothesis, no point of $S - M$ is a limit point of M. Hence, any point x in $S - M$ must have some neighborhood containing no point of M and, therefore, containing only points of $S - M$. It follows that x is an interior point of $S - M$, that $S - M$ is open, and that M is closed. This proves the theorem.

The theorem clearly allows the following alternative definition for a closed set: *A closed set contains all its limit points.*

Theorem 1-10.2. *In a metric space S, a boundary point of a set M either belongs to M or is a limit point of M.*

PROOF. If x is a boundary point of M, then every neighborhood of x contains at least one point of M (and one point of $S-M$). If x does not belong to M, then every deleted neighborhood of x contains at least one point of M so that x is a limit point of M.

Theorem 1-10.3. *In a metric space S, a limit point of a set M either belongs to M or is a boundary point of M.*

PROOF. If x is a limit point of M, then every deleted neighborhood of x contains at least one point of M. Consequently, if x does not belong to M, every neighborhood of x contains at least one point of M and at least one point of $S-M$. Hence x is a boundary point of M.

Corollary 1-10.2 and 1-10.3. *A necessary and sufficient condition that a set M contain all its limit points is that it contain all its boundary points.*

From this we obtain the following second alternative definition for a closed set: *A closed set contains all its boundary points.*

All of the vector spaces previously described for which a norm was defined serve as examples of metric spaces. The following examples provide additional illustration of the preceding definitions.

Example 1. Let S consist of all the points with integral coordinates in Euclidean two-space which lie inside or on the square determined by $x = 0$, $x = 3$, $y = 0$, $y = 3$. Let the metric be the ordinary Euclidean distance function. This is a finite space containing 16 points. Let M be the subset given by

$$M = \{(0,0), (0,1), (0,2), (1,0), (1,1), (1,2)\} .$$

M is a bounded set, since $M \subset K(x_0, 2)$, where x_0 is the point $(0, 1)$. The space S itself is also bounded. If x is any point in M, the neighborhood $K(x, \frac{1}{2})$ contains only the point x. Hence every point of M is an inner point and M is open. The same argument shows that $S-M$ is open so that M is closed. Clearly every subset of S is both open and closed.

Example 2. Let S consist of all points with rational coordinates in the square of Example 1, and let M be as in Example 1. M is still bounded but, in this case, every neighborhood of a point in M contains points in $S-M$. Hence, M has no interior points and is not open. Every point in $S-M$ is an interior point, so that M is closed. Each point of M is a boundary point of M and is also a boundary point of $S-M$.

Example 3. In the square of Example 1, let all the points with real coordinates constitute the space S and all the points with rational coordinates constitute the set M. Every neighborhood of each point x in S contains points of both M and $S-M$. Hence, M has no interior points, and $S-M$ has no interior points. It follows that M is neither open nor closed and that every point in S is a boundary point of M. It is also clear that every point in S is a limit point of M. Hence, $M' = \overline{M} = S$.

The spherical neighborhoods associated with any metric space play a fundamental role in defining the concepts of limit of a sequence and of continuity of a function (or transformation).

Definition 1-10.9. *A sequence of points*

$$\{x_j\} = \{x_j : j = 1, 2, \ldots\}$$

in a metric space S is said to ***converge*** *to a point x in S if for every positive real number ε there is a natural number N such that*

$$\rho(x, x_n) < \varepsilon \quad \text{if } n \geqq N \ .$$

The point x is called the ***limit of the sequence.***

Definition 1-10.10. *A sequence of points $\{x_j\}$ in S is a* ***Cauchy sequence*** *if, for every positive real number ε, there is a natural number N such that*

$$\rho(x_n, x_m) < \varepsilon$$

if $n \geqq N$ and $m \geqq N$.

Definition 1-10.11. *If in a metric space S every Cauchy sequence has a limit in S, then S is* ***complete.***

Theorem 1-10.4. *If S is a complete metric space and M is a nonempty closed subset of S, then M is a complete metric space where the metric for M is the same as the metric for S.*

PROOF. By using the metric of S to define the distance between any two points in M, we automatically make M a metric space. To prove that it is complete, let $\{x_j\}$ be any Cauchy sequence in M. Since S is complete, the sequence converges to some point x in S. Let $K(x, \varepsilon)$ be any neighborhood of x, and let the natural number N be determined so that

$$\rho(x, x_j) < \varepsilon$$

if $j > N$. This implies that all the points in the sequence beyond the Nth point belong to $K(x, \varepsilon)$. Thus, every neighborhood of x contains points of M. Hence, x belongs to M or is a limit point of M. Since M is closed, by hypothesis, x must belong to M and we infer that M is complete.

The most familiar example of a complete metric space is the set of real numbers with the distance between two points defined as the absolute value of their difference. This space is commonly called Euclidean one-space and designated by R^1. Some elementary calculus texts refer to the completeness property as the "completeness postulate." Other texts state the equivalent "postulate" that "every bounded set of real numbers has a least upper bound." It should be noted, however, that when real numbers are defined as Cauchy sequences of rational numbers or, alternatively, as Dedekind cuts, the property of completeness can be derived. Completeness is a basic property of the real number system, and many of the developments of elementary analysis depend upon it. Further, the completeness of Euclidean one-space insures the completeness of Euclidean n-space (see Exercise 3 of Section 1-11). The familiar Euclidean distance in n-space may be replaced by other metrics without destroying the property of completeness (see Remark following Theorem 1-11.1).

1-11. MATRIX SPACES

Matrices play an important role in the study of differential equations, and it is therefore pertinent to set down some of their metric properties. Let S consist of all finite dimensional matrices with real components.

Definition 1-11.1. *A norm for an m by n matrix* $\mathbf{A}$ *in S may be defined as*

$$\|\mathbf{A}\| = \sum_{i=1}^{m} \sum_{j=1}^{n} |a_{ij}| \ .$$

This norm has the following properties:

$$\text{(i)} \quad \|\mathbf{A}\| > 0 \ , \quad \|\mathbf{A}\| = 0 \text{ if and only if } \mathbf{A} = \mathbf{0} \ .$$

$$\text{(ii)} \quad \|\alpha\mathbf{A}\| = |\alpha| \, \|\mathbf{A}\| \ .$$

$$\text{(iii)} \quad \|\mathbf{A}+\mathbf{B}\| \leqq \|\mathbf{A}\| + \|\mathbf{B}\| \ .$$

$$\text{(iv)} \quad \|\mathbf{AB}\| \leqq \|\mathbf{A}\| \, \|\mathbf{B}\| \ .$$

The first three properties are easily verified. The fourth property is meaningful only if the product **AB** is defined. Under the restriction, therefore, that **A** is an m by r matrix and **B** is an r by n matrix, we may establish the fourth property as follows:

$$\|\mathbf{A}\| \, \|\mathbf{B}\| = \left\{ \sum_{i=1}^{m} \sum_{k=1}^{r} |a_{ik}| \right\} \left\{ \sum_{l=1}^{r} \sum_{j=1}^{n} |b_{lj}| \right\} = \sum_{i,k,l,j} |a_{ik} b_{lj}|$$

$$= \sum_{i=1}^{m} \sum_{k=1}^{r} \sum_{j=1}^{n} \left\{ |a_{ik} b_{kj}| + \sum_{l=1,\, l\neq k}^{r} |a_{ik} b_{lj}| \right\} .$$

By simply deleting some of the nonnegative terms on the right-hand side, we get

$$\|\mathbf{A}\| \, \|\mathbf{B}\| \geqq \sum_{i=1}^{m} \sum_{j=1}^{n} \sum_{k=1}^{r} |a_{ik} b_{kj}|$$

$$\geqq \sum_{i=1}^{m} \sum_{j=1}^{n} \left| \sum_{k=1}^{r} a_{ik} b_{kj} \right| .$$

Since

$$\sum_{k=1}^{r} a_{ik} b_{kj}$$

is the ith row and jth column component of $\mathbf{AB}$, the right-hand side is the norm of $\mathbf{AB}$. Hence

$$\| \mathbf{AB} \| \leqq \| \mathbf{A} \| \, \| \mathbf{B} \| \ .$$

A distance function $\rho(\mathbf{A}, \mathbf{B})$ between any two matrices $\mathbf{A}$ and $\mathbf{B}$, of the same dimension, is given by

$$\rho(\mathbf{A}, \mathbf{B}) = \| \mathbf{A}-\mathbf{B} \| = \sum_{i=1}^{m} \sum_{j=1}^{n} | a_{ij}-b_{ij} | \ .$$

It is easily verified that this function has the required properties [relations (1-7.2)], namely:

(i) $\rho(\mathbf{A}, \mathbf{B}) \geqq 0$ and $\rho(\mathbf{A}, \mathbf{B}) = 0$ if and only if $\mathbf{A} = \mathbf{B}$.

(ii) $\rho(\mathbf{A}, \mathbf{B}) = \rho(\mathbf{B}, \mathbf{A})$.

(iii) $\rho(\mathbf{A}, \mathbf{B}) \leqq \rho(\mathbf{A}, \mathbf{C})+\rho(\mathbf{C}, \mathbf{B})$.

Theorem 1-11.1. *The space S of all m by n matrices with real components is complete relative to the above metric.*

PROOF. Let

$$\{\mathbf{A}_r\} = \{\mathbf{A}_1, \mathbf{A}_2, \ldots\}$$

be a Cauchy sequence of m by n matrices. For any positive real number ε, there is a natural number N such that

$$\rho(\mathbf{A}_r, \mathbf{A}_s) < \varepsilon$$

if $r, s \geqq N$. By virtue of the definition of the distance function this may be written as

$$\sum_{i=1}^{m} \sum_{j=1}^{n} | a_{ij}^{(r)} - a_{ij}^{(s)} | < \varepsilon$$

if $r, s \geqq N$, where $a_{ij}^{(r)}$ and $a_{ij}^{(s)}$, respectively, represent components of $\mathbf{A}_r$ and $\mathbf{A}_s$. Each term of the sum on the left-hand side is clearly no larger than the whole sum. Hence, for each value of i and j,

$$|a_{ij}^{(r)} - a_{ij}^{(s)} | < \varepsilon$$

if $r, s \geqq N$. The sequence

$$\{a_{ij}^{(r)} : r = 1, 2, \ldots\}$$

is therefore a Cauchy sequence of real numbers. Since the real numbers form a complete space, the sequence must converge to some real number a_{ij}. Hence, if ε is any positive real number, there is a natural number N corresponding to ε/mn such that

$$| a_{ij}- a_{i,j}^{(r)} | < \frac{\varepsilon}{mn}$$

if $r \geqq N$. Since this inequality is valid for each pertinent value of i and j,

$$\sum_{i=1}^{m}\sum_{j=1}^{n} |a_{ij}-a_{ij}^{(r)}| < mn\frac{\varepsilon}{mn} = \varepsilon$$

if $r \geqq N$.
That is,

$$\| \mathbf{A}-\mathbf{A}_r \| < \varepsilon$$

if $r \geqq N$, where $\mathbf{A} = (a_{ij})$ is a matrix in S. This proves that every Cauchy sequence has a limit in S and, hence, that the space S is complete.

Corollary 1-11.1. *A sequence of matrices converges if and only if each of its component sequences converges.*

Remark. If $n = 1$, the elements of S are m-vectors. The space of m-vectors is therefore complete. This does not establish the completeness of the space relative to the ordinary Euclidean distance function, but that fact can be inferred from this result. (See Exercise 3 of this section.)

The relation between infinite series and infinite sequences of matrices is entirely analogous to the relation between series and sequences of real numbers. Thus, let

$$\sum_{j=1}^{\infty} \mathbf{A}_j = \mathbf{A}_1+\mathbf{A}_2+ \cdots$$

be an infinite series of matrices where $\mathbf{A}_j, j = 1, 2, \ldots$ is an m by n matrix. The nth partial sum of the series is represented by $\mathbf{S}_n$, where

$$\mathbf{S}_n + \sum_{j=1}^{n} \mathbf{A}_j \ .$$

The series is said to converge to a matrix $\mathbf{A}$ if and only if the sequence $\{\mathbf{S}_n\}$ converges to $\mathbf{A}$.

Theorem 1-11.2. *The exponential series*

$$\sum_{j=1}^{\infty}\frac{1}{(j-1)!}\mathbf{A}^{j-1} \ , \tag{1-11.1}$$

where $\mathbf{A}$ *is any* n *by* n *matrix and* $\mathbf{A}^0 = \mathbf{I}$, *converges.*

PROOF. The sequence of partial sums is easily shown to be a Cauchy sequence, for, if

$$\mathbf{S}_n = \sum_{j=1}^{n}\frac{1}{(j-1)!}\mathbf{A}^{j-1} \ ,$$

then

$$\| \mathbf{S}_n - \mathbf{S}_m \| = \left\| \frac{1}{m!}\mathbf{A}^m + \frac{1}{(m+1)!}\mathbf{A}^{m+1} + \cdots + \frac{1}{(n-1)!}\mathbf{A}^{n-1} \right\|$$

$$\leq \left\| \frac{1}{m!} \mathbf{A}^m \right\| + \left\| \frac{1}{(m+1)!} \mathbf{A}^{m+1} \right\| + \cdots + \left\| \frac{1}{(n-1)!} \mathbf{A}^{n-1} \right\|$$

$$\leq \frac{1}{m!} R^m + \frac{1}{(m+1)!} R^{m+1} + \cdots + \frac{1}{(n-1)!} R^{n-1} ,$$

where $\| \mathbf{A} \| = R$. The right-hand side of the last inequality is, however, the difference between the nth partial sum and the mth partial sum of the series expansion for e^R. Hence, for any positive real number ε there must exist a natural number N such that

$$\| \mathbf{S}_n - \mathbf{S}_m \| < \varepsilon$$

if $m, n \geqq N$. This proves that $\{\mathbf{S}_j\}$ is a Cauchy sequence. Since the space of n by n matrices is complete, the sequence, and hence the series, converges to an n by n matrix, designated by $e^{\mathbf{A}}$ and called an *exponential matrix.*

Sequences and series of matrices have many properties in common with sequences and series of real or complex numbers (see Exercises 5, 6, and 7 of this section). A useful property of an exponential matrix is stated as the following theorem.

Theorem 1-11.3. *If* $\mathbf{T}$ *is any nonsingular matrix, then*

$$\mathbf{T}^{-1} e^{\mathbf{A}} \mathbf{T} = e^{\mathbf{T}^{-1}\mathbf{A}\mathbf{T}} .$$

PROOF. Since $(\mathbf{T}^{-1}\mathbf{A}\mathbf{T})^j = \mathbf{T}^{-1}\mathbf{A}^j\mathbf{T}$,

$$\mathbf{T}^{-1} e^{\mathbf{A}} \mathbf{T} = \mathbf{T}^{-1} \left\{ \sum_{j=1}^{\infty} \frac{1}{(j-1)!} \mathbf{A}^{j-1} \right\} \mathbf{T}$$

$$= \sum_{j=1}^{\infty} \frac{1}{(j-1)!} (\mathbf{T}^{-1}\mathbf{A}\mathbf{T})^{j-1}$$

$$= e^{\mathbf{T}^{-1}\mathbf{A}\mathbf{T}} .$$

This proves the theorem.

It was pointed out in Section 1-2 that the set $C[0, 1]$ is a vector space. It may be made a normed vector space by defining the norm of a function f by

$$\|f\| = \max_{0 \leqq t \leqq 1} |f(t)| ;$$

the distance function between two elements f and g then becomes

$$\rho(f, g) = \|f-g\|$$

$$= \max_{0 \leqq t \leqq 1} |f(t)-g(t)| .$$

The definition is such that, if $\{f_j\}$ is a Cauchy sequence in $C[0, 1]$, then the sequence $\{f_j(t)\}$ converges uniformly in the Cauchy sense on [0, 1]. It is known[3] that such a sequence converges to a continuous limit on [0, 1]. It follows that $C[0, 1]$ is a complete metric space relative to the given metric.

A norm for matrices whose components are functions is given in the following definition.

Definition 1-11.2. *The norm of an m by n matrix* **A** *whose components are bounded functions on an interval I is*

$$\| \mathbf{A} \| = \sup_{t \in I} \| \mathbf{A}(t) \| \ .$$

The corresponding distance function is

$$\rho(\mathbf{A}, \mathbf{B}) = \| \mathbf{A} - \mathbf{B} \| \ .$$

Theorem 1-11.4. *The space of all m by n matrices whose components belong to C[a, b] is a complete metric space.*

PROOF. Let S be the space of all m by n matrices with components in $C[a, b]$. Let $\{\mathbf{A}_j\}$ be any Cauchy sequence in S. Corresponding to any positive real number ε, there is, by hypothesis, a natural number N such that

$$\sup_{t \in [a, b]} \| \mathbf{A}_r(t) - \mathbf{A}_s(t) \| < \varepsilon$$

if $r, s \geqq N$. For each t in $[a, b]$, therefore, $\{\mathbf{A}_j(t)\}$ is a Cauchy sequence of scalar matrices which, in view of Theorem 1-11.1, converges to a matrix $\mathbf{A}(t)$. As in the proof of Theorem 1-11.1, we may fix our attention on the component in the ith row and jth column of each matrix in the sequence. The sequence of continuous functions resulting from this selection must converge uniformly to a continuous function on $[a, b]$. It follows that the components of $\mathbf{A}(t)$ are continuous and, hence, that S is complete.

A useful relationship between the norm of an integral of a matrix and the norm of the matrix is stated in the following theorem.

Theorem 1-11.5. *If the components of an m by n matrix* **A** *are bounded and integrable functions on an interval [a, b], then*

$$\left\| \int_a^b \mathbf{A}(t)\, dt \right\| \leqq \| \mathbf{A} \| \, |b - a| \ .$$

PROOF.

$$\left\| \int_a^b \mathbf{A}(t)\, dt \right\| = \sum_{i=1}^{m} \sum_{j=1}^{n} \left| \int_a^b a_{ij}(t)\, dt \right|$$

[3] Olmsted [37], page 279.

$$\leqq \sum_{i=1}^{m} \sum_{j=1}^{n} \left| \int_a^b | a_{ij}(t) | \, dt \right| .$$

The exterior numerical value signs are needed only if $b < a$. Since each integrand is positive, the summation symbols can be moved inside the numerical value bars and, since the order of summation and integration are interchangeable, we have

$$\left\| \int_a^b \mathbf{A}(t) \, dt \right\| \leqq \left| \int_a^b \sum_{i=1}^{m} \sum_{j=1}^{n} | a_{ij}(t) | \, dt \right|$$

$$\leqq \left| \int_a^b \sup_{t \in [a, b]} \sum_{i=1}^{m} \sum_{j=1}^{n} | a_{ij}(t) | \, dt \right|$$

$$\leqq \| \mathbf{A} \| \, | b - a | .$$

This proves the theorem.

Exercises

1. Prove that if a sequence $\{x_j\}$ converges to a point x in a metric space S then x is unique.

2. Let the norm of a matrix **A** be given by

$$\| \mathbf{A} \| = \left\{ \sum_{i=1}^{m} \sum_{j=1}^{n} a_{ij}^2 \right\}^{1/2} .$$

Show that the space of m by n matrices is complete relative to the distance function associated with this norm.

3. Let $n = 1$ in Exercise 2 and prove that Euclidean m-space is complete relative to the standard norm for that space.

4. Let the norm of a matrix **A** be given by $\| \mathbf{A} \| = \max_{i,j} | a_{ij} |$.

Show that the space of m by n matrices is complete relative to this norm.

5. (a) If $\{\mathbf{A}_j\}$ is a Cauchy sequence of n by n matrices and **B** and **C** are any two n by n matrices, show that $\{\mathbf{B}\mathbf{A}_j\mathbf{C}\}$ is a Cauchy sequence.
(b) State and prove a corresponding result for a series.

6. Show that the sum of two Cauchy sequences is a Cauchy sequence.

7. Prove that $\sum_{j=1}^{\infty} \mathbf{A}_j$ converges if $\sum_{j=1}^{\infty} \| \mathbf{A}_j \|$ converges.

8. Show that if $\mathbf{AB} = \mathbf{BA}$, then

$$e^{\mathbf{A}+\mathbf{B}} = e^{\mathbf{A}} e^{\mathbf{B}} .$$

9. Prove that $e^{\mathbf{A}}$ is nonsingular and that $\{e^{\mathbf{A}}\}^{-1} = e^{-\mathbf{A}}$.

1-12. MAPPINGS ON METRIC SPACES

In this section we discuss the continuity of a function (or mapping) defined on a metric space. Following the first two preliminary theorems, a fixed point theorem is proved. This latter theorem provides an easy proof for the fundamental existence theorem for a first-order system of differential equations, the subject of Chapter 2.

Definition 1-12.1. *Let S_1 and S_2 be metric spaces with distance functions ρ_1 and ρ_2, respectively. A function f with domain M in S_1 and range in S_2 is* ***continuous*** *at a point x_0 in M if for every positive real number ε there is a positive real number δ such that*

$$\rho_2(f(x), f(x_0)) < \varepsilon$$

if $x \in M$ and $\rho_1(x, x_0) < \delta$. The function is continuous on any subset of M, if it is continuous at each point of that subset.

Theorem 1-12.1. *If f maps S_1, with metric ρ_1, into S_2, with metric ρ_2, and $\bar{x}$ is a limit point of S_1, then f is continuous at $\bar{x}$ if and only if for every sequence $\{x_j\}$ in S_1 which converges to $\bar{x}$ the corresponding sequence $\{f(x_j)\}$ in S_2 converges to $f(\bar{x})$.*

PROOF. (i) Suppose f is continuous at $\bar{x}$. Let $\{x_j\}$ be any sequence in S_1 converging to $\bar{x}$. Let any positive real number ε be chosen. Corresponding to ε, we may determine a positive real number δ such that

$$\rho_2(f(x), f(\bar{x})) < \varepsilon$$

if $\rho_1(x, \bar{x}) < \delta$. Corresponding to δ, we may, further, determine a natural number N such that

$$\rho_1(x_j, \bar{x}) < \delta$$

if $j \geqq N$. It follows immediately that

$$\rho_2(f(x_j), f(\bar{x})) < \varepsilon$$

if $j \geqq N$. This proves that $\{f(x_j)\}$ converges to $f(\bar{x})$.

(ii) Suppose that for every sequence $\{x_j\}$ in S_1 which converges to $\bar{x}$, the corresponding sequence $f(x_j)$ in S_2 converges to $f(\bar{x})$. In order to provide an indirect proof, we assume that f is not continuous at $\bar{x}$. This implies that for some positive real number ε there is no positive real number δ such that

$$\rho_2(f(x), f(\bar{x})) < \varepsilon$$

for all x satisfying $\rho_1(x, \bar{x}) < \delta$. Thus for each positive δ, and in particular for

$$\delta = \frac{1}{j}, \quad j = 1, 2, \ldots,$$

there is a point x_j in S_1 such that

$$\rho_1(x_j, \bar{x}) < \frac{1}{j} \quad \text{and} \quad \rho_2(f(x_j), f(\bar{x})) \geqq \varepsilon .$$

Clearly the sequence $\{x_j\}$ converges to $\bar{x}$, and the sequence $\{f(x_j)\}$ does not converge to $f(\bar{x})$. This contradicts the supposition and completes the proof.

Definition 1-12.2. *A mapping f of a metric space into itself is a* ***contraction mapping*** *if and only if there exists a real number* α *such that* $0 < \alpha < 1$ *and*

$$\rho(f(x_1), f(x_2)) \leqq \alpha\rho(x_1, x_2) ,$$

for any pair of points x_1 *and* x_2 *in S;* α *is the* ***contraction constant*** *of the mapping.*

Theorem 1-12.2. *A contraction mapping is continuous.*

PROOF. Let f be a contraction mapping of S into itself. If $\bar{x}$ is any point in S, then

$$\rho(f(x), f(\bar{x})) \leqq \alpha\rho(x, \bar{x}) .$$

Hence, if ε is any positive real number

$$\rho(f(x), f(\bar{x})) < \varepsilon$$

if $\rho(x, \bar{x}) < \varepsilon$. This implies that f is continuous on S.

Definition 1-12.3. *A point* $\bar{x}$ *in S is a* ***fixed point*** *of the mapping f if*

$$f(\bar{x}) = \bar{x} .$$

Theorem 1-12.3. *A contraction mapping f on a complete metric space S has one and only one fixed point.*

PROOF. Let x_0 be any point in S which is not a fixed point. That is,

$$f(x_0) \neq x_0 .$$

Define x_1 by

$$x_1 = f(x_0) ,$$

and in general define x_j by

(1-12.1) $$x_j = f(x_{j-1}) , \quad j = 1, 2, \ldots .$$

For the sequence $\{x_j\}$, so defined, we have by repeated application of the triangle property

(1-12.2) $$\rho(x_n, x_m) \leqq \sum_{= m+1}^{n} \rho(x_j, x_{j-1}) .$$

Further, using (1-12.1), we get

$$\rho(x_j, x_{j-1}) = \rho(f(x_{j-1}), f(x_{j-2}))$$
$$\leqq \alpha\rho(x_{j-1}, x_{j-2}) ,$$

where α is the contraction constant. By iteration, the above relation yields

$$\rho(x_j, x_{j-1}) \leqq \alpha^{j-1}\rho(x_1, x_0) .$$

Substituting this in (1-12.2), we get

$$\rho(x_n, x_m) \leqq \rho(x_1, x_0) \sum_{j=m+1}^{n} \alpha^{j-1} .$$

Since

$$\sum_{j=m+1}^{n} \alpha^{j-1}$$

is the difference between the nth and mth partial sums of the convergent geometric series

$$\sum_{j=1}^{\infty} \alpha^{j-1} ,$$

it follows that $\{x_j\}$ is a Cauchy sequence. The completeness of S insures that the sequence converges to a point x in S.

Since the contraction mapping is continuous, Theorem 1-12.1 implies that the sequence

$$\{f(x_j)\}$$

converges to $f(x)$. However, the latter sequence may be written as $\{x_{j+1}\}$, and this sequence converges to x. That is,

$$f(x) = x ,$$

and we have established that x is a fixed point of the mapping.

This fixed point is obviously unique. For, if x and y are two distinct fixed points, $f(x) = x$ and $f(y) = y$, and

$$\rho(f(x), f(y)) = \rho(x, y) .$$

This contradicts the hypothesis that the mapping is a contraction mapping.

Exercises

1. The relation

$$f(t) = \tfrac{1}{2}t$$

defines a mapping of R^1 into R^1. Show that f is a contraction mapping.

2. Let the space S consist of all continuous functions on the interval $[-1, 1]$ whose graphs pass through the origin. That is,

$$S = \{x : x \in C[-1, 1], x(0) = 0\} .$$

Let a norm for the space be

$$\| x \| = \max_{t \in [-1, 1]} |x(t)| .$$

If k is a function in S such that $\| k \| < 1$,

$$y(t) = \int_0^t k(s)x(s)\,ds, \quad -1 \leqq t \leqq 1 ,$$

defines a mapping, $y = F(x)$, of S into itself. Prove that F is a contraction mapping.

2

Existence and Uniqueness of Solutions

2-1. INTRODUCTION

The most elementary differential equation is

$$y' = f \ ,$$

where f is a given continuous function on the interval $[a, b]$. The problem associated with this equation is to find a function y whose first derivative is the function f. For each real constant c and for $a \leqq t \leqq b$ it is clear that

$$y(t) = \int_a^t f(s)\,ds + c$$

is a solution of the equation.

The general first-order differential equation is

$$y' = f(t, y) \ .$$

Here for $a \leqq t \leqq b$ and f assumed to be continuous the problem is to find a function y with a continuous first derivative such that

$$y'(t) = f(t, y(t)) \ .$$

The conditions under which a solution for this equation can be found are discussed in Section 2-2.

For the present, we consider the existence of a solution for a particular case, namely,

$$y' = ay \ , \tag{2-1.1}$$

where a is any real constant. This equation, like the previous one, appears in elementary calculus. Its solutions are given by

$$y(t) = ce^{at} \ ,$$

where c is an arbitrary constant. The solutions, therefore, form a one-dimensional vector space, and the function

$$u(t) = e^{at}$$

is a convenient basis for this space. It is easily verified that there is a unique solution satisfying the condition

(2-1.2) $$y(0) = y_0\ ,$$

where y_0 is an arbitrary real number. This solution is

$$y = y_0 u\ .$$

Equation (2-1.1) together with the condition (2-1.2) are referred to as an *initial-value problem.*

The second-order differential equation

$$y'' - 3y' + 2y = 0$$

is satisfied by the function $y = u_1$, where

$$u_1(t) = e^t\ .$$

It is also satisfied by the function $y = u_2$, where

$$u_2(t) = e^{2t}\ .$$

It is easily verified that for any two real constants c_1 and c_2

$$y = c_1 u_1 + c_2 u_2$$

is a solution of the given second-order differential equation. That every real solution can be expressed in this form is subsequently demonstrated. Consequently, since u_1 and u_2 are linearly independent, the solutions of the equation constitute a two-dimensional vector space over the field of real numbers. That the solutions of a general homogeneous nth-order linear equation form an n-dimensional vector space is established in Section 3-2.

As a third example of the formation of a vector space by the solutions of equations let us consider the system

(2-1.3) $$\begin{aligned} y_1' &= y_2\ , \\ y_2' &= -2y_1 + 3y_2\ . \end{aligned}$$

It is easily verified that the pair of functions $y_1 = u_1$ and $y_2 = u_2$, where

$$\begin{aligned} u_1(t) &= e^t\ , \\ u_2(t) &= e^t\ , \end{aligned}$$

satisfy the system. Similarly, the pair $y_1 = v_1$ and $y_2 = v_2$, where

$$\begin{aligned} v_1(t) &= e^{2t}\ , \\ v_2(t) &= 2e^{2t}\ , \end{aligned}$$

is another solution. Each of the vectors $\mathbf{u}$ and $\mathbf{v}$, therefore, where

(2-1.4) $$\mathbf{u}(t) = \begin{pmatrix} u_1(t) \\ u_2(t) \end{pmatrix} \quad \text{and} \quad \mathbf{v}(t) = \begin{pmatrix} v_1(t) \\ v_2(t) \end{pmatrix}\ ,$$

has a pair of components which satisfies the system. Clearly, for any two real numbers α and β, the vector

(2-1.5) $$\mathbf{y} = \alpha\mathbf{u} + \beta\mathbf{v}$$

has components which satisfy the system. In Chapter 3 it is shown that every pair of functions which satisfy the system are the components of some linear combination of **u** and **v**. Hence the solutions of the system form a two-dimensional vector space having **u** and **v** as a basis.

The vector differential equation

$$\mathbf{y}' = \begin{pmatrix} 0 & 1 \\ -2 & 3 \end{pmatrix} \mathbf{y} \tag{2-1.6}$$

is equivalent, in an obvious sense, to the scalar system (2-1.3). Each of the two vectors in (2-1.4) is a solution of this vector equation, and its general solution is given by (2-1.5). The distinction between (2-1.3) and (2-1.6) is merely a notational distinction, and we refer to (2-1.3) as the *scalar system* corresponding to the vector differential equation (2-1.6).

The solutions in each of these examples form finite-dimensional vector spaces. This holds for all the solutions of any given homogeneous linear differential equation. Therefore some knowledge of finite-dimensional vector algebra is a necessary prerequisite to an understanding of the theory of differential equations. It is obvious that vector notation effectively simplifies some of the mechanical aspects of this development.

2-2. EXISTENCE AND UNIQUENESS THEOREM

The system of equations

$$\begin{aligned} y_1' &= f_1(t, y_1, \ldots, y_n) \ , \\ y_2' &= f_2(t, y_1, \ldots, y_n) \ , \\ &\ \ \vdots \\ y_n' &= f_n(t, y_1, \ldots, y_n) \ , \end{aligned} \tag{2-2.1}$$

is equivalent to the vector equation

$$\mathbf{y}' = \mathbf{f}(t, \mathbf{y}) \ , \tag{2-2.2}$$

where **f** is an n-vector whose components are functions of the real variable t and the n-vector **y** [*cf.* (2-1.3) and (2-1.6)]. The domain of **f**, therefore, lies in the product space $R^1 \times V_n$. Because of the notational advantage, our discussion is in terms of (2-2.2) rather than (2-2.1). Also, for convenience, the space $R^1 \times V_n$ is referred to as $(t, \mathbf{y})$ space. It should be noted that the case $n = 1$ is not excluded so that the classical first-order equation is included as a special case of the system.

Definition 2-2.1. *A* ***solution*** *of equation* (2-2.2) *on an interval I is an n-vector* **y** *whose components have continuous derivatives on I and which, for each t on I, satisfies*

$$\mathbf{y}'(t) = \mathbf{f}(t, \mathbf{y}(t)) \ .$$

A diagrammatic representation of a solution, when $n = 2$, can be obtained by drawing a curve in three-space. Let us examine Figure 2-2.1. Values of t are plotted on the horizontal axis, and values of the vector $\mathbf{y}$ are plotted on the $y_1 y_2$-plane. The curve C represents the solution on the interval $[a, b]$ in the sense that the projection of C on the ty_i-plane is the graph of the component $y_i(t)$ of the vector $\mathbf{y}(t)$, $i = 1, 2$.

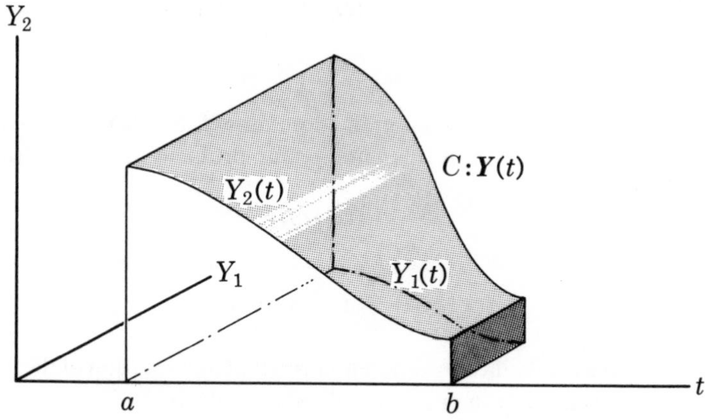

Figure 2-2.1

In the existence theorem, the vector $\mathbf{f}$ is restricted to be continuous in some region of $(t, \mathbf{y})$ space. Therefore, we need a definition of continuity for $\mathbf{f}$. The norm used here is the one given by Definition 1-11.2 with $n = 1$.

Definition 2-2.2. *A vector* $\mathbf{f}$ *is* ***continuous*** *at a point* $(t_0, \mathbf{y}_0)$ *in a region D of* $(t, \mathbf{y})$ *space if, for every positive real number* ε, *there are two positive real numbers* δ_1 *and* δ_2 *such that*

$$\| \mathbf{f}(t, \mathbf{y}) - \mathbf{f}(t_0, \mathbf{y}_0) \| < \varepsilon \ ,$$

if $(t, \mathbf{y}) \in D$, $| t - t_0) < \delta_1$, *and* $\| \mathbf{y} - \mathbf{y}_0 \| < \delta_2$. *The vector* $\mathbf{f}$ *is continuous in D if it is continuous at each point of D.*

It is not hard to verify that $\mathbf{f}$ is continuous according to this definition if and only if each of the functions on the right-hand sides of the equations (2-2.1) is continuous in $(n+1)$-space.

In order to be able to achieve a unique solution in the existence theorem, we now impose a Lipschitz condition on the vector $\mathbf{f}$. The nature of this condition is specified in the next definition.

Definition 2-2.3. *The vector* $\mathbf{f}$ *satisfies a* ***Lipschitz condition,*** *with respect to* $\mathbf{y}$, *in a region* D, *if there exists a positive real constant* K *such that for every* $(t, \mathbf{y}_1)$ *and* $(t, \mathbf{y}_2)$ *in* D,

$$\|\mathbf{f}(t, \mathbf{y}_1)-\mathbf{f}(t, \mathbf{y}_2)\| \leqq K\|\mathbf{y}_1-\mathbf{y}_2\| .$$

The constant K *is called a* ***Lipschitz constant.***

The problem of finding a solution $\mathbf{y}$ of the differential equation

$$\mathbf{y}' = \mathbf{f}(t, \mathbf{y})$$

given

$$\mathbf{y}(t_0) = \mathbf{y}_0 ,$$

where $(t_0, \mathbf{y}_0)$ is any specified point in the domain of $\mathbf{f}$, is called an *initial-value problem.* If $\mathbf{y}$ is any solution of this initial-value problem, it is clear from the integration of

$$\mathbf{y}'(s) = \mathbf{f}(s, \mathbf{y}(s))$$

that

$$\mathbf{y}(t) = \mathbf{y}_0+\int_{t_0}^{t} \mathbf{f}(s, \mathbf{y}(s))\, ds . \tag{2-2.3}$$

Conversely, it is easily verified by differentiation that any solution of the integral equation (2-2.3) is a solution of the initial-value problem.

Theorem 2-2.1. Existence and Uniqueness Theorem. *If* $\mathbf{f}$ *is continuous and satisfies a Lipschitz condition with respect to* $\mathbf{y}$ *on some open connected*[1] *region* R *of* $(t, \mathbf{y})$ *space and if* $(t_0, \mathbf{y}_0)$ *is any point in this region, then the initial-value problem*

$$\mathbf{y}' = \mathbf{f}(t, \mathbf{y}) ,$$

$$\mathbf{y}(t_0) = \mathbf{y}_0$$

has a unique solution on some real interval containing the point t_0.

PROOF. Since R is open there must exist two positive real constants δ_1 and b such that the region

$$D_1: \ |t-t_0| \leqq \delta_1 , \quad \|\mathbf{y}-\mathbf{y}_0\| \leqq b ,$$

is a subset of R. Since D_1 is closed, the components of $\mathbf{f}$ are bounded in D_1. Hence the norm of $\mathbf{f}$ relative to D_1 exists, and we may write, for some positive real number M,

$$\|\mathbf{f}\| = \sup_{(t, \mathbf{y}) \in D_1} \|\mathbf{f}(t, \mathbf{y})\| = M .$$

Let K be the Lipschitz constant for $\mathbf{f}$, and let δ be any positive real number which is smaller than each of the three numbers

$$\delta_1 , \quad b/M , \quad \text{and} \quad 1/K .$$

[1] For a definition of "connected," see Buck [9], page 29.

The region

$$D:\quad |t-t_0| \leqq \delta\ ,\quad \|\mathbf{y}-\mathbf{y}_0\| \leqq b$$

is a closed subset of D_1. It follows that

$$\|\mathbf{f}(t,\mathbf{y})\|_{(t,\mathbf{y})\in D} \leqq M\ .$$

Let I represent the closed interval $[t_0-\delta,\ t_0+\delta]$, and let T be the space of all n-vectors whose components are continuous functions on I. Let S be the subset of T defined by

$$S = \{\mathbf{y}:\mathbf{y}\in T,\ \|\mathbf{y}(t)-\mathbf{y}_0\| \leqq b\}\ .$$

For the case $n = 2$, Figure 2-2.2 shows the boxlike region D of length 2δ which contains the graphs of all elements in S. In order to show that S is a closed subset, let $\bar{\mathbf{y}}$ be any element in $T-S$. With reference to Figure 2-2.2, such an element must have a graph that is not entirely in the region D. Hence, for some point t_1 on I and some positive real number ε

$$\|\bar{\mathbf{y}}(t_1)-\mathbf{y}_0\| = b+\varepsilon\ .$$

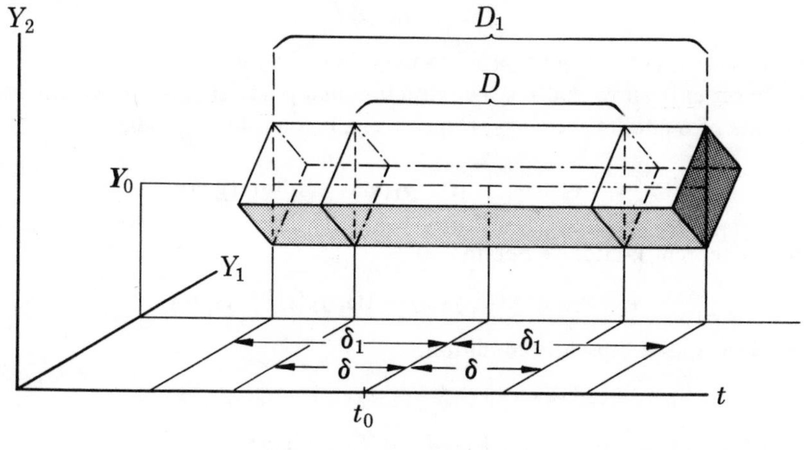

Figure 2-2.2

If $\mathbf{y}$ is any element of T in the spherical neighborhood $K(\bar{\mathbf{y}},\varepsilon/2)$ of $\bar{\mathbf{y}}$, we may write

$$\begin{aligned}\|\mathbf{y}(t_1)-\mathbf{y}_0\| &= \|\mathbf{y}(t_1)-\bar{\mathbf{y}}(t_1)+\bar{\mathbf{y}}(t_1)-\mathbf{y}_0\|\\ &\geqq \|\bar{\mathbf{y}}(t_1)-\mathbf{y}_0\| - \|\mathbf{y}(t_1)-\bar{\mathbf{y}}(t_1)\|\\ &\geqq (b+\varepsilon)-\varepsilon/2\\ &\geqq b+\varepsilon/2\ .\end{aligned}$$

This implies that $\mathbf{y} \in T-S$ and that $\bar{\mathbf{y}}$ is an interior point of $T-S$. Thus, $T-S$ is open, and S is closed. By Theorem 1-11.4, T is complete. Hence, Theorem 1-10.4 guarantees that S is a complete metric space.

Let F be a mapping with domain S defined by

$$\mathbf{v} = F(\mathbf{y}) \ ,$$

where

$$\mathbf{v}(t) = \mathbf{y}_0 + \int_{t_0}^{t} \mathbf{f}(s, \mathbf{y}(s))\, ds \ , \quad t \in I \ .$$

It is obvious that the range of F is contained in T. That it is, in fact, contained in S can be established as follows, using Theorem 1-11.5:

$$\begin{aligned} \| \mathbf{v}(t) - \mathbf{y}_0 \| &= \left\| \int_{t_0}^{t} \mathbf{f}(s, \mathbf{y}(s))\, ds \right\| \\ &\leqq \| \mathbf{f} \| \, | t - t_0 | \\ &\leqq M | t - t_0 | \ . \end{aligned}$$

Since $| t - t_0 | < \delta$ and δ was chosen less than b/M, we infer that

$$\| \mathbf{v}(t) - \mathbf{y}_0 \| \leqq b \ .$$

This insures that $\mathbf{v} \in S$ and that F is a mapping of S into S.

In order to show that F is a contraction mapping, let $\mathbf{y}_1$ and $\mathbf{y}_2$ be any two elements of S and let $\mathbf{v}_1$ and $\mathbf{v}_2$, respectively, be their images. Then,

$$\| \mathbf{v}_1 - \mathbf{v}_2 \| = \left\| \int_{t_0}^{t} [\mathbf{f}(s, \mathbf{y}_1(s)) - \mathbf{f}(s, \mathbf{y}_2(s))]\, ds \right\| \ .$$

Using Theorem 1-11.5, we obtain

$$\| \mathbf{v}_1 - \mathbf{v}_2 \| \leqq \| \mathbf{f}(s, \mathbf{y}_1(s)) - \mathbf{f}(s, \mathbf{y}_2(s)) \| \, | t - t_0 | \ .$$

Since $\mathbf{f}$ satisfies a Lipschitz condition,

$$\| \mathbf{v}_1 - \mathbf{v}_2 \| \leqq K \| \mathbf{y}_1 - \mathbf{y}_2 \| \, | t - t_0 | \ .$$

Recalling that $| t - t_0 | \leqq \delta$ and that $\delta < 1/K$, we have

$$\| \mathbf{v}_1 - \mathbf{v}_2 \| \leqq \alpha \| \mathbf{y}_1 - \mathbf{y}_2 \| \ ,$$

where $\alpha = \delta K < 1$. Hence, F is a contraction mapping.

It follows from Theorem 1-12.3, that F has a unique fixed point in S. If this point is designed by $\mathbf{x}$, we have

$$\mathbf{x}(t) = \mathbf{y}_0 + \int_{t_0}^{t} \mathbf{f}(s, \mathbf{x}(s))\, ds \ ,$$

and $\mathbf{x}$ is a unique solution of the integral equation (2-2.3). This is equivalent to saying that it is a unique solution of the initial-value problem, and the proof of the theorem is complete.

Exercises

1. Obtain a sequence of functions which converges to a solution for each of the following initial-value problems:

(a) $u' = u$,

$u(0) = 1$;

(*Hint:* Define $u_j(t)$ by

$$u_j(t) = 1 + \int_0^t u_{j-1}(s)\,ds$$

and use $u_0(t) = 1$ for the initial function.)

(b) $u' = tu,$

$u(0) = 1$.

2. Obtain a sequence of vectors which converges to a solution for each of the following initial-value problems:

(a) $\mathbf{y}' = \begin{pmatrix} 0 & 1 \\ -2 & 3 \end{pmatrix}\mathbf{y}$, $\mathbf{y}(0) = \begin{pmatrix} 1 \\ 1 \end{pmatrix}$;

(b) $\mathbf{y}' = \begin{pmatrix} 0 & 1 \\ -2 & 3 \end{pmatrix}\mathbf{y}$, $\mathbf{y}(0) = \begin{pmatrix} 1 \\ 2 \end{pmatrix}$;

(c) $\mathbf{y}' = \mathbf{A}\mathbf{y}$, $\mathbf{y}(0) = \mathbf{b}$, where $\mathbf{A}$ is a constant matrix.

3. Show that the functional equation

$$f(x_1 + x_2) = f(x_1)f(x_2) ,$$

with the initial condition $f(0) = 1$, has a unique solution in the space C^1. (*Hint:* Deduce that $f'(x) = f(x)$ and that $f(0) = 1$ and then apply the Existence Theorem 2-2.1.)

4. If $f(t, y)$ is a function of 2 variables and if $\partial f(t, y)/\partial y$ is continuous in a region R, show that f satisfies a Lipschitz condition with respect to y in R.

5. If $\mathbf{f}(t, \mathbf{y})$ is a vector-valued function of t and the vector variable $\mathbf{y}$ and if $\partial f_i/\partial y_j, i, j = 1, 2, \ldots, n$, is continuous in a region R show that $\mathbf{f}(t, \mathbf{y})$ satisfies a Lipschitz condition with respect to $\mathbf{y}$ in R.

2-3. CONTINUATION OF SOLUTIONS

The Existence Theorem 2-2.1 provides a local result in the sense that the interval I on which a solution is guaranteed may be short relative to the domain of $\mathbf{f}$. However, any point $(t_1, \mathbf{x}(t_1))$, $t_1 \in I$, on the graph of a solution $\mathbf{x}$ may be taken as an initial point for an application of the existence theorem. This second application establishes a second boxlike region containing the points of a solution $\bar{\mathbf{x}}$. Because of the uniqueness property the two solutions are identical at points which lie in both boxlike regions. The points of $\bar{\mathbf{x}}$ which are associated with values of t outside I provide a continuation of the solution $\mathbf{x}$. The process can be repeated and, in general, yields a solution $\mathbf{y}$ whose graph is a curve with boundary points on the boundary of the domain R of the vector function $\mathbf{f}$.

Much of our attention is devoted to linear differential equations whose coefficients are defined and continuous on some fundamental finite interval $[a, b]$. The basic existence theorem and the process of continuation insures the existence of solutions for all such equations.[2]

2-4. DEPENDENCE OF SOLUTIONS ON INITIAL CONDITIONS[3]

Let the vector-valued function $\mathbf{f}$ in

$$\mathbf{y}' = \mathbf{f}(t, \mathbf{y}) \tag{2-4.1}$$

satisfy the hypotheses of the existence theorem. Let $\mathbf{x}$ be a solution of equation (2-4.1), and let its graph C, consisting of the points $\{(t, \mathbf{x}(t)) : a \leqq t \leqq b\}$, lie entirely in the open connected region of R of $(t, \mathbf{y})$ space. Let the region $U_{\mathbf{x}\delta}$ be defined by

$$U_{\mathbf{x}\delta} = \{(t, \mathbf{y}) : a \leqq t \leqq b,\ \|\mathbf{y} - \mathbf{x}(t)\| < \delta\} .$$

Figure 2-2.3 shows the nature of $U_{\mathbf{x}\delta}$ when $\mathbf{y}$ is a two-dimensional vector with components y_1 and y_2. A physical realization of a region of this type can be obtained by squeezing toothpaste from a tube with a square orifice, the length of the diagonal of the square being 2δ. The curve C forms the axis of the ribbon of toothpaste.

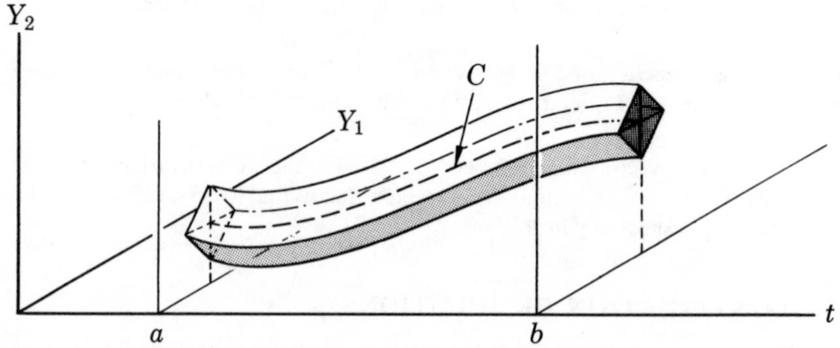

Figure 2-2.3

[2] For more information on "continuation of solutions," the reader is referred to other texts Coddington and Levinson [11] or Lefschetz [32].

[3] The treatment given to this problem follows from Strauss [44], pages 649–652.

The solution $\mathbf{x}$ is an element of the space T consisting of all n-vectors whose components belong to $C[a, b]$. A norm for this space is provided by Definition 1-11.2, and the spherical neighborhood

$$K(\mathbf{x}, \delta) = \{\mathbf{y} : \mathbf{y} \in T, \ \| \mathbf{y} - \mathbf{x} \| < \delta\}$$

(defined in terms of this norm) contains precisely those elements of T whose graphs are in the region $U_{\mathbf{x}\delta}$.

It should be observed that if δ is sufficiently small the region $U_{\mathbf{x}\delta}$ lies entirely in R. Hence, we may choose a positive real number δ_1 such that $U_{\mathbf{x}\delta} \subset R$ if $\delta \leqq \delta_1$. Intuitively one would suppose that any spherical neighborhood of $\mathbf{x}$ would contain solutions (other than $\mathbf{x}$ itself) of equation (2-4.1). This conjecture is supported by the proof of the next theorem.

Theorem 2-4.1. *If $\mathbf{x}$ is a solution of equation* (2-4.1) *then, corresponding to any positive real ε, there exists a positive real δ such that the solution for which $(\tau, \mathbf{b})$ is an initial point is in the spherical neighborhood $K(\mathbf{x}, \varepsilon)$ if $(\tau, \mathbf{b})$ is in $U_{\mathbf{x}\delta}$.*

PROOF. Let ε be any positive real number no larger than δ_1. This is not an essential restriction on ε; it is imposed to insure that $U_{\mathbf{x}\varepsilon}$ lies entirely in R. Let δ be a positive real number such that

$$\delta < \varepsilon e^{-K(b-a)} , \tag{2-4.2}$$

where K is the Lipschitz constant for $\mathbf{f}$. If $(\tau, \mathbf{b})$ is any point in $U_{\mathbf{x}\delta}$, the symbol $\mathbf{y}$ may be used to designate the solution of equation (2-4.1) for which $\mathbf{y}(\tau) = \mathbf{b}$. This solution must be regarded as a local solution, and the discussion is temporarily restricted to values of t in some neighborhood of τ. Let $\hat{\mathbf{b}}$ be defined by $\mathbf{x}(\tau) = \hat{\mathbf{b}}$. The solutions $\mathbf{x}$ and $\mathbf{y}$ must satisfy the following integral relations:

$$\mathbf{x}(t) = \hat{\mathbf{b}} + \int_\tau^t \mathbf{f}(s, \mathbf{x}(s))\, ds ,$$

$$\mathbf{y}(t) = \mathbf{b} + \int_\tau^t \mathbf{f}(s, \mathbf{y}(s))\, ds .$$

Subtracting the first of these from the second and taking the norm of both sides we obtain, for each value of t for which $t \geqq \tau$,

$$\| \mathbf{y}(t) - \mathbf{x}(t) \| \leqq \| \mathbf{b} - \hat{\mathbf{b}} \| + \int_\tau^t \| \mathbf{f}(s, \mathbf{y}(s)) - \mathbf{f}(s, \mathbf{x}(s)) \| \, ds$$

$$\leqq \delta + \int_\tau^t K \| \mathbf{y}(s) - \mathbf{x}(s) \| \, ds .$$

This inequality may be written as

$$\frac{1}{K} R'(t) \leqq \delta + R(t) , \tag{2-4.3}$$

where

$$R(t) = \int_{\tau}^{t} K \| \mathbf{y}(s) - \mathbf{x}(s) \| \, ds \ .$$

Multiplying both sides of relation (2-4.3) by Ke^{-Kt} and transposing part of the right-hand side to the left-hand side, we get

$$R'(t)e^{-Kt} - R(t)Ke^{-Kt} \leqq \delta K e^{-Kt} \ .$$

Since the left-hand side is the derivative of $R(t)e^{-Kt}$ and since $R(\tau) = 0$, integration of both sides from τ to t yields

$$R(t)e^{-Kt} \leqq -\delta e^{-Kt} + \delta e^{-K\tau} \ .$$

Hence,

$$\delta + R(t) \leqq \delta e^{K(t-\tau)} \ .$$

In view of (2-4.3), therefore,

$$\frac{1}{K} R'(t) \leqq \delta e^{K(t-\tau)} \ .$$

This implies that

$$\| \mathbf{y}(t) - \mathbf{x}(t) \| \leqq \delta e^{K(t-\tau)} \leqq \delta e^{K(b-a)} \ .$$

The same result can be achieved when it is assumed that $t < \tau$. Hence, recalling (2-4.2), we may write

(2-4.4) $$\| \mathbf{y}(t) - \mathbf{x}(t) \| < \varepsilon \ .$$

It follows that the graph of $\mathbf{y}$ lies in the region $U_{\mathbf{x}\varepsilon}$ for all values of t for which the existence of the local solution $\mathbf{y}$ was guaranteed. However, since $U_{\mathbf{x}\varepsilon}$ lies in the region R, the continuation of the local solution $\mathbf{y}$ may be effected over the entire interval $[a, b]$. The inequality (2-4.4) is, therefore, valid over that interval. Thus, we insure that $\mathbf{y}$ is nowhere farther than ε from $\mathbf{x}$ by restricting its initial point to be no farther than δ from $\mathbf{x}$. This proves the theorem.

The solution of equation (2-4.1) whose graph contains the point $(\tau, \mathbf{b})$ may be represented by $\mathbf{x}(t, \tau, \mathbf{b})$. Every such symbol, providing $(\tau, \mathbf{b}) \in R$, represents a unique solution of equation (2-4.1). However, since any point on the graph of a solution determines that solution, it is clear that each solution has infinitely many representations of this form. A point $(\tau, \mathbf{b})$ in R which is used to determine the solution $\mathbf{x}(t, \tau, \mathbf{b})$ is called an *initial point* for that solution. It is relevant to ask if a solution depends continuously on its initial point. It is intuitively clear that this question has an affirmative answer. Theorem 2-4.1 shows, in effect, that for any fixed value of τ, a solution depends continuously on the value of $\mathbf{b}$. This fact is used in the proof of the following theorem.

Theorem 2-4.2. *The solution represented by* $\mathbf{x}(t, \tau, \mathbf{b})$ *depends continuously on the initial point* $(\tau, \mathbf{b})$.

PROOF. Let $\mathbf{x}_0$ represent the solution $\mathbf{x}(t, \tau_0, \mathbf{b}_0)$ for which $(\tau_0, \mathbf{b}_0)$ is an initial point. If the point $(\tau_1, \mathbf{b}_1)$ is close to $(\tau_0, \mathbf{b}_0)$, it is close to $\mathbf{x}_0$ in the sense that it lies in some region $U_{\mathbf{x}_0\delta}$. This statement can be made precise as follows. Let $\delta \leqq \delta_1$ be a positive real number. The continuity of $\mathbf{x}_0(t)$ insures the existence of a positive real number η_1 such that

$$\| \mathbf{x}_0(\tau_1) - \mathbf{x}_0(\tau_0) \| < \tfrac{1}{2}\delta \quad \text{if} \quad |\tau_1 - \tau_0| < \eta_1 .$$

It follows that

$$\begin{aligned} \| \mathbf{b}_1 - \mathbf{x}_0(\tau_1) \| &= \| \mathbf{b}_1 - \mathbf{x}_0(\tau_0) + \mathbf{x}_0(\tau_0) - \mathbf{x}_0(\tau_1) \| \\ &\leqq \| \mathbf{b}_1 - \mathbf{b}_0 \| + \| \mathbf{x}_0(\tau_1) - \mathbf{x}_0(\tau_0) \| \\ &< \tfrac{1}{2}\delta + \tfrac{1}{2}\delta = \delta , \end{aligned}$$

if $\| \mathbf{b}_1 - \mathbf{b}_0 \| < \tfrac{1}{2}\delta$ and $|\tau_1 - \tau_0| < \eta_1$.

If η is the smaller of η_1 and $\tfrac{1}{2}\delta$, the above statement implies that

$$\| \mathbf{b}_1 - \mathbf{x}_0(\tau_1) \| < \delta \tag{2-4.5}$$

if $\| \mathbf{b}_1 - \mathbf{b}_0 \| + |\tau_1 - \tau_0| < \eta$. The natural metric ρ for $(t, \mathbf{y})$ space is

$$\rho((t_1, \mathbf{y}_1), (t_2, \mathbf{y}_2)) = \| \mathbf{y}_1 - \mathbf{y}_2 \| + |t_1 - t_2| .$$

Hence, relation (2-4.5) may be rewritten as

$$(\tau_1, \mathbf{b}_1) \in U_{\mathbf{x}_0\delta}$$

if $\rho((\tau_0, \mathbf{b}_0), (\tau_1, \mathbf{b}_1)) < \eta$.

In order to complete the proof of the theorem, let $\varepsilon \leqq \delta_1$ be a positive real number and let δ satisfy relation (2-4.2). If η is determined as above, Theorem 2-4.1 implies that the solution represented by $\mathbf{x}(t, \tau_1, \mathbf{b}_1)$ lies in $K(\mathbf{x}_0, \varepsilon)$ if $\rho((\tau_0, \mathbf{b}_0), (\tau_1, \mathbf{b}_1)) < \eta$. This proves the theorem.

The symbol $\mathbf{x}(t, \tau, \mathbf{b})$ may be regarded as a function of $n+2$ variables. These variables are t, τ, and the components of $\mathbf{b}$. The following corollary states an easily verified consequence of the above theorem.

Corollary 2-4.2. *The function* $\mathbf{x}(t, \tau, \mathbf{b})$ *is a continuous function of its* $n+2$ *variables.*

Exercises

1. Prove Corollary 2-4.2.
2. Find the solution of

$$\mathbf{y}' = \begin{pmatrix} 0 & 1 \\ -1 & 0 \end{pmatrix} \mathbf{y} ,$$

$$\mathbf{y}(\tau) = \mathbf{b} ,$$

and use it to illustrate the result of Theorem 2-4.1.

2-5. DEPENDENCE OF SOLUTIONS ON PARAMETERS

Frequently one or more parameters are present in a differential equation. The solutions are bound to depend upon these parameters, and it is helpful to determine if this dependence is continuous. Let us consider

$$\mathbf{y}' = \mathbf{f}(t, \mathbf{y}, \mathbf{p}) \ , \tag{2-5.1}$$

where the components of the k-vector $\mathbf{p}$ play the role of parameters. It is assumed that $\mathbf{f}$ is continuous over a region which may be described as the Cartesian product of an open connected region R in $(t, \mathbf{y})$ space and an interval $I_{\mathbf{p}}$ in the parameter space. This interval is

$$I_{\mathbf{p}} = \{\mathbf{p} : \| \mathbf{p} - \mathbf{a} \| < c\}$$

for some k-vector $\mathbf{a}$ and some positive real number c. It is assumed that $\mathbf{f}$ satisfies a Lipschitz condition with respect to $\mathbf{y}$ for every $\mathbf{p}$ in $I_{\mathbf{p}}$.

Theorem 2-5.1. *A solution of equation* (2-5.1) *depends continuously on the parameter.*

PROOF. Let $\mathbf{x}_0$ be the solution of $\mathbf{y}' = \mathbf{f}(t, \mathbf{y}, \mathbf{p}_0)$ determined by the initial point $(\tau, \mathbf{b})$. If $\varepsilon \leqq \delta_1$ is a positive real number, we can choose a number δ such that

$$\| \mathbf{f}(t, \mathbf{x}_0(t), \mathbf{p}_1) - \mathbf{f}(t, \mathbf{x}_0(t), \mathbf{p}_0) \| < \frac{\varepsilon}{b-a} e^{-K(b-a)} \ , \tag{2-5.2}$$

for all t in $[a, b]$, if $\| \mathbf{p}_1 - \mathbf{p}_0 \| < \delta$. Let $\mathbf{x}_1$ be the solution of $\mathbf{y}' = \mathbf{f}(t, \mathbf{y}, \mathbf{p}_1)$ determined by the same initial point $(\tau, \mathbf{b})$ mentioned above. For the two solutions $\mathbf{x}_0$ and $\mathbf{x}_1$, we may write the integral relations

$$\mathbf{x}_0(t) = \mathbf{b} + \int_\tau^t \mathbf{f}(s, \mathbf{x}_0(s), \mathbf{p}_0)\, ds \ ,$$

$$\mathbf{x}_1(t) = \mathbf{b} + \int_\tau^t \mathbf{f}(s, \mathbf{x}_1(s), \mathbf{p}_1)\, ds \ .$$

It follows that, for $t \geqq \tau$,

$$\begin{aligned} \| \mathbf{x}_0(t) - \mathbf{x}_1(t) \| &\leqq \int_\tau^t \| \mathbf{f}(s, \mathbf{x}_0(s), \mathbf{p}_0) - \mathbf{f}(s, \mathbf{x}_1(s), \mathbf{p}_1) \| \, ds \\ &\leqq \int_\tau^t \| \mathbf{f}(s, \mathbf{x}_0(s), \mathbf{p}_0) - \mathbf{f}(s, \mathbf{x}_0(s), \mathbf{p}_1) \| \, ds \\ &\quad + \int_\tau^t \| \mathbf{f}(s, \mathbf{x}_0(s), \mathbf{p}_1) - f(s, \mathbf{x}_1(s), \mathbf{p}_1) \| \, ds \ . \end{aligned}$$

In view of (2-5.2), under the assumption that $\| \mathbf{p}_1 - \mathbf{p}_0 \| < \delta$, we have

$$\| \mathbf{x}_0(t) - \mathbf{x}_1(t) \| < \varepsilon e^{-K(b-a)} + \int_\tau^t K \| \mathbf{x}_0(s) - \mathbf{x}_1(s) \| \, ds \ .$$

Exactly as in Theorem 2-4.1, we deduce that

$$\| \mathbf{x}_0(t) - \mathbf{x}_1(t) \| < \varepsilon$$

for all t on $[a, b]$. Since

$$\| \mathbf{x}_0 - \mathbf{x}_1 \| = \sup_{t \in [a, b]} \| \mathbf{x}_0(t) - \mathbf{x}_1(t) \| ,$$

we can write

$$\mathbf{x}_1 \in K(\mathbf{x}_0, \varepsilon)$$

if $\| \mathbf{p}_1 - \mathbf{p}_0 \| < \delta$. This proves the theorem.

The solution of equation (2-5.1) determined by the initial point $(\tau, \mathbf{b})$ may be represented by $\mathbf{x}(t, \tau, \mathbf{b}, \mathbf{p})$.

Corollary 2-5.1a. *For any positive real ε there exists a positive real δ such that the solution represented by $\mathbf{x}(t, \tau, \mathbf{b}, \mathbf{p})$ is in the spherical neighborhood $K(\mathbf{x}_0, \varepsilon)$ if $|\tau - \tau_0| + \| \mathbf{b} - \mathbf{b}_0 \| + \| \mathbf{p} - \mathbf{p}_0 \| < \delta$, where $\mathbf{x}_0$ is the solution represented by $\mathbf{x}(t, \tau_0, \mathbf{b}_0, \mathbf{p}_0)$.*

Corollary 2-5.1b. *The function $\mathbf{x}(t, \tau, \mathbf{b}, \mathbf{p})$ is a continuous function of its $n+k+2$ variables.*

Assuming that $\mathbf{f}(t, \mathbf{y}, \mathbf{p})$ has continuous partial derivatives with respect to the components of $\mathbf{y}$ and $\mathbf{p}$, it can be shown that a solution of equation (2-5.1) is differentiable with respect to the coordinates of the initial point and the components of the parameter vector.[4]

Exercises

1. Prove Corollary 2-5.1a.

2. Prove Corollary 2-5.1b.

3. Find the solution of

$$\mathbf{y}' = \begin{pmatrix} 0 & 1 \\ -\lambda^2 & 0 \end{pmatrix} \mathbf{y} ,$$

$$\mathbf{y}(\tau) = \mathbf{b} ,$$

and use it to illustrate the results of Theorem 2-5.1.

[4] A thorough discussion of this topic is found in Coddington and Levinson [11] and Hartman [23].

3

General Theory for Linear Differential Equations

3-1. EXISTENCE OF SOLUTIONS

The linear system

$$y_i' = \sum_{j=1}^{n} a_{ij}(t) y_j \ , \quad i = 1, 2, \ldots, n \tag{3-1.1}$$

is a special case of the system (2-2.1). It is obtained by restricting $f_i(t, y_1, \ldots, y_n)$, $i = 1, 2, \ldots, n$, to the linear form

$$\sum_{j=1}^{n} a_{ij}(t) y_j \ .$$

The corresponding vector equation is readily seen to be

$$\mathbf{y}' = \mathbf{A}\mathbf{y} \ , \tag{3-1.2}$$

where

$$\mathbf{A} = \mathbf{A}(t) = (a_{ij}(t)) \ .$$

We assume that the components of $\mathbf{A}$ are continuous functions of t on the interval $[a, b]$. Therefore the region R on which the right-hand side of equation (3-1.2) is defined is

$$R: a \leqq t \leqq b \ , \quad \| y \| < \infty \ .$$

Since the components of $\mathbf{A}$ are continuous on a closed interval, they are bounded. Hence the norm of $\mathbf{A}$ relative to $[a, b]$ exists and may be designated by some positive real number M. It follows that for $t \in [a, b]$

$$\| \mathbf{A}(t) \| \leqq M \ .$$

If $(t, \mathbf{y}_1)$ and $(t, \mathbf{y}_2)$ are two points in R then

$$\begin{aligned} \| \mathbf{A}(t)\mathbf{y}_1 - \mathbf{A}(t)\mathbf{y}_2 \| &\leqq \| \mathbf{A}(t) \| \, \| \mathbf{y}_1 - \mathbf{y}_2 \| \\ &\leqq M \| \mathbf{y}_1 - \mathbf{y}_2 \| \ . \end{aligned}$$

Thus, the equation satisfies a Lipschitz condition in R. It follows that for any t_0 in $[a, b]$ and any $\mathbf{y}_0$ in $V_n(R)$ the initial-value problem

$$\mathbf{y}' = \mathbf{A}\mathbf{y} \ ,$$

$$\mathbf{y}(t_0) = \mathbf{y}_0 \ ,$$

has a unique solution. Moreover, by an application of the continuation process this solution can be shown to be valid on the fundamental interval $[a, b]$.[1]

It should be recalled that this solution is a continuous function of the initial conditions. In addition, if the matrix $\mathbf{A}$ depends continuously on a set of parameters, the solution is a continuous function of these parameters.

3-2. SOLUTION SPACE

In Section 2-1 examples were given illustrating that the solutions of any linear differential equation (or system of equations) form a finite-dimensional vector space. This will now be established for the general equation (3-1.2).

Theorem 3-2.1. *The solutions of the linear differential equation* (3-1.2) *form a vector space, called the solution space.*

PROOF. Let $\mathbf{y}_1$ and $\mathbf{y}_2$ be any two solutions of (3-1.2), and let α_1 and α_2 be any two real constants.

$$\begin{aligned}(\alpha_1\mathbf{y}_1+\alpha_2\mathbf{y}_2)' &= \alpha_1\mathbf{y}_1'+\alpha_2\mathbf{y}_2' \\ &= \alpha_1\mathbf{A}\mathbf{y}_1+\alpha_2\mathbf{A}\mathbf{y}_2 \\ &= \mathbf{A}(\alpha_1\mathbf{y}_1+\alpha_2\mathbf{y}_2) \ .\end{aligned}$$

This implies that $\alpha_1\mathbf{y}_1+\alpha_2\mathbf{y}_2$ is a solution of equation (3-1.2). The solutions, therefore, form a vector space that is a subspace of the space of all n-vectors with components in $C^1[a\ b,]$.

The next theorem establishes the dimension of the solution space.

Theorem 3-2.2. *The equation* (3-1.2) *has n linearly independent solutions, and every solution of the equation is expressible as a linear combination of these n solutions.*

PROOF. Let t_0 be any point in $[a, b]$, and let $\mathbf{b}_1, \mathbf{b}_2, \ldots, \mathbf{b}_n$ be any set of n linearly independent n-vectors in $V_n(R)$. Let $\mathbf{u}_j$ be the solution of (3-1.2) which satisfies the initial condition

$$\mathbf{y}(t_0) = \mathbf{b}_j \ , \quad j = 1, 2, \ldots, n \ .$$

If the set $\{\mathbf{u}_j\}$ were a linearly dependent set, there would exist scalars $\alpha_1, \alpha_2, \ldots,$ α_n, not all zero, such that

$$\sum_{j=1}^{n} \alpha_j \mathbf{u}_j = \mathbf{o} \ .$$

This would imply that

$$\sum_{j=1}^{n} \alpha_j \mathbf{u}_j(t_0) = \mathbf{o}$$

[1] For the development of this process, see Coddington and Levinson [11], Chapter 1, Section 5.

and, hence, that the set $\{\mathbf{b}_j\}$ is a linearly dependent set. Since this is contrary to our assumption for $\{\mathbf{b}_j\}$, we must infer that $\{\mathbf{u}_j\}$ is a linearly independent set.

To prove the second part of the theorem, let $\mathbf{u}$ be any solution of equation (3-1.2). Since the set $\{\mathbf{b}_j\}$ is a basis for $V_n(R)$, there exists a set of scalars $\{\alpha_j\}$ such that

$$\sum_{j=1}^{n} \alpha_j \mathbf{b}_j = \mathbf{u}(t_0) \ .$$

Using these scalars, we may define the vector $\mathbf{v}$ by

$$\mathbf{v} = \sum_{j=1}^{n} \alpha_j \mathbf{u}_j \ .$$

Clearly $\mathbf{v}$ is a solution of (3-1.2) such that

$$\mathbf{v}(t_0) = \mathbf{u}(t_0) \ .$$

The uniqueness property, therefore, insures that

$$\mathbf{v} = \mathbf{u}$$

and, hence, that

$$\mathbf{u} = \sum_{j=1}^{n} \alpha_j \mathbf{u}_j \ .$$

This proves the theorem and establishes the fact that the solutions of equation (3-1.2) form an n-dimensional vector space.

Corollary 3-2.2a. *Any set of n linearly independent solutions of equation* (3-1.2) *is a basis for its solution space.*

Corollary 3-2.2b. *If all the components of a solution $\mathbf{u}$ of equation* (3-1.2) *are zero at some point t_0 of $[a, b]$, then $\mathbf{u} = \mathbf{o}$.*

Corollary 3-2.2c. *If a set of solutions $\mathbf{u}_1, \mathbf{u}_2, \ldots, \mathbf{u}_k$ is such that their functional values $\mathbf{u}_1(t_0), \mathbf{u}_2(t_0), \ldots, \mathbf{u}_k(t_0)$ is a linearly dependent set for any t_0 in $[a, b]$, then the solutions are linearly dependent and their functional values are linearly dependent at every t on $[a, b]$.*

Definition 3-2.1. *Any set of n linearly independent solutions of* (3-1.2) *is a **fundamental set of solutions** of the equation. The matrix with these particular solutions as columns is a **fundamental matrix** for the given equation.*

Let $\mathbf{y}_1, \mathbf{y}_2, \ldots, \mathbf{y}_n$ be a fundamental set of solutions of equation (3-1.2) and let

$$\mathbf{Y} = (\mathbf{y}_1, \mathbf{y}_2, \ldots, \mathbf{y}_n)$$

be the corresponding fundamental matrix. Clearly, for any constant n-vector $\mathbf{c}$, $\mathbf{Yc}$ is a solution of (3-1.2), and every solution of that equation can be expressed in this form. Corollary 3-2.2c implies that $\mathbf{Y}(t)$ is nonsingular at each point t of $[a, b]$. Hence, its inverse $\mathbf{Y}^{-1}(t)$ is defined on $[a, b]$, and its determinant $|\mathbf{Y}(t)|$ is not zero for any t in $[a, b]$. In addition, if $\mathbf{C}$ is any constant nonsingular matrix of order n, then $\mathbf{YC}$ is a fundamental matrix and every fundamental matrix can be expressed in this form.

The matrix equation

$$\mathbf{Y}' = \mathbf{AY} \tag{3-2.1}$$

can be regarded as a generalization of the vector equation (3-1.2). It is easily seen that a matrix is a solution of (3-2.1) if and only if its columns regarded as vectors are solutions of (3-1.2). A fundamental matrix for (3-1.2) will also be called a fundamental matrix for (3-2.1). The solutions of the matrix equation are given by $\mathbf{YC}$, where $\mathbf{C}$ is an arbitrary constant matrix with n rows.

Theorem 3-2.3. *A vector (or matrix) equation is completely determined by one of its fundamental matrices.*

PROOF. If $\mathbf{Y}$ is a fundamental matrix for

$$\mathbf{y}' = \mathbf{Ay} \ ,$$

then

$$\mathbf{Y}' = \mathbf{AY} \ .$$

It follows that

$$\mathbf{A} = \mathbf{Y}'\mathbf{Y}^{-1} \ .$$

Since the equation is determined by the matrix $\mathbf{A}$, the proof of the theorem is complete.

Definition 3-2.2. *The **trace** of an n by n matrix $\mathbf{B}$, designated by* tr$\mathbf{B}$, *is defined by*

$$\mathrm{tr}\mathbf{B} = \sum_{j=1}^{n} b_{jj} \ .$$

It is a familiar fact that the trace and the determinant of a matrix are invariant under a similarity transformation.

The following interesting result involving the determinant of a fundamental matrix is given as a theorem.

Theorem 3-2.4. *If $\mathbf{Y}$ is a fundamental matrix for the equation* (3-2.1) *and if Y designates the determinant of $\mathbf{Y}$, then for all t_0, $t \in [a, b]$*

$$Y(t) = Y(t_0) \exp\left[\int_{t_0}^{t} \mathrm{tr}\mathbf{A}(s)\, ds\right] \ .$$

PROOF. Using the basic definition of a determinant as the sum of the products of the elements, we have (see Exercise 4 of this section)

$$Y' = \begin{vmatrix} y_{11}' & y_{12}' & \cdots & y_{1n}' \\ y_{21} & y_{22} & \cdots & y_{2n} \\ \cdot & \cdot & \cdot & \cdot \\ \cdot & \cdot & \cdot & \cdot \\ \cdot & \cdot & \cdot & \cdot \\ y_{n1} & y_{n2} & \cdots & y_{nn} \end{vmatrix} + \begin{vmatrix} y_{11} & y_{12} & \cdots & y_{1n} \\ y_{21}' & y_{22}' & \cdots & y_{2n}' \\ \cdot & \cdot & \cdot & \cdot \\ \cdot & \cdot & \cdot & \cdot \\ \cdot & \cdot & \cdot & \cdot \\ y_{n1} & y_{n2} & \cdots & y_{nn} \end{vmatrix} + \cdots$$

$$+ \begin{vmatrix} y_{11} & y_{12} & \cdots & y_{1n} \\ y_{21} & y_{22} & \cdots & y_{2n} \\ \cdot & \cdot & \cdot & \cdot \\ \cdot & \cdot & \cdot & \cdot \\ \cdot & \cdot & \cdot & \cdot \\ y_{n1}' & y_{n2}' & \cdots & y_{nn}' \end{vmatrix} .$$

Let $\mathbf{I}_{hl}$ be defined as a matrix of zeros except for a single unit element in the hth row and lth column. That is,

$$\mathbf{I}_{hl} = (\delta_{ih}\delta_{lj}) \; ,$$

where δ_{ij} is Kronecker's delta. Also, let $\mathbf{I}^{hh}$ be defined by

$$\mathbf{I}^{hh} = \mathbf{I} - \mathbf{I}_{hh} \; , \quad h = 1, 2, \ldots, n \; .$$

Using this notation, we can write the above expression for the derivative of Y as

$$Y' = \sum_{j=1}^{n} |\mathbf{I}^{jj}\mathbf{Y} + \mathbf{I}_{jj}\mathbf{Y}'| \; .$$

Since $\mathbf{Y}$ is a solution of (3-2.1), we have

$$\begin{aligned} Y' &= \sum_{j=1}^{n} |\mathbf{I}^{jj}\mathbf{Y} + \mathbf{I}_{jj}\mathbf{A}\mathbf{Y}| \\ &= \sum_{j=1}^{n} |\mathbf{I}^{jj} + \mathbf{I}_{jj}\mathbf{A}| \, |\mathbf{Y}| \\ &= \sum_{j=1}^{n} a_{jj} Y \\ &= (\mathrm{tr}\mathbf{A})Y \; . \end{aligned}$$

Since $Y \neq 0$ on $[a, b]$,

$$Y(t) = Y(t_0) \exp\left[\int_{t_0}^{t} \mathrm{tr}\, \mathbf{A}(s)\, ds\right] \; .$$

This proves the theorem.

The essential result of this section is the demonstration that the solution space of the equation $\mathbf{y}' = \mathbf{A}\mathbf{y}$ is an n-dimensional vector space. The space is the column space of any fundamental matrix for the equation, since the columns of that matrix form a basis for the solution space.

Example 1. For the purpose of illustration, we consider a previous example,

$$\mathbf{y}' = \begin{pmatrix} 0 & 1 \\ -2 & 3 \end{pmatrix} \mathbf{y} . \tag{3-2.2}$$

The two solutions given in Section 2-1 are

$$\mathbf{u}_1(t) = \begin{pmatrix} e^t \\ e^t \end{pmatrix} \quad \text{and} \quad \mathbf{u}_2(t) = \begin{pmatrix} e^{2t} \\ 2e^{2t} \end{pmatrix} .$$

Since $\mathbf{u}_1(0)$ and $\mathbf{u}_2(0)$ are linearly independent, we know from Theorem 3-2.2 that $\mathbf{u}_1$ and $\mathbf{u}_2$ form a basis for the solution space of the equation. The fundamental matrix with these solutions as columns is

$$\mathbf{Y}(t) = \begin{pmatrix} e^t & e^{2t} \\ e^t & 2e^{2t} \end{pmatrix} .$$

The determinant of $\mathbf{Y}(t)$ is $|\mathbf{Y}(t)| = e^{3t}$. Since the trace of the coefficient matrix in equation (3-2.2) is 3, this determinant satisfies the formula of Theorem 3-2.4 with $t_0 = 0$. Finally we may illustrate a result from Theorem 3-2.3 by noting that

$$\mathbf{Y}'(t)\mathbf{Y}^{-1}(t) = \begin{pmatrix} 0 & 1 \\ -2 & 3 \end{pmatrix} .$$

Exercises

1. In each of the following cases determine whether or not the given matrix **Y** is a fundamental matrix for the corresponding equation.

(a) $\mathbf{y}' = \begin{pmatrix} 1 & 1 \\ 0 & -1 \end{pmatrix} \mathbf{y}$, $\quad \mathbf{Y} = \begin{pmatrix} e^t & e^{-t} \\ 0 & -2e^{-t} \end{pmatrix}$;

(b) $\mathbf{y}' = \begin{pmatrix} 0 & 1 \\ 2 & 1 \end{pmatrix} \mathbf{y}$, $\quad \mathbf{Y} = \begin{pmatrix} e^{2t} & e^{-t} \\ 2e^{2t} & -e^{-t} \end{pmatrix}$;

(c) $\mathbf{y}' = \begin{pmatrix} 0 & 1 \\ -2 & -3 \end{pmatrix} \mathbf{y}$, $\quad \mathbf{Y} = \begin{pmatrix} e^{-2t} & -3e^{-2t} \\ -2e^{-2t} & 6e^{-2t} \end{pmatrix}$;

(d) $\mathbf{y}' = \begin{pmatrix} 1 & 1 \\ -1 & -1 \end{pmatrix} \mathbf{y}$, $\quad \mathbf{Y} = \begin{pmatrix} 1 & 2t+1 \\ -1 & -2t+1 \end{pmatrix}$;

(e) $\mathbf{y}' = \begin{pmatrix} 1 & 1 \\ 0 & 1 \end{pmatrix} \mathbf{y}$, $\quad \mathbf{Y} = \begin{pmatrix} e^t & (t+1)e^t \\ 0 & e^t \end{pmatrix}$.

2. Find the vector differential equations for which the following are fundamental matrices.

(a) $\begin{pmatrix} e^{-t} & e^{-2t} \\ -e^{-t} & -2e^{-2t} \end{pmatrix}$; $\quad$ (b) $\begin{pmatrix} \sin t & \cos t \\ \cos t & -\sin t \end{pmatrix}$;

(c) $\begin{pmatrix} 2e^{-t} & e^{t/2} \\ -e^{-t} & e^{t/2} \end{pmatrix}$; $\quad$ (d) $\begin{pmatrix} e^t & te^t \\ e^t & (t+1)e^t \end{pmatrix}$;

(e) $\begin{pmatrix} e^{-t} & e^t & te^t \\ -e^{-t} & e^t & (t+1)e^t \\ e^{-t} & e^t & (t+2)e^t \end{pmatrix}$; (f) $\begin{pmatrix} 1 & t & t^2 \\ 0 & 1 & t \\ 0 & 0 & 1 \end{pmatrix}$;

(g) $\begin{pmatrix} 1 & t & t^2 \\ 0 & 1 & 2t \\ 0 & 0 & 2 \end{pmatrix}$; (h) $\sum_{j=1}^{n} \mathbf{k}(t^{j-1})\tilde{\mathbf{d}}_j$.

3. Check the results of Theorem 3-2.4 for some of the matrices given in Exercise 2.

4. Derive the formula, quoted in Theorem 3-2.4, for the derivative of a determinant.

5. If $\mathbf{Y}$ is a fundamental matrix for the vector equation $\mathbf{y}' = \mathbf{A}\mathbf{y}$ and if $\mathbf{T}$ is any constant, nonsingular, n by n matrix, find the vector equation for which $\mathbf{TY}$ is a fundamental matrix.

3-3. THE NONHOMOGENEOUS EQUATION

The equation

(3-3.1) $$\mathbf{y}' = \mathbf{A}\mathbf{y} + \mathbf{f} \ ,$$

where $f_j \in C[a, b]$, is commonly referred to as the *nonhomogeneous* equation corresponding to the *homogeneous* equation

(3-3.2) $$\mathbf{y}' = \mathbf{A}\mathbf{y} \ .$$

We shall see that the solutions of (3-3.1) do not form a vector space (unless $\mathbf{f} = \mathbf{o}$) but that they can be simply expressed in terms of the solutions of the homogeneous equation. The following theorem shows this.

Theorem 3-3.1. *If* $\bar{\mathbf{y}}$ *is any "particular" solution of the nonhomogeneous equation* (3-3.1) *and* $\mathbf{Y}$ *is a fundamental matrix for the corresponding homogeneous equation* (3-3.2), *then* $\mathbf{y}$ *defined by*

(3-3.3) $$\mathbf{y} = \bar{\mathbf{y}} + \mathbf{Y}\mathbf{c}$$

is a solution of (3-3.1) *for every* $\mathbf{c}$ *in* $V_n(R)$, *and every solution is of this form.*

PROOF. It is easily verified that $\mathbf{y}$, defined by (3-3.3), is a solution of equation (3-3.1) for any constant n-vector $\mathbf{c}$. Further, if $\mathbf{u}$ is any solution of (3-3.1), then

$$(\mathbf{u} - \bar{\mathbf{y}})' = \mathbf{A}(\mathbf{u} - \bar{\mathbf{y}}) \ .$$

Hence, $(\mathbf{u} - \bar{\mathbf{y}})$ is a solution of equation (3-3.2). It follows, that for some constant vector $\mathbf{c}$,

$$\mathbf{u} - \bar{\mathbf{y}} = \mathbf{Y}\mathbf{c} \ .$$

Hence,

$$\mathbf{u} = \bar{\mathbf{y}} + \mathbf{Y}\mathbf{c} \ .$$

This proves the theorem.

The following theorem provides a formula for a particular solution of the nonhomogeneous equation. The formula is derived by a device that is commonly known as the *method of variation of parameters.*

Theorem 3-3.2. *A particular solution* $\bar{\mathbf{y}}$ *of the nonhomogeneous equation* (3-3.1) *is given by*

$$\bar{\mathbf{y}}(t) = \mathbf{Y}(t) \int_a^t \mathbf{Y}^{-1}(s)\mathbf{f}(s)\, ds \ ,$$

where $\mathbf{Y}$ *is any fundamental matrix for the corresponding homogeneous equation* (3-3.2).

PROOF. Let $\mathbf{Y}$ be a fundamental matrix for equation (3-3.2). The vector

$$\bar{\mathbf{y}} = \mathbf{Y}\mathbf{h} \ , \tag{3-3.4}$$

is a solution of (3-3.2) if $\mathbf{h}$ is any constant vector. However, by considering $\mathbf{h}$ to be a function of the variable t, we may assume that $\bar{\mathbf{y}}$ is a solution of (3-3.1) and attempt to determine $\mathbf{h}$ so that this is the case. Substituting from (3-3.4) into equation (3-3.1), we have

$$\mathbf{Y}\mathbf{h}' + \mathbf{Y}'\mathbf{h} = \mathbf{A}\mathbf{Y}\mathbf{h} + \mathbf{f} \ .$$

Since $\mathbf{Y}$ satisfies the homogeneous equation, this reduces to

$$\mathbf{Y}\mathbf{h}' = \mathbf{f}$$

or

$$\mathbf{h}' = \mathbf{Y}^{-1}\mathbf{f} \ .$$

The vector $\mathbf{h}$ satisfies this condition, if

$$\mathbf{h}(t) = \int_a^t \mathbf{Y}^{-1}(s)\mathbf{f}(s)\, ds \ .$$

Hence,

$$\bar{\mathbf{y}}(t) = \mathbf{Y}(t) \int_a^t \mathbf{Y}^{-1}(s)\mathbf{f}(s)\, ds \tag{3-3.5}$$

determines a possible solution of equation (3-3.1). The proof of the theorem is completed by verifying that this evaluation of $\bar{\mathbf{y}}$ satisfies the equation.

Corollary 3-3.2. *The matrix equation*

$$\mathbf{Y}' = \mathbf{A}\mathbf{Y} + \mathbf{B} \ ,$$

where $\mathbf{B}$ *is any* n *by* k *matrix with components in* $C[a, b]$, *has a particular solution given by*

$$\bar{\mathbf{Y}}(t) = \mathbf{Y}(t) \int_a^t \mathbf{Y}^{-1}(s)\mathbf{B}(s)\, ds \ .$$

It should be noted that an equally suitable particular solution of the nonhomogeneous equation is defined by formula (3-3.5) if the lower limit of integration a is replaced by t_0, where t_0 is any point in $[a, b]$.

Example 1. Consider

(3-3.6)
$$\mathbf{y}' = \begin{pmatrix} 0 & 1 \\ -2 & 3 \end{pmatrix} \mathbf{y} + \begin{pmatrix} 1 \\ 1 \end{pmatrix} .$$

For the corresponding homogeneous equation, a fundamental matrix and its inverse are given by (see Example 1 of Section 3-2)

$$\mathbf{Y}(t) = \begin{pmatrix} e^t & e^{2t} \\ e^t & 2e^{2t} \end{pmatrix} , \quad \mathbf{Y}^{-1}(t) = \begin{pmatrix} 2e^{-t} & -e^{-t} \\ -e^{-2t} & e^{-2t} \end{pmatrix} .$$

In view of formula (3-3.5), a solution $\bar{\mathbf{y}}$ of equation (3-3.6) is given by

$$\bar{\mathbf{y}}(t) = \begin{pmatrix} e^t & e^{2t} \\ e^t & 2e^{2t} \end{pmatrix} \int_0^t \begin{pmatrix} 2e^{-s} & -e^{-s} \\ -e^{-2s} & e^{-2s} \end{pmatrix} \begin{pmatrix} 1 \\ 1 \end{pmatrix} ds$$

$$= (e^t - 1) \begin{pmatrix} 1 \\ 1 \end{pmatrix} .$$

It is easily verified that this is, in fact, a particular solution of (3-3.6).

Exercises

1. Find particular solutions for the following equations (see Exercise 1 of Section 3-2).

(a) $\mathbf{y}' = \begin{pmatrix} 1 & 1 \\ 0 & -1 \end{pmatrix} \mathbf{y} + \begin{pmatrix} 1 \\ 0 \end{pmatrix}$; (b) $\mathbf{y}' = \begin{pmatrix} 1 & 1 \\ 0 & -1 \end{pmatrix} \mathbf{y} + \begin{pmatrix} e^{2t} \\ e^{-2t} \end{pmatrix}$;

(c) $\mathbf{y}' = \begin{pmatrix} 0 & 1 \\ 2 & 1 \end{pmatrix} \mathbf{y} + \begin{pmatrix} 1 \\ 1 \end{pmatrix}$; (d) $\mathbf{y}' = \begin{pmatrix} 1 & 1 \\ -1 & -1 \end{pmatrix} \mathbf{y} + \begin{pmatrix} t \\ 1 \end{pmatrix}$;

2. (a) Derive a formula for the solution of the initial-value problem

$$\mathbf{y}' = \mathbf{A}\mathbf{y} + \mathbf{f} ,$$

$$\mathbf{y}(a) = \mathbf{b} .$$

(b) Do part (a) when the initial condition is replaced by $\mathbf{y}(t_0) = \mathbf{b}$, where t_0 is any point in $[a, b]$.

3-4. THE nth-ORDER LINEAR HOMOGENEOUS EQUATION

Let a differential form Lu be defined by

(3-4.1)
$$Lu = u^{[n]} + p_1 u^{[n-1]} + \cdots + p_n u ,$$

where

$$p_j \in C[a, b] .$$

The equation

$$Lu = 0 \tag{3-4.2}$$

is an nth-*order homogeneous linear differential equation.* To avoid a consideration of singular points we have specified a unit coefficient for the nth derivative of u.

Definition 3-4.1. *A function u is a* ***solution*** *of* (3-4.2) *if it belongs to* $C^n[a, b]$ *and satisfies the equation at each point of* $[a, b]$.

Equation (3-4.2), together with the auxiliary conditions

$$\begin{aligned} u(t_0) &= b_1 \ , \\ u'(t_0) &= b_2 \ , \\ &\ \ \vdots \\ u^{[n-1]}(t_0) &= b_n \ , \end{aligned} \tag{3-4.3}$$

is an *initial-value problem.* Recalling the definition of a Wronskian vector in Section 1-3, we observe that equation (3-4.2) can be written as

$$u^{[n]} + \tilde{\mathbf{p}}\mathbf{k}(u) = 0 \ , \tag{3-4.4}$$

where

$$\tilde{\mathbf{p}} = (p_n, p_{n-1}, \ldots, p_1) \ ,$$

and the initial conditions (3-4.3) are written as

$$\mathbf{k}(u(t_0)) = \mathbf{b} \ . \tag{3-4.5}$$

A solution of equation (3-4.2) which also satisfies the conditions (3-4.3) is a solution of the initial-value problem.

Before investigating the existence of solutions it is desirable to establish the linear properties of the equation. To this end, we note that

$$v = Lu \tag{3-4.6}$$

defines a mapping of $C^n[a, b]$ into $C[a, b]$. If u_1 and u_2 are any two functions in $C^n[a, b]$ and if α_1 and α_2 are any two scalars, then (with p_0 defined to be 1)

$$\begin{aligned} L(\alpha_1 u_1 + \alpha_2 u_2) &= \sum_{j=0}^{n} p_j(\alpha_1 u_1 + \alpha_2 u_2)^{[n-j]} \\ &= \alpha_1 \sum_{j=0}^{n} p_j u_1^{[n-j]} + \alpha_2 \sum_{j=0}^{n} p_j u_2^{[n-j]} \\ &= \alpha_1 L u_1 + \alpha_2 L u_2 \ . \end{aligned}$$

This implies that the transformation is linear and justifies the calling of equation (3-4.2) a linear equation.

The solutions of equation (3-4.2) are precisely those functions whose images, under (3-4.6), are zero functions. That is to say, the solutions constitute the *kernel* of the transformation. It is easily verified that the solutions form a vector subspace of $C^n[a, b]$. This subspace is the *solution space* of equation (3-4.2).

The properties of the solution space of equation (3-4.2) can be inferred from the corresponding properties of a related vector equation. This vector equation, which is called the *companion equation* of (3-4.2), is

$$\mathbf{y}' = \mathbf{A}\mathbf{y} \ , \tag{3-4.7}$$

where

$$\mathbf{A} = \begin{bmatrix} 0 & 1 & 0 & \cdots & 0 \\ 0 & 0 & 1 & \cdots & 0 \\ \cdot & \cdot & \cdot & \cdot & \cdot \\ \cdot & \cdot & \cdot & \cdot & \cdot \\ \cdot & \cdot & \cdot & \cdot & \cdot \\ 0 & 0 & 0 & \cdots & 1 \\ -p_n & -p_{n-1} & -p_{n-2} & \cdots & -p_1 \end{bmatrix} . \tag{3-4.8}$$

The correspondence between the nth-order equation and its companion vector equation can be appreciated by writing the vector equation in scalar form. The scalar relations corresponding to the vector equation are

$$\begin{aligned} y_1' &= y_2 \,, \\ y_2' &= \quad y_3 \,, \\ &\ \cdot \\ &\ \cdot \\ &\ \cdot \\ y_{n-1}' &= \qquad y_n \,, \\ y_n' &= -p_n y_1 - p_{n-1} y_2 - p_{n-2} y_3 - \cdots - p_1 y_n \ . \end{aligned} \tag{3-4.9}$$

The first $n-1$ of these relations merely specify that the functions $y_1, y_2, \ldots, y_n$ are the components of the Wronskian vector $\mathbf{k}(y_1)$. This being so, the last relation can be written as

$$y_1^{[n]} = -\tilde{\mathbf{p}}\mathbf{k}(y_1) \ , \tag{3-4.10}$$

which [see equation (3-4.4)] is equivalent to

$$Ly_1 = 0 \ .$$

It follows, therefore, that any vector whose components satisfy (3-4.9) is a Wronskian vector with a first component which is a solution of $Lu = 0$. Conversely, the Wronskian vector of any solution of $Lu = 0$ is readily seen to have components which satisfy (3-4.9).

We can now prove the following theorem which plays the role of an existence theorem for equation (3-4.2).

Theorem 3-4.1. *The solution space of the* nth-*order homogeneous linear differential equation* (3-4.2) *has dimension n.*

PROOF. Let $\mathbf{u}$ represent the vector whose components are the components of the first row of some specific fundamental matrix for equation (3-4.7). Since the matrix must be a Wronskian matrix it can be represented by $\mathbf{K}(\mathbf{u})$. The components of $\mathbf{u}$ obviously belong to $C^n[a, b]$, and each one must be a solution of equation (3-4.2) since the corresponding column of $\mathbf{K}(\mathbf{u})$ is a solution of (3-4.7). Moreover, if the components of $\mathbf{u}$ were linearly dependent, we should be forced to conclude that the columns of $\mathbf{K}(\mathbf{u})$ were linearly dependent. Since $\mathbf{K}(\mathbf{u})$ is nonsingular, it follows that the components of $\mathbf{u}$ are linearly independent.

Let v be any solution of equation (3-4.2). It follows that $\mathbf{k}(v)$ is a solution of (3-4.7). Since $\mathbf{K}(\mathbf{u})$ is a fundamental matrix for (3-4.7), there exists a vector $\mathbf{c}$ such that

$$\mathbf{k}(v) = \mathbf{K}(\mathbf{u})\mathbf{c} \ .$$

This implies that

$$v = \tilde{\mathbf{u}}\mathbf{c}$$

and, hence, that the components of $\mathbf{u}$ form a basis for the solution space of equation (3-4.2). The solution space is, therefore, an n-dimensional vector space.

Definition 3-4.2. *Any vector whose components form a basis for the solution space of the* nth-*order homogeneous linear differential equation* (3-4.2) *is a* ***fundamental vector*** *for that equation.*

Corollary 3-4.1. *A Wronskian matrix is a fundamental matrix for the companion vector equation* (3-4.7) *if and only if its first row forms a fundamental vector for the* nth-*order equation* (3-4.2).

It is common practice in developing the theory of the nth-order linear differential equation to present the next theorem as the basic existence theorem and then to deduce the equivalent of our Theorem 3-4.1. We have reversed this order and, in fact, we only present the next theorem because of the major role it played in the classical treatment of this subject.

Theorem 3-4.2. *The initial-value problem* (3-4.2) *and* (3-4.3) *has a unique solution.*

PROOF. Let $\mathbf{u}$ be a fundamental vector for (3-4.2). Every solution v of this equation can be expressed as

$$v = \tilde{\mathbf{u}}\mathbf{c} \ ,$$

where $\mathbf{c}$ is a constant n-vector. This solution satisfies (3-4.3), or the equivalent condition (3-4.5), if and only if

$$\mathbf{k}(v(t_0)) = \mathbf{b} \ ,$$

that is, if and only if

$$\mathbf{K}(\mathbf{u}(t_0))\mathbf{c} = \mathbf{b} \ .$$

Since $\mathbf{K}(\mathbf{u}(t_0))$ is nonsingular, the vector $\mathbf{c}$ is determined uniquely and the theorem is proved.

At this point it is convenient to introduce the matrix $\mathbf{J}$ defined by

$$\mathbf{J} = \begin{bmatrix} 0 & 1 & 0 & \cdots & 0 \\ 0 & 0 & 1 & \cdots & 0 \\ \cdot & \cdot & \cdot & \cdot & \cdot \\ \cdot & \cdot & \cdot & \cdot & \cdot \\ \cdot & \cdot & \cdot & \cdot & \cdot \\ 0 & 0 & 0 & \cdots & 1 \\ 0 & 0 & 0 & \cdots & 0 \end{bmatrix} \ .$$

If this matrix is used as a left multiplier of any matrix $\mathbf{T}$, it raises each row of $\mathbf{T}$ one stage and replaces the last row by a row of zeros. As a right multiplier of $\mathbf{T}$, it moves each column of $\mathbf{T}$ one stage to the right and replaces the first column by a column of zeros. It is easily inferred that the multiplication of $\mathbf{T}$ by $\tilde{\mathbf{J}}$ translates the rows (or columns) of $\mathbf{T}$ in the reverse direction.

It is also pertinent to note that an n-dimensional column vector multiplied on the right by an n-dimensional row vector yields an n by n matrix. Such a matrix is called a *dyad* by some writers. An instance of this occurs when one of the vectors in the product is $\mathbf{d}_j$ (see definition of $\mathbf{d}_j$ in Section 1-3). Thus, $\mathbf{d}_j\tilde{\mathbf{c}}$ is a matrix whose jth row consists of the components of the vector $\mathbf{c}$ and whose other rows consist entirely of zeros.

The following discussion provides an exercise in the use of these notational devices and further illuminates the relationship between an nth-order differential equation and its companion vector equation. Let $\mathbf{u}$ be a fundamental vector for equation (3-4.2) and $\mathbf{K}(\mathbf{u})$ a fundamental matrix for (3-4.7). In view of Theorem 3-2.3, the matrix $\mathbf{A}$ in the latter equation is

(3-4.11) $$\mathbf{A} = \mathbf{K}'(\mathbf{u})\mathbf{K}^{-1}(u) \ .$$

In order to verify this identity, we write

(3-4.12) $$\mathbf{K}'(\mathbf{u}) = \mathbf{J}\mathbf{K}(\mathbf{u}) + \mathbf{d}_n\tilde{\mathbf{u}}^{[n]} \ .$$

Since each element of $\mathbf{u}$ satisfies (3-4.4), we have

$$\tilde{\mathbf{u}}^{[n]} = -\tilde{\mathbf{p}}\mathbf{K}(\mathbf{u}) \ .$$

Substituting this into (3-4.12), we get

$$\mathbf{K}'(\mathbf{u}) = \mathbf{J}\mathbf{K}(\mathbf{u}) - \mathbf{d}_n\tilde{\mathbf{p}}\mathbf{K}(\mathbf{u}) \ .$$

It follows that

$$\mathbf{K}'(\mathbf{u})\mathbf{K}^{-1}(\mathbf{u}) = \mathbf{J} - \mathbf{d}_n\tilde{\mathbf{p}} \ .$$

This completes the illustration since the right-hand side is clearly the matrix **A** defined by (3-4.8).

The following theorem is the analogue of Theorem 3-2.3. It establishes that an nth-order differential equation is uniquely determined by a fundamental set of solutions.

Theorem 3-4.3. *If* **u** *is any vector whose components are linearly independent functions in* $C^n[a, b]$, *then the differential equation for which* **u** *is a fundamental vector is* $Ly = 0$, *where*

$$Ly = y^{[n]} - \tilde{\mathbf{d}}_n \mathbf{K}'(\mathbf{u})\mathbf{K}^{-1}(\mathbf{u})\mathbf{k}(y) \ . \tag{3-4.13}$$

PROOF. The vector equation for which $\mathbf{K}(\mathbf{u})$ is a fundamental matrix is $\mathbf{y}' = \mathbf{A}\mathbf{y}$, where **A** is given by (3-4.11). The last equation in the scalar system corresponding to this vector equation may be written as [see (3-4.10)]

$$y_1^{[n]} = \tilde{\mathbf{d}}_n \mathbf{K}'(\mathbf{u})\mathbf{K}^{-1}(\mathbf{u})\mathbf{k}(y_1) \ .$$

If the subscript on y_1 is omitted, this can be written as $Ly = 0$ where Ly is defined by (3-4.13). This nth-order equation is obviously satisfied by every component of **u**, and its uniqueness follows from the uniqueness of the matrix **A**.

REMARK. The relation[2]

$$\frac{1}{|\mathbf{K}(\mathbf{u})|}\begin{vmatrix} u_1 & u_2 & \cdots & u_n & y \\ u_1' & u_2' & \cdots & u_n' & y' \\ \cdot & \cdot & \cdot & \cdot & \cdot \\ \cdot & \cdot & \cdot & \cdot & \cdot \\ \cdot & \cdot & \cdot & \cdot & \cdot \\ u_1^{[n]} & u_2^{[n]} & \cdots & u_n^{[n]} & y^{[n]} \end{vmatrix} = 0$$

is obviously an nth-order linear differential equation. Moreover, the coefficient of $y^{[n]}$ is unity. The equation is clearly satisfied by each component of the vector **u**. It must be realized, therefore, that this equation is identical with the equation of Theorem 3-4.3. The identification of the left-hand side of the above equation with Ly, defined in (3-4.13), is left as an exercise. The determinant $|\mathbf{K}(\mathbf{u})|$ is commonly called the *Wronskian* of the components of **u**.

The following theorem is essentially a corollary of Theorem 3-2.4.

Theorem 3-4.4. *If* **u** *is any fundamental vector for the* n*th-order homogeneous equation* (3-4.2), *then*

$$|\mathbf{K}(\mathbf{u}(t))| = |\mathbf{K}(\mathbf{u}(t_0))| \exp\left[-\int_{t_0}^{t} p_1(s)\,ds\right] \ .$$

[2] Coddington and Levinson [11], page 83.

PROOF. Since **u** is a fundamental vector for (3-4.2), **K**(**u**) is a fundamental matrix for the companion vector equation (3-4.7). In view of the definition of **A** [formula (3-4.8)],

$$\operatorname{tr}\mathbf{A}(s) = -p_1(s) \ .$$

The desired result follows directly from Theorem 3-2.4.

Example 1. The equation

$$u'' - 3u' + 2u = 0 \tag{3-4.14}$$

has for its companion vector equation

$$\mathbf{y}' = \begin{pmatrix} 0 & 1 \\ -2 & 3 \end{pmatrix} \mathbf{y} \ .$$

These equations are also used as examples in Sections 2-1, 3-2, and 3-3. We may recall that

$$\mathbf{Y}(t) = \begin{pmatrix} e^t & e^{2t} \\ e^t & 2e^{2t} \end{pmatrix}$$

is a fundamental matrix for this vector equation. It is clear that it is a Wronskian matrix and that its first row is a fundamental vector for equation (3-4.14). If this vector is represented by **u** we have

$$\mathbf{K}(\mathbf{u}) = \mathbf{Y} \ .$$

Using formula (3-4.13), we may write

$$\begin{aligned} Ly &= y^{[2]} - (0, 1)\begin{pmatrix} e^t & 2e^{2t} \\ e^t & 4e^{2t} \end{pmatrix} \begin{pmatrix} 2e^{-t} & -e^{-t} \\ -e^{-2t} & e^{-2t} \end{pmatrix} \begin{pmatrix} y \\ y' \end{pmatrix} \\ &= y^{[2]} - (0, 1)\begin{pmatrix} 0 & 1 \\ -2 & 3 \end{pmatrix} \begin{pmatrix} y \\ y' \end{pmatrix} \\ &= y^{[2]} - 3y' + 2y \ . \end{aligned}$$

We can observe by application of Theorem 3-4.3 that $Lu = 0$ is equation (3-4.14).

Exercises

1. If each component of a vector **u** is a solution of the equation $Lu = 0$, the vector is a fundamental vector if and only if $|\mathbf{K}(u(t))| \neq 0$ for every t in the interval $[a, b]$.

2. In each case, determine whether or not **u** is a fundamental vector for the given equation.

(a) $u'' - 3u' + 2u = 0$, $\quad \tilde{\mathbf{u}}(t) = (e^t, e^{2t})$;

(b) $u''' - 6u'' + 11u' - 6u = 0$, $\quad \tilde{\mathbf{u}}(t) = (e^t, e^{2t}, e^{3t})$;

(c) $u''' = 0$, $\quad \tilde{\mathbf{u}}(t) = (1, t, t^2)$;

(d) $u'' + u = 0$, $\quad \tilde{\mathbf{u}}(t) = (\sin t, \cos t)$;

(e) $u'' + 2u' + u = 0$, $\quad \tilde{\mathbf{u}}(t) = (e^{-t}, te^{-t})$.

3. Find the companion vector equation for each of the equations in Exercise 2, and find a fundamental matrix for each vector equation.

4. Find the companion vector equation for $u''-u'-2u = 0$. Compare this result with Exercise 1(b) of Section 3-2 and, hence, determine a fundamental vector for the given equation.

5. Find equations, with unit coefficient for the leading term, to correspond with the following fundamental vectors:

(a) $(\sin\alpha t, \cos\alpha t)$; (b) $(1, e^t)$;

(c) (e^t, e^{-t}); (d) (e^t, te^t, t^2e^t).

6. Show that

$$\frac{1}{|\mathbf{K}(\mathbf{u})|}\begin{vmatrix} u_1 & \cdot & \cdot & \cdot & u_n & y \\ u_1' & \cdot & \cdot & \cdot & u_n' & y' \\ \cdot & \cdot & \cdot & \cdot & \cdot & \cdot \\ \cdot & \cdot & \cdot & \cdot & \cdot & \cdot \\ \cdot & \cdot & \cdot & \cdot & \cdot & \cdot \\ u_1^{[n]} & \cdot & \cdot & \cdot & u_n^{[n]} & y^{[n]} \end{vmatrix} = y^{[n]} - \tilde{\mathbf{d}}_n\mathbf{K}'(\mathbf{u})\mathbf{K}^{-1}(\mathbf{u})\mathbf{k}(y)\,,$$

7. Solve the following initial-value problems: (a) $u''+u = 0$, $\tilde{\mathbf{k}}(u(0)) = (1, 1)$, given that $\tilde{\mathbf{u}}(t) = (\sin t, \cos t)$ is a fundamental vector. (b) $u''' = 0$, $\tilde{\mathbf{k}}(u(1)) = (1, 2, 1)$, given that $\tilde{\mathbf{u}}(t) = (1, t, t^2)$ is a fundamental vector.

3-5. THE *n*th-ORDER NONHOMOGENEOUS EQUATION

The nonhomogeneous equation associated with the *n*th-order homogeneous equation (3-4.2) is

$$Lu = f\,, \tag{3-5.1}$$

where $f \in C[a, b]$. If the matrix $\mathbf{A}$ is given by (3-4.8), it is apparent that the vector equation

$$\mathbf{y}' = \mathbf{A}\mathbf{y} + f\mathbf{d}_n \tag{3-5.2}$$

is associated with (3-5.1) in the same way that the companion vector equation (3-4.7) is associated with equation (3-4.2). That is to say, if v is any solution of (3-5.1), then $\mathbf{k}(v)$ is a solution of (3-5.2). Conversely, any solution of (3-5.2) must be a Wronskian vector, and its first component must be a solution of (3-5.1). In view of this, Theorems 3-3.1 and 3-3.2 provide immediate proofs for a corresponding pair of theorems to be associated with equation (3-5.1).

Theorem 3-5.1. *If $\bar{u}$ is a particular solution of the nonhomogeneous equation (3-5.1) and* $\mathbf{u}$ *is a fundamental vector for the corresponding homogeneous equation (3-4.2), then*

$$u = \bar{u} + \tilde{\mathbf{u}}\mathbf{c}$$

is a solution of the nonhomogeneous equation for every $\mathbf{c}$ *in $V_n(R)$. Every solution is of this form.*

PROOF. Since $\mathbf{u}$ is a fundamental vector for (3-4.2), $\mathbf{K}(\mathbf{u})$ is a fundamental matrix for (3-4.7). Further, since $\bar{u}$ is a particular solution of (3-5.1), $\mathbf{k}(\bar{u})$ is a particular solution of (3-5.2). By Theorem 3-3.1, the solutions of (3-5.2) are represented by

$$\mathbf{y} = \mathbf{k}(\bar{u}) + \mathbf{K}(\mathbf{u})\mathbf{c} \ .$$

If y_1, the first component of $\mathbf{y}$, is replaced by the symbol u, we may write

$$\begin{aligned} u &= \tilde{\mathbf{d}}_1 \mathbf{k}(\bar{u}) + \tilde{\mathbf{d}}_1 \mathbf{K}(\mathbf{u})\mathbf{c} \\ &= \bar{u} + \tilde{\mathbf{u}}\mathbf{c} \ . \end{aligned}$$

It follows that u is a solution of (3-5.1) for every $\mathbf{c}$ and that every solution of (3-5.1) has this form. This proves the theorem.

Theorem 3-5.2. *A particular solution $\bar{u}$ of the nonhomogeneous equation* (3-5.1) *is given by*

(3-5.3) $$\bar{u}(t) = \tilde{\mathbf{u}}(t) \int_a^t \mathbf{K}^{-1}(\mathbf{u}(s))\,\mathbf{d}_n f(s)\, ds \ ,$$

where $\mathbf{u}$ *is any fundamental vector for the corresponding homogeneous equation* (3-4.2).

PROOF. If $\mathbf{u}$ is a fundamental vector for (3-4.2), then $\mathbf{K}(\mathbf{u})$ is a fundamental matrix for the companion vector equation (3-4.7). It follows from Theorem 3-3.2 that

$$\bar{\mathbf{y}}(t) = \mathbf{K}(\mathbf{u}(t)) \int_a^t \mathbf{K}^{-1}(\mathbf{u}(s))\,\mathbf{d}_n f(s)\, ds \ ,$$

is a particular solution of (3-5.2). The first component of this solution is clearly a particular solution of (3-5.1). It may be represented by the symbol $\bar{u}(t)$, and it is easily seen to be given by the formula (3-5.3). This proves the theorem.

Corollary 3-5.2. *If the coefficient of $u^{[n]}$ in Lu is p_0 instead of unity, then a particular solution of the nonhomogeneous equation is given by*

(3-5.4) $$\bar{u}(t) = \tilde{\mathbf{u}}(t) \int_a^t \mathbf{K}^{-1}(\mathbf{u}(s))\,\mathbf{d}_n p_0^{-1}(s) f(s)\, ds \ .$$

Exercises

1. Find particular solutions of the following nonhomogeneous equations. The fundamental vectors for the corresponding homogeneous equations are given in Exercise 2 of Section 3-4.

(a) $u'' - 3u' + 2u = e^{-t}$;

(b) $u''' - 6u'' + 11u' - 6u = e^{t}$;

(c) $u''' = 1 - t^2$;

(d) $u'' + u = \sin 2t$.

2. Derive a formula for the solution of the initial-value problem

$$Lu = f,$$
$$\mathbf{k}(u(t_0)) = \mathbf{b},$$

where t_0 is any point in $[a, b]$.

3. Solve the following initial-value problems:

(a) $u'' - u = e^{2t}, \mathbf{k}(u(0)) = \mathbf{o}$, given that $\tilde{\mathbf{u}}(t) = (e^t, e^{-t})$ is a fundamental vector for $u'' - u = 0$.

(b) $u'' - 3u' + 2u = e^{-t}$, $\tilde{\mathbf{k}}(u(0)) = (\frac{7}{6}, -\frac{1}{6})$.

3-6. THE ADJOINT VECTOR EQUATION

The adjoint equation is of considerable significance in the field of differential equations. This notion was originally introduced by Lagrange in connection with the problem of finding integrating factors. It is introduced here from the same point of view.

Let M be a linear operator defined by

$$M\mathbf{y} = \mathbf{y}' - \mathbf{A}\mathbf{y} \ ,$$

where $\mathbf{A}$ is an n by n matrix with components in $C[a, b]$. The operator maps any vector $\mathbf{y}$, whose components are in $C^1[a, b]$, into a vector whose components are in $C[a, b]$. It is clear that the equation $M\mathbf{y} = \mathbf{o}$ is equivalent to the vector equation

$$\mathbf{y}' = \mathbf{A}\mathbf{y} \ . \tag{3-6.1}$$

We consider the problem of finding a vector $\mathbf{z}$ such that the inner product $\tilde{\mathbf{z}}M\mathbf{y}$ is an exact derivative. We have

$$\begin{aligned}\tilde{\mathbf{z}}M\mathbf{y} &= \tilde{\mathbf{z}}(\mathbf{y}' - \mathbf{A}\mathbf{y}) \\ &= \tilde{\mathbf{z}}\mathbf{y}' + \tilde{\mathbf{z}}'\mathbf{y} - \tilde{\mathbf{z}}'\mathbf{y} - \tilde{\mathbf{z}}\mathbf{A}\mathbf{y} \\ &= (\tilde{\mathbf{z}}\mathbf{y})' + (-\tilde{\mathbf{z}}' - \tilde{\mathbf{z}}\mathbf{A})\mathbf{y} \\ &= (\tilde{\mathbf{z}}\mathbf{y})' + (\widetilde{M^*\mathbf{z}})\mathbf{y} \ ,\end{aligned}$$

where

$$M^*\mathbf{z} = -\mathbf{z}' - \tilde{\mathbf{A}}\mathbf{z} \ . \tag{3-6.2}$$

It can be inferred that $\tilde{\mathbf{z}}M\mathbf{y}$ is an exact derivative if

$$M^*\mathbf{z} = \mathbf{o} \ . \tag{3-6.3}$$

That is, $\mathbf{z}$ can be regarded as an integrating factor for $M\mathbf{y}$ if it satisfies equation (3-6.3) or the equivalent equation

$$\mathbf{z}' = -\tilde{\mathbf{A}}\mathbf{z} \ . \tag{3-6.4}$$

The operator M^* is the *adjoint* of the operator M, and the equation (3-6.4) is the adjoint of the equation (3-6.1).

The identity derived above may be rewritten as

$$\tilde{\mathbf{z}}M\mathbf{y}-(\widetilde{M^*\mathbf{z}})\,\mathbf{y}=(\tilde{\mathbf{z}}\mathbf{y})' \ . \tag{3-6.5}$$

It is valid for every pair of vectors **y** and **z** with components in $C^1[a, b]$ and is known as the *Lagrange identity*. By integrating both sides of (3-6.5), we obtain *Green's formula*

$$\int_a^b (\tilde{\mathbf{z}}M\mathbf{y}-(\widetilde{M^*\mathbf{z}})\,\mathbf{y})\,dt=\tilde{\mathbf{z}}(b)\,\mathbf{y}(b)-\tilde{\mathbf{z}}(a)\,\mathbf{y}(a)\ . \tag{3-6.6}$$

The operators M and M^* can be applied to matrices as well as to vectors. It is easily concluded that the Lagrange identity remains valid if the vectors **y** and **z** are replaced, respectively, by matrices **Y** and **Z**. Let such a replacement be made and, further, specify that **Y** is a fundamental matrix for the vector equation (3-6.1) and that **Z** is a fundamental matrix for the adjoint equation (3-6.4). It follows that $M\mathbf{Y}=\mathbf{0}$ and $M^*\mathbf{Z}=\mathbf{0}$ and, hence, that

$$(\tilde{\mathbf{Z}}\mathbf{Y})'=\mathbf{0}\ .$$

This implies that

$$\tilde{\mathbf{Y}}\mathbf{Z}=\mathbf{C}\ ,$$

where **C** is some nonsingular constant matrix. We are able to deduce at once that $\mathbf{Z}=\tilde{\mathbf{Y}}^{-1}\mathbf{C}$ and, therefore, that $\tilde{\mathbf{Y}}^{-1}$ is a fundamental matrix for the adjoint equation.

Example 1. Let M be defined by

$$M\mathbf{y}=\mathbf{y}'-\begin{pmatrix}0 & 1\\ -2 & 3\end{pmatrix}\mathbf{y}\ .$$

Then its adjoint operator is

$$M^*\mathbf{z}=-\mathbf{z}'-\begin{pmatrix}0 & -2\\ 1 & 3\end{pmatrix}\mathbf{z}\ .$$

The equation $M\mathbf{y}=\mathbf{o}$ is the Example of Sections 2-1, 3-2, 3-3, and 3-4. A fundamental matrix for this equation is

$$\mathbf{Y}(t)=\begin{pmatrix}e^t & e^{2t}\\ e^t & 2e^{2t}\end{pmatrix}.$$

The inverse of this matrix (see Section 3-3) yields a fundamental matrix **Z** for $M^*\mathbf{z}=\mathbf{o}$,

$$\mathbf{Z}(t)=\tilde{\mathbf{Y}}^{-1}(t)=\begin{pmatrix}2e^{-t} & -e^{-2t}\\ -e^{-t} & e^{-2t}\end{pmatrix}.$$

Exercises

1. Write down the adjoint equations for each vector equation in Exercise 1 of Section 3-2 and find the fundamental matrices.

3-7. THE ADJOINT *n*th-ORDER EQUATION

The *n*th-order differential form Lu is defined here as

$$Lu = \sum_{k=0}^{n} p_{-nk} u^{[k]} , \tag{3-7.1}$$

where $p_j \in C^{n-j}[a, b]$, $p_0(t) \neq 0$, and $t \in [a, b]$. The use of p_0 instead of unity as the coefficient for $u^{[n]}$ provides a notational advantage and an increase in generality. The differentiability condition imposed on p_j is necessary for the subsequent development of this section. The adjoint form corresponding to Lu is

$$L^*v = \sum_{k=0}^{n} (-1)^k (p_{n-k} v)^{[k]} . \tag{3-7.2}$$

The motivation for the development of the relationship between Lu and L^*v is the same here as for the vector equation and its adjoint in Section 3-6. That is, we need to determine what condition must be imposed on a function v in order to make vLu an exact derivative.

The development of the adjoint of the vector operator was accomplished with ease. It would be a great convenience to be able to obtain L^*v from the adjoint vector form,

$$M^*\mathbf{z} = -\mathbf{z}' - \tilde{\mathbf{A}}\mathbf{z} ,$$

where $\mathbf{A}$ is the matrix defined by (3-4.8). Unfortunately, the relationship between $M^*\mathbf{z}$ and L^*v becomes clear only after L^*v has been derived independently. Reluctantly, therefore, we present the rather involved and tedious classical derivation of the Lagrange identity for an *n*th-order differential equation.

Theorem 3-7.1. The Lagrange Identity. *If u and v are any two functions in* $C^n[a, b]$, *then*

$$vLu - uL^*v = [\tilde{\mathbf{k}}(v)\mathbf{P}\mathbf{k}(u)]' , \tag{3-7.3}$$

where the components of the matrix $\mathbf{P}$ *are*

$$p_{ij} = \begin{cases} \displaystyle\sum_{h=i}^{n-j+1} (-1)^{h-1} \binom{h-1}{i-1} p_{n-h-j+1}{}^{[h-i]} , & i \leqq n-j+1 , \\ 0 , & i > n-j+1 , \end{cases}$$

[*This is formula* (3-7.8), *which is derived in the proof.*]

PROOF. The obvious identity

$$[wu^{[k-1]} - w'u^{[k-2]} + \cdots + (-1)^{k-1} w^{[k-1]} u]' = wu^{[k]} - (-1)^k w^{[k]} u$$

may be rewritten as

$$\text{(3-7.4)} \qquad wu^{[k]} = \left[\sum_{j=1}^{k} (-1)^{k-j} w^{[k-j]} u^{[j-1]}\right]' + (-1)^k w^{[k]} u \ , \qquad k = 1, 2, \ldots, n \ .$$

If the form Lu is multiplied by v, the result can be expressed as

$$\text{(3-7.5)} \qquad vLu = p_n vu + \sum_{k=1}^{n} (p_{n-k} v) u^{[k]} \ .$$

Replacing w by $p_{n-k} v$ in (3-7.4) and substituting into (3-7.5), we obtain

$$vLu = p_n vu + \sum_{k=1}^{n} \left\{ \left[\sum_{j=1}^{k} (-1)^{k-j} (p_{n-k} v)^{[k-j]} u^{[j-1]}\right]' + (-1)^k (p_{n-k} v)^{[k]} u \right\} .$$

This relation can be written as

$$vLu - uL^* v = [P(u, v)]' \ ,$$

where $L^* v$ is given by (3-7.2) and

$$\text{(3-7.6)} \qquad P(u, v) = \sum_{k=1}^{n} \sum_{j=1}^{k} (-1)^{k-j} (p_{n-k} v)^{[k-j]} u^{[j-1]} \ .$$

It is clear that $P(u, v)$ is a bilinear form in the components of the vectors $\mathbf{k}(u)$ and $\mathbf{k}(v)$. This form is called the *bilinear concomitant*, and the remaining part of this derivation is devoted to finding an explicit expression for its matrix.

If the order of summation on the right-hand side of formula (3-7.6) is changed, we get

$$\text{(3-7.7)} \qquad P(u, v) = \sum_{j=1}^{n} \sum_{k=j}^{n} (-1)^{k-j} (p_{n-k} v)^{[k-j]} u^{[j-1]} \ .$$

The rule for changing the order of summation[3] can be understood by first plotting the index pairs on a Cartesian plane and then observing that the pairs form a triangular array. It is convenient, at this point, to replace the index k by $h+j-1$. As a result of this substitution

$$P(u, v) = \sum_{j=1}^{n} \sum_{h=1}^{n-j+1} (-1)^{h-1} (p_{n-h-j+1} v)^{[h-1]} u^{[j-1]} \ .$$

Expansion of $(p_{n-h-j+1} v)^{[h-1]}$ on the right-hand side yields

$$P(u, v) = \sum_{j=1}^{n} \sum_{h=i}^{n-j+1} \sum_{i=1}^{h} (-1)^{h-1} \binom{h-1}{i-1} p_{n-h-j+1}{}^{[h-i]} v^{[i-1]} u^{[j-1]} \ .$$

Again, we change the order of summation for the indices h and i to get

$$P(u, v) = \sum_{j=1}^{n} \sum_{i=1}^{n-j+1} \sum_{h=i}^{n-j+1} (-1)^{h-1} \binom{h-1}{i-1} p_{n-h-j+1}{}^{[h-i]} v^{[i-1]} u^{[j-1]} \ .$$

[3] Buck [9], Footnote, page 119.

Consequently, if we define the components of the matrix $\mathbf{P} = (p_{ij})$ by

$$(3\text{-}7.8) \quad p_{ij} = \begin{cases} \sum_{h=i}^{n-j+1} (-1)^{h-1} \binom{h-1}{i-1} p_{n-h-j+1}{}^{[h-i]} , & i \leqq n-j+1 , \\ 0 , & i > n-j+1 , \end{cases}$$

then it is readily seen that

$$P(u, v) = \tilde{\mathbf{k}}(v)\mathbf{P}\mathbf{k}(u) \ .$$

This proves the theorem.

Corollary 3-7.1. *If v is a solution of $L^*v = 0$, then vLu is an exact derivative.*

The corollary follows from the fact that if $L^*v = 0$ then the Lagrange identity reduces to

$$vLu = [\tilde{\mathbf{k}}(v)\mathbf{P}\mathbf{k}(u)]' \ .$$

From this it may be inferred that the effect of the integrating factor is to permit reduction of the equation to

$$\tilde{\mathbf{k}}(v)\mathbf{P}\mathbf{k}(u) = c \ ,$$

where c is an arbitrary constant. Since this equation is now of order $n-1$, it is clear that *the order of a linear differential equation can be reduced if a solution of its adjoint equation is known.*

The matrix $\mathbf{P}$ of the bilinear concomitant is called the *concomitant matrix.* Since the matrix plays an important part in subsequent discussions, it is useful to examine its structure. The structure is indicated by giving the concomitant matrix for the general third-order equation,

$$\mathbf{P} = \begin{pmatrix} p_0'' - p_1' + p_2 & -p_0' + p_1 & p_0 \\ 2p_0' - p_1 & -p_0 & 0 \\ p_0 & 0 & 0 \end{pmatrix} .$$

In the course of proving the following theorem we show that the structure for the *n*th-order case is similar.

Theorem 3-7.2. *The concomitant matrix is nonsingular, and the value of its determinant is $p_0{}^n$.*

PROOF. From formula (3-7.8)

$$p_{n-j+1,j} = (-1)^{n-j} p_0 \ .$$

Thus the components on the secondary diagonal of $\mathbf{P}$ are alternately $+p_0$ and $-p_0$, with $+p_0$ in the upper right-hand corner. Further, it is also clear from formula (3-7.8) that every component of $\mathbf{P}$ below the secondary diagonal is zero. It follows, therefore that the determinant of $\mathbf{P}$ has the stated value, and that $\mathbf{P}$ is nonsingular.

Corollary 3-7.2. *Every component of* $\mathbf{P}^{-1}$ *above the secondary diagonal is zero. The components on the secondary diagonal are alternately* $+(1/p_0)$ *and* $-(1/p_0)$, *with* $(-1)^{n-1}(1/p_0)$ *in the upper right-hand corner.*

In the following two theorems, we develop further the intimate relation that exists between an nth-order linear differential form and its adjoint.

Theorem 3-7.3. *If* $\mathbf{u}$ *and* $\mathbf{v}$ *are fundamental vectors for* $Lu = 0$ *and* $L^*v = 0$, *respectively, then*

$$\tilde{\mathbf{K}}(\mathbf{v})\mathbf{P}\mathbf{K}(\mathbf{u}) = \mathbf{C} \ ,$$

where $\mathbf{C}$ *is a nonsingular constant matrix.*

PROOF. Let u_j be the jth component of $\mathbf{u}$ and v_i be the ith component of $\mathbf{v}$, then $\mathbf{k}(u_j)$ is the jth column of $\mathbf{K}(\mathbf{u})$ and $\tilde{\mathbf{k}}(v_i)$ is the ith row of $\tilde{\mathbf{K}}(\mathbf{v})$. In view of the Lagrange identity, we can deduce that

$$\tilde{\mathbf{k}}(v_i)\mathbf{P}\mathbf{k}(u_j) = c_{ij} \ ,$$

where c_{ij} is some constant. This implies that

$$\tilde{\mathbf{K}}(\mathbf{v})\mathbf{P}\mathbf{K}(\mathbf{u}) = \mathbf{C} \ ,$$

where $\mathbf{C} = (c_{ij})$. Since each of the matrices on the left-hand side of this relation is nonsingular, the matrix $\mathbf{C}$ must also be nonsingular.

Corollary 3-7.3. *The fundamental vectors* $\mathbf{u}$ *and* $\mathbf{v}$ *can be so chosen that*

$$\tilde{\mathbf{K}}(\mathbf{v})\mathbf{P}\mathbf{K}(\mathbf{u}) = \mathbf{I} \ .$$

The corollary is a direct result of the theorem and the fact that $\mathbf{K}(\mathbf{u})\mathbf{C}^{-1}$ is a Wronskian matrix of a fundamental vector for $Lu = 0$.

Definition 3-7.1. *If* $L^* = L$ *we say the differential form* L *is* ***self-adjoint*** *and, also, that the equation* $Lu = 0$ *is* ***self-adjoint***.

Theorem 3-7.4. *The adjoint relationship for differential forms is a reciprocal relationship.*

PROOF. With L, L^*, and $\mathbf{P}$ having the same meanings as previously, we designate the adjoint form of L^* by L^{**} and the corresponding concomitant matrix by $\mathbf{Q}$, We then have the two Lagrange identities

$$vLu - uL^*v = [\tilde{\mathbf{k}}(v)\mathbf{P}\mathbf{k}(u)]' \ ,$$
$$uL^*v - vL^{**}u = [\tilde{\mathbf{k}}(u)\mathbf{Q}\mathbf{k}(v)]' \ .$$

The addition of these yields the identity

$$v(Lu - L^{**}u) = [\tilde{\mathbf{k}}(v)(\mathbf{P}+\tilde{\mathbf{Q}})k(u)]' \ .$$

This may be written as

$$hv = (a_1 v + a_2 v' + \cdots + a_n v^{[n-1]})' \ ,$$

where $h = Lu - L^{**}u$ and a_j is the jth component of the vector $(\mathbf{P}+\tilde{\mathbf{Q}})\mathbf{k}(u)$. Since the relation is valid for every v in $C^n[a, b]$ and since the left-hand side has no term involving $v^{[n]}$, we must deduce that $a_n = 0$. Since this is true and since the left-hand side has no term involving $v^{[n-1]}$, we conclude that $a_{n-1} = 0$. Therefore, by induction,

$$a_j = 0 \ , \quad j = 1, 2, \ldots, n \ . \tag{3-7.9}$$

This implies that

$$h = Lu - L^{**}u = 0$$

and, hence, that for $u \in C^n[a, b]$

$$L^{**}u = Lu \ .$$

This proves the theorem.

Corollary 3-7.4a. *The matrices* $\mathbf{P}$ *and* $\mathbf{Q}$ *are such that* $\mathbf{P} = -\tilde{\mathbf{Q}}$.
This result follows from the fact that relation (3-7.9) is valid for every u in $C^n[a, b]$.

Corollary 3-7.4b. *If the differential form L is self-adjoint then*

$$\mathbf{P} = -\tilde{\mathbf{P}} \ ,$$

that is, $\mathbf{P}$ *is skew-symmetric.*

REMARK. Recalling the structure of the matrix $\mathbf{P}$, we are able to infer that an equation of odd order with real coefficients cannot be self-adjoint. It should be noted, however, that if the coefficients of the equation are complex, then an equation of odd order can be self-adjoint.

Example 1. To illustrate the concepts developed in this section we reconsider the operator (see the Examples of Sections 2-1, 3-2, 3-3, 3-4, and 3-6)

$$Lu = u'' - 3u' + 2u \ .$$

Using formulas (3-7.2) and (3-7.8), we get for the adjoint operator L^* and the concomitant matrix $\mathbf{P}$,

$$L^*v = v'' + 3v' + 2v \ ,$$

$$\mathbf{P} = \begin{pmatrix} -3 & 1 \\ -1 & 0 \end{pmatrix} .$$

The concomitant matrix for L^* is $-\tilde{\mathbf{P}}$, which is consistent with Corollary 3-7.4a.

Fundamental vectors for $Lu = 0$ and $L^*v = 0$ are, respectively,

$$\mathbf{u}(t) = \begin{pmatrix} e^t \\ e^{2t} \end{pmatrix} \quad \text{and} \quad \mathbf{v}(t) = \begin{pmatrix} e^{-t} \\ e^{-2t} \end{pmatrix} .$$

We may illustrate the application of Theorem 3-7.3 by noting that the product

$$\tilde{\mathbf{K}}(\mathbf{v})\mathbf{P}\mathbf{K}(\mathbf{u}) = \begin{pmatrix} e^{-t} & -e^{-t} \\ e^{-2t} & -2e^{-2t} \end{pmatrix} \begin{pmatrix} -3 & 1 \\ -1 & 0 \end{pmatrix} \begin{pmatrix} e^{t} & e^{2t} \\ e^{t} & 2e^{2t} \end{pmatrix}$$

$$= \begin{pmatrix} -1 & 0 \\ 0 & 1 \end{pmatrix}$$

is a constant matrix. We may also illustrate the application of Corollary 3-7.3 by noting that if the sign of the first component of $\mathbf{u}(t)$ is changed, then the constant matrix becomes the identity matrix.

Finally, we may illustrate the result of Theorem 3-7.4 by noting that the adjoint of L^* is L.

Exercises

1. For each equation in Exercise 2 of Section 3-4, find the concomitant matrix, the adjoint equation, and a fundamental vector for the adjoint equation.

2. (a) Show that $p_0 u'' + p_1 u' + p_2 u = 0$ is self-adjoint if $p_1 = p_0'$.
(b) If $p_1 = p_0'$, show that the equation of part (a) can be written as $(pu')' + qu = 0$.

3. Show that $u'' + fu' + gu = 0$ may be made self-adjoint by multiplying it by the integrating factor

$$\exp \int_a^t f(s)\, ds \ .$$

3-8. THE RELATIONSHIP BETWEEN SCALAR AND VECTOR ADJOINTS

It is assumed in this section that the coefficient p_0 in the differential form Lu is restricted by $p_0 = 1$ and that $\mathbf{A}$ represents the matrix defined by (3-4.8). With these specifications, the scalar equation

$$Lu = 0 \tag{3-8.1}$$

and its companion vector equation

$$\mathbf{y}' = \mathbf{A}\mathbf{y} \tag{3-8.2}$$

are "equivalent" in the sense described in Section 3-4. We intend to explore the relationship between

$$L^* v = 0 \ , \tag{3-8.3}$$

the adjoint of equation (3-8.1) and

$$\mathbf{z}' = -\tilde{\mathbf{A}}\mathbf{z} \ , \tag{3-8.4}$$

the adjoint of equation (3-8.2).
The following theorems reveal this relationship.

Theorem 3-8.1. *The last component in any vector solution of* (3-8.4) *is a solution of* (3-8.3).

PROOF. The scalar relations corresponding to (3-8.4) are

$$
\begin{aligned}
z_1' &= && && p_n z_n \\
z_2' &= -z_1 && && +p_{n-1} z_n \\
&\ \vdots \\
z_{i+1}' &= && -z_i && +p_{n-i} z_n \\
&\ \vdots \\
z_n' &= && && -z_{n-1} + p_1 z_n \ .
\end{aligned}
\tag{3-8.5}
$$

Let the $(i+1)$st relation be multiplied by $(-1)^i$ and differentiated i times, $i = 0, 1, \ldots, n-1$. If the resulting relations are added, we get

$$(-1)^{n-1} z_n^{[n]} = \sum_{i=0}^{n-1} (-1)^i (p_{n-i} z_n)^{[i]} \ .$$

If the single term on the left-hand side of this relation is transposed to the right-hand side, it becomes

$$L^* z_n = 0 \ .$$

It follows that if $\mathbf{z}$ satisfies equation (3-8.4), its last component satisfies equation (3-8.3). This proves the theorem.

Theorem 3-8.2. *If* $\mathbf{z}$ *is any solution of equation* (3-8.4), *Wronskian vector of its last component satisfies*

$$\tilde{\mathbf{z}} = \tilde{\mathbf{k}}(z_n)\mathbf{P} \ ,$$

where $\mathbf{P}$ *is the concomitant matrix for Lu.*

PROOF. Let the first relation in the system (3-8.5) be deleted, and let the trivial relation, $(p_0 = 1)$

$$0 = -z_n + p_0 z_n$$

be adjoined as a last relation to form a new set of n relations. It is clear that the new set can be written in matrix notation as

$$\mathbf{J}\mathbf{z}' = -\mathbf{z} + z_n \mathbf{q} \ , \tag{3-8.6}$$

where

$$\tilde{\mathbf{q}} = (p_{n-1}, p_{n-2}, \ldots, p_0) \ .$$

It is also clear that relation (3-8.6) is satisfied by any solution of (3-8.4). Transposing the first term on the right-hand side of (3-8.6) to the left-hand side, differentiating i times, and left-multiplying both sides of the relation by

$(-1)^i \mathbf{J}^i$, we get

$$(-1)^i \mathbf{J}^i \mathbf{z}^{[i]} + (-1)^i \mathbf{J}^{i+1} \mathbf{z}^{[i+1]} = (-1)^i \mathbf{J}^i (z_n \mathbf{q})^{[i]} \ , \qquad i = 0, 1, \ldots, n-1 \ .$$

Summing these relations, we have

$$\sum_{i=0}^{n-1} (-1)^i \mathbf{J}^i \mathbf{z}^{[i]} - \sum_{i=0}^{n-1} (-1)^{i+1} \mathbf{J}^{i+1} \mathbf{z}^{[i+1]} = \sum_{i=0}^{n-1} (-1)^i \mathbf{J}^i (z_n \mathbf{q})^{[i]} \ .$$

If the index $i+1$ in the second sum on the left-hand side is replaced by j, we find that the terms of the two sums on the left cancel each other with the exception of the first term of the first sum and the last term of the second sum. The last term of the second sum is $(-1)^n \mathbf{J}^n \mathbf{z}^{[n]}$ and is, therefore, the zero vector, since $\mathbf{J}^n = \mathbf{O}$. Consequently, the above relation reduces to

(3-8.7) $$\mathbf{z} = \sum_{i=0}^{n-1} (-1)^i \mathbf{J}^i (z_n \mathbf{q})^{[i]} \ .$$

A vector $\mathbf{z}$ must satisfy this relation (3-8.7) if it is a solution of equation (3-8.4). A formula for the jth component of such a vector is easily obtained from relation (3-8.7) by left-multiplying both sides by $\tilde{\mathbf{d}}_j$. That is,

$$z_j = \tilde{\mathbf{d}}_j \mathbf{z} = \sum_{i=0}^{n-1} (-1)^i \tilde{\mathbf{d}}_j \mathbf{J}^i (z_n \mathbf{q})^{[i]} \ .$$

In view of the fact that

$$\tilde{\mathbf{d}}_j \mathbf{J}^i = \begin{cases} \tilde{\mathbf{d}}_{j+i} \ , & i \leqq n-j \ , \\ \mathbf{0} \ , & i > n-j \ , \end{cases}$$

we may write

$$z_j = \sum_{i=0}^{n-j} (-1)^i \tilde{\mathbf{d}}_{j+i} (z_n \mathbf{q})^{[i]}$$
$$= \sum_{i=0}^{n-j} (-1)^i (z_n p_{n-j-i})^{[i]} \ .$$

If the index i is replaced by $k-j$, this formula becomes

(3-8.8) $$z_j = \sum_{k=j}^{n} (-1)^{k-j} (z_n p_{n-k})^{[k-j]} \ .$$

At this point it is clear that each component of $\mathbf{z}$ is a linear combination of z_n and its first $n-1$ derivatives. That is to say, there is a matrix $\mathbf{Q}$ such that $\tilde{\mathbf{z}} = \tilde{\mathbf{k}}(z_n)\mathbf{Q}$. It is gratifying to note that the computation involved in the explicit determination of $\mathbf{Q}$ has already been done. This matrix is, in fact, the concomitant matrix $\mathbf{P}$. To establish this, we note that if v is replaced by z_n in relation (3-7.7) we may write, in view of (3-8.8),

$$P(u, z_n) = \sum_{j=1}^{n} z_j u^{[j-1]}$$
$$= \tilde{\mathbf{z}}\mathbf{k}(u) \ .$$

Since $P(u, z_n) = \tilde{\mathbf{k}}(z_n)\mathbf{P}\mathbf{k}(u)$, we must conclude that

$$\tilde{\mathbf{z}} = \tilde{\mathbf{k}}(z_n)\mathbf{P} \ . \tag{3-8.9}$$

This proves the theorem.

Corollary 3-8.2a. *If* $\mathbf{Z}$ *is a fundamental matrix for equation* (3-8.4), *and* $\mathbf{v}$ *is the vector whose components form the last row of* $\mathbf{Z}$, *then*

$$\tilde{\mathbf{Z}} = \tilde{\mathbf{K}}(\mathbf{v})\mathbf{P} \ . \tag{3-8.10}$$

Corollary 3-8.2b. *The last row of any fundamental matrix for equation* (3-8.4) *is a fundamental vector for equation* (3-8.3).

PROOF. If $\mathbf{Z}$ is a fundamental matrix for equation (3-8.4), we can deduce from Corollary 3-8.2a that $\mathbf{K}(\mathbf{v})$ is nonsingular. It follows that the components of $\mathbf{v}$ are linearly independent. By Theorem 3-8.1, they are solutions of equation (3-8.3). Hence, $\mathbf{v}$ is a fundamental vector for that equation.

Corollary 3-8.2c. *If* $\mathbf{u}$ *is any fundamental vector for* $Lu = 0$ *and* $\mathbf{v}$ *is the vector whose components form the last column of* $\mathbf{K}^{-1}(\mathbf{u})$, *then* $\mathbf{v}$ *is a fundamental vector for* $L^*v = 0$ *and*

$$\tilde{\mathbf{K}}(\mathbf{v})\mathbf{P}\mathbf{K}(\mathbf{u}) = \mathbf{I} \ . \tag{3-8.11}$$

PROOF. Since $\tilde{\mathbf{K}}^{-1}(\mathbf{u})$ is a fundamental matrix for $\mathbf{z}' = -\tilde{\mathbf{A}}\mathbf{z}$, it may be substituted for $\mathbf{Z}$ in formula (3-8.10). Multiplication on the right by $\mathbf{K}(\mathbf{u})$, then, yields the desired result.

The existence of relation (3-8.11) was established in Corollary 3-7.3. Here, however, we have been able to state the precise relationship that exists between $\mathbf{u}$ and $\mathbf{v}$ in order that (3-8.11) should hold. This information is useful in the derivation of the properties of Green's function.

The following theorem is not used in the subsequent development of this text and can, therefore, be omitted without affecting the continuity of the exposition. It does, however, complete the set of vector equations associated with the general nth-order linear differential equation and its adjoint.

Theorem 3-8.3. *The companion vector equation for* $L^*v = 0$ *is*

$$\mathbf{w}' = \mathbf{B}\mathbf{w} \ , \tag{3-8.12}$$

where

$$\tilde{\mathbf{B}} = -(\mathbf{P}\mathbf{A}+\mathbf{P}')\mathbf{P}^{-1} \ .$$

PROOF. Let **Z** be any fundamental matrix for equation (3-8.4) and let **v** be the vector whose components form the last row of **Z**. Theorem 3-8.2 and Corollaries 3-8.2a, b, c imply that **v** is a fundamental vector for $L^*v = 0$ and that

$$\tilde{\mathbf{Z}} = \tilde{\mathbf{K}}(\mathbf{v})\mathbf{P} \ .$$

Since **Z** was chosen as a fundamental matrix for equation (3-8.4), we may write

$$(\tilde{\mathbf{K}}(\mathbf{v})\mathbf{P})' = -(\tilde{\mathbf{K}}(\mathbf{v})\mathbf{P})\mathbf{A} \ .$$

This is equivalent to

$$\tilde{\mathbf{K}}'(\mathbf{v}) = -\tilde{\mathbf{K}}(\mathbf{v})(\mathbf{PA}+\mathbf{P}')\mathbf{P}^{-1} \ .$$

It follows at once that $\mathbf{K}(\mathbf{v})$ is a fundamental matrix for equation (3-8.12) and, hence, that equation (3-8.12) is the companion vector equation associated with $L^*v = 0$.

Exercises

1. Prove that

$$L^*v = p_n v - (\tilde{\mathbf{k}}(\mathbf{v})\mathbf{P}\mathbf{d}_1)' \ .$$

(*Hint:* Use relation (3-8.8) with $j = 1$.[4])

[4] Cole [14], Section 3.

4

Linear Equations with Constant Coefficients

4-1. INTRODUCTION

In this chapter the n by n matrix $\mathbf{A}$ in

$$\mathbf{y}' = \mathbf{A}\mathbf{y} \tag{4-1.1}$$

is restricted to real, constant components. We first note that when $n = 1$ equation (4-1.1) reduces to

$$y' = ay \ , \tag{4-1.2}$$

for which a fundamental solution (see Section 2-1) is

$$y(t) = e^{at} \ .$$

Using the definition of an exponential matrix in Theorem 1-11.2, we define a matrix $\mathbf{U}$ by

$$\mathbf{U}(t) = e^{t\mathbf{A}} \ .$$

That is, $\mathbf{U}(t)$ is the matrix to which the series [see (1-11.1)]

$$\sum_{j=1}^{\infty} \frac{1}{(j-1)!}(t\mathbf{A})^{j-1}$$

converges. It is easily deduced that this series converges uniformly to $\mathbf{U}(t)$ on any finite real interval. Since the derivative of the series may be written as

$$\mathbf{A} \sum_{j=1}^{\infty} \frac{1}{(j-1)!}(t\mathbf{A})^{j-1} \ ,$$

we must conclude that

$$\mathbf{U}' = \mathbf{A}\mathbf{U} \ .$$

This implies that $\mathbf{U}$ is a solution matrix for equation (4-1.1). Since $\mathbf{U}$ is non-singular (we examine this later in the text), it is also a fundamental matrix for equation (4-1.1).

It is gratifying to obtain a representation of a fundamental matrix for (4-1.1) that is identical in form with a fundamental solution for the scalar equation (4-1.2). It must be recognized, however, that $e^{t\mathbf{A}}$ is a more complicated entity than e^{ta}. We show that the character of the matrix $e^{t\mathbf{A}}$ is determined by the character of the Jordan canonical form of $\mathbf{A}$. Consequently, the classification of n by n matrices according to their Jordan canonical form implies a similar classification of solutions of equation (4-1.1).

A brief description of the Jordan canonical form and a brief outline of its algebraic significance follows.[1, 2] Two square matrices $\mathbf{A}$ and $\mathbf{B}$ are said to be *similar* if there exists a nonsingular matrix $\mathbf{T}$ such that

$$\mathbf{T}^{-1}\mathbf{A}\mathbf{T} = \mathbf{B} \ .$$

It is easily verified that "similarity" is an equivalence relation. Hence, the set of all n by n matrices may be separated into equivalence classes in such a way that each matrix in a class is similar to every other matrix in that class. One matrix from each class is then selected to be a canonical or representative matrix for that class. The Jordan set of canonical matrices is such a representative set. Each member $\mathbf{M}$ of the set has the form

$$\mathbf{M} = \begin{pmatrix} \mathbf{M}_1 & \mathbf{0} & \cdots & \mathbf{0} \\ \mathbf{0} & \mathbf{M}_2 & \cdots & \mathbf{0} \\ \cdot & \cdot & \cdot & \cdot \\ \cdot & \cdot & \cdot & \cdot \\ \cdot & \cdot & \cdot & \cdot \\ \mathbf{0} & \mathbf{0} & \cdots & \mathbf{M}_r \end{pmatrix}, \tag{4-1.3}$$

where $\mathbf{M}_i$ is a square submatrix of order n_i given by

$$\mathbf{M}_i = \lambda_i \mathbf{I} + \mathbf{J} \ .$$

(For the definition of the matrix $\mathbf{J}$ see Section 3-4 following Theorem 3-4.2.) Clearly

$$\sum_{i=1}^{r} n_i = n$$

and the symbol $\mathbf{0}$ in the ith row and jth column of the partitioned form of $\mathbf{M}$ represents an n_i by n_j zero-matrix. It should be noted that if n_i equals 1 then $\mathbf{M}_i$ is a 1 by 1 matrix with a single component λ_i. Further, it is not implied that λ_i is necessarily distinct from λ_j when $i \neq j$.

A specific matrix of the form exhibited in (4-1.3) may be referred to as the (*Jordan*) *canonical form* of any matrix that is similar to it. That is to say, it is the canonical form of any matrix in its equivalence class. A scalar λ is an *eigenvalue* of a matrix $\mathbf{A}$ if there exists a nonzero vector $\mathbf{x}$, called an *eigenvector*, such that $\mathbf{A}\mathbf{x} = \lambda\mathbf{x}$. Since the eigenvalues of a matrix are invariant under a similarity transformation, the eigenvalues of any matrix are the eigenvalues of its canonical form. Hence, the eigenvalues of any matrix similar to $\mathbf{M}$ are the distinct members of the set

$$\lambda_1, \lambda_2, \ldots, \lambda_r \ .$$

[1] Hoffman and Kunze [25].
[2] Nering [36].

Moreover, the multiplicity of each eigenvalue is equal to the number of times it appears as a diagonal element of **M**.

The significance of the similarity transformation relative to the problem of finding solutions of a vector equation is shown by the following theorem. It is assumed that **A**, **B**, and **S** are constant, square matrices.

Theorem 4-1.1. *If* **V** *is a fundamental matrix for*

$$\mathbf{v}' = \mathbf{B}\mathbf{v} \ ,$$

then, with **S** *nonsingular,*

$$\mathbf{Y} = \mathbf{S}\mathbf{V}$$

is a fundamental matrix for

$$\mathbf{y}' = \mathbf{A}\mathbf{y} \ ,$$

where $\mathbf{A} = \mathbf{S}\mathbf{B}\mathbf{S}^{-1}$.

PROOF. By hypothesis, we have

$$\mathbf{V}' = \mathbf{B}\mathbf{V} \ .$$

Since $\mathbf{V} = \mathbf{S}^{-1}\mathbf{Y}$, this becomes

$$\mathbf{Y}' = \mathbf{S}\mathbf{B}\mathbf{S}^{-1}\mathbf{Y} \ ,$$

and the theorem is proved by noting that **Y** is nonsingular.

Theorem 4-1.1 implies that we can find a solution for a vector equation with coefficient matrix **A** by finding a solution for any vector equation whose coefficient matrix is similar to **A**. Because of its simplicity, the vector equation whose coefficient matrix is the canonical form of **A** offers obvious advantages relative to the task of finding a solution.

At this point it is clear that the problem of solving equation (4-1.1) has been reduced to the problem of solving

$$\mathbf{v}' = \mathbf{M}\mathbf{v} \ ,$$

where **M** is given by (4-1.3). This problem is treated in Sections 4-2 and 4-3. The treatment given there yields a complex-valued solution for every complex eigenvalue. Since we have agreed to limit our attention to real-valued solutions, we have a complication which is removed in Section 4-5. In that section, complex-valued solutions are shown to occur as conjugate pairs which can readily be replaced by an equivalent pair of real-valued solutions.

4-2. REAL DISTINCT EIGENVALUES

In this section the simplest case is treated to provide an introduction for the general case. Consider

$$\mathbf{y}' = \mathbf{A}\mathbf{y} \ , \tag{4-2.1}$$

where the eigenvalues $\lambda_1, \lambda_2, \ldots, \lambda_n$ of the matrix **A** are real and distinct. The canonical form of **A** is a diagonal matrix given by

$$\mathbf{M} = (\delta_{ij}\lambda_j) \ .$$

Let $\mathbf{s}_j$ be an eigenvector of **A** corresponding to the eigenvalue λ_j, and let the matrix S be

$$\mathbf{S} = (\mathbf{s}_1, \mathbf{s}_2, \ldots, \mathbf{s}_n) \ ,$$

where the jth column is the vector $\mathbf{s}_j$. It follows that

$$\mathbf{AS} = \mathbf{SM} \ ,$$

and, since S is nonsingular, that

$$\mathbf{S}^{-1}\mathbf{AS} = \mathbf{M} \ .$$

If

$$\mathbf{v}' = \mathbf{M}\mathbf{v} \tag{4-2.2}$$

is written in scalar form, it is obvious that

$$\mathbf{v}_j = e^{\lambda_j t}\mathbf{d}_j \ , \quad j = 1, 2, \ldots, n \ ,$$

is a solution and that the matrix

$$\mathbf{E} = (\delta_{ij} e^{\lambda_j t})$$

is a fundamental matrix for the equation. It follows readily that a fundamental matrix **Y** for equation (4-2.1) is

$$\mathbf{Y} = \mathbf{SE} \ .$$

This completes the solution of equation (4-2.1), but it is pertinent to note that the jth column of **Y** is

$$\mathbf{y}_j = e^{\lambda_j t}\mathbf{s}_j \ , \quad j = 1, 2, \ldots, n \ ,$$

where $\mathbf{s}_j$ is an eigenvector of **A** corresponding to the eigenvalue λ_j. Also, recalling the discussion in Section 4-1, it is instructive to note that

$$\mathbf{E} = (\delta_{ij} e^{t\lambda_j}) = e^{t(\delta_{ij}\lambda_j)} = e^{t\mathbf{M}} \ .$$

Finally, it is clear that $\mathbf{YS}^{-1}$ is a fundamental matrix for (4-2.1) and, for this matrix, we have

$$\mathbf{YS}^{-1} = \mathbf{S}e^{t\mathbf{M}}\mathbf{S}^{-1} = e^{t\mathbf{SMS}^{-1}} = e^{t\mathbf{A}} \ .$$

Example 1. A simple example illustrates these results. We wish to find a fundamental matrix for the following equation

$$\mathbf{Y}' = \begin{pmatrix} 1 & 1 & 1 \\ 0 & 2 & 1 \\ 0 & 0 & 3 \end{pmatrix} \mathbf{y} \ .$$

The eigenvalues of the coefficient matrix are

$$\lambda_1 = 1, \ \lambda_2 = 2, \ \lambda_3 = 3 \ .$$

The corresponding eigenvectors are

$$\mathbf{s}_1 = \begin{pmatrix} 1 \\ 0 \\ 0 \end{pmatrix}, \quad \mathbf{s}_2 = \begin{pmatrix} 1 \\ 1 \\ 0 \end{pmatrix}, \quad \mathbf{s}_3 = \begin{pmatrix} 1 \\ 1 \\ 1 \end{pmatrix}.$$

Hence, a fundamental set of solutions is given by

$$\mathbf{y}_1 = e^t \begin{pmatrix} 1 \\ 0 \\ 0 \end{pmatrix}, \quad \mathbf{y}_2 = e^{2t} \begin{pmatrix} 1 \\ 1 \\ 0 \end{pmatrix}, \quad \mathbf{y}_3 = e^{3t} \begin{pmatrix} 1 \\ 1 \\ 1 \end{pmatrix}.$$

The matrix

$$\begin{aligned} \mathbf{Y} &= \begin{pmatrix} e^t & e^{2t} & e^{3t} \\ 0 & e^{2t} & e^{3t} \\ 0 & 0 & e^{3t} \end{pmatrix} \\ &= \begin{pmatrix} 1 & 1 & 1 \\ 0 & 1 & 1 \\ 0 & 0 & 1 \end{pmatrix} \begin{pmatrix} e^t & 0 & 0 \\ 0 & e^{2t} & 0 \\ 0 & 0 & e^{3t} \end{pmatrix} \end{aligned}$$

is a fundamental matrix for the equation.

Exercises

1. Find fundamental matrices for the following equations. (Answers are given below.)

(a) $\mathbf{y}' = \begin{pmatrix} -1 & 3 & 0 \\ 0 & 2 & 0 \\ -2 & 3 & 1 \end{pmatrix} \mathbf{y}$;

(b) $\mathbf{y}' = \begin{pmatrix} 1 & 0 & -1 \\ 2 & 3 & 2 \\ 0 & 0 & 2 \end{pmatrix} \mathbf{y}$;

(c) $y_1' = 2y_2$,
$y_2' = 2y_2$,
$y_3' = -y_1 + 2y_2 + y_3$;

(d) $y_1' = y_2$,
$y_2' = y_3$,
$y_3' = 4y_2$;

(e) $\mathbf{y}' = \begin{pmatrix} 0 & 1 \\ a^2 & 0 \end{pmatrix} \mathbf{y}$;

(f) $\mathbf{y}' = \begin{pmatrix} 0 & 1 \\ -6 & -5 \end{pmatrix} \mathbf{y}$;

(g) $\mathbf{y}' = \begin{pmatrix} 0 & 1 & 0 \\ 0 & 0 & 1 \\ 0 & 1 & 0 \end{pmatrix} \mathbf{y}$;

(h) $\mathbf{y}' = \begin{pmatrix} 0 & 1 & 0 \\ 0 & 0 & 1 \\ 2 & 1 & -2 \end{pmatrix} \mathbf{y}$.

2. Find a particular solution of

$$\mathbf{y}' = \begin{pmatrix} -1 & 3 & 0 \\ 0 & 2 & 0 \\ -2 & 3 & 1 \end{pmatrix} \mathbf{y} + \begin{pmatrix} 1 \\ 1 \\ 0 \end{pmatrix}.$$

See Exercise 1(a).

3. Find the solution of the following initial-value problem:

$$\mathbf{y}' = \begin{pmatrix} 1 & 0 & -1 \\ 2 & 3 & 2 \\ 0 & 0 & 2 \end{pmatrix} \mathbf{y} + \begin{pmatrix} 1 \\ 0 \\ 0 \end{pmatrix},$$

$$\mathbf{y}(0) = \mathbf{o} .$$

See Exercise 1(b).

ANSWERS

1\.

(a) $\begin{pmatrix} e^{-t} & 0 & e^{2t} \\ 0 & 0 & e^{2t} \\ e^{-t} & e^{t} & e^{2t} \end{pmatrix}$; (b) $\begin{pmatrix} e^{t} & -e^{2t} & 0 \\ -e^{t} & 0 & e^{3t} \\ 0 & e^{2t} & 0 \end{pmatrix}$;

(c) $\begin{pmatrix} 1 & 0 & e^{2t} \\ 0 & 0 & e^{2t} \\ 1 & e^{t} & e^{2t} \end{pmatrix}$; (d) $\begin{pmatrix} 1 & e^{2t} & e^{-2t} \\ 0 & 2e^{2t} & -2e^{-2t} \\ 0 & 4e^{2t} & 4e^{-2t} \end{pmatrix}$;

(e) $\begin{pmatrix} e^{at} & e^{-at} \\ ae^{at} & -ae^{-at} \end{pmatrix}$; (f) $\begin{pmatrix} e^{-2t} & e^{-3t} \\ -2e^{-2t} & -3e^{-3t} \end{pmatrix}$;

(g) $\begin{pmatrix} 1 & e^{t} & e^{-t} \\ 0 & e^{t} & -e^{-t} \\ 0 & e^{t} & e^{-t} \end{pmatrix}$; (h) $\begin{pmatrix} e^{t} & e^{-t} & e^{-2t} \\ e^{t} & -e^{-t} & -2e^{-2t} \\ e^{t} & e^{-t} & 4e^{-2t} \end{pmatrix}$.

4-3. THE GENERAL CASE

We have already shown that a solution of

$$\mathbf{y}' = \mathbf{A}\mathbf{y} , \tag{4-3.1}$$

where $\mathbf{A}$ is any constant real n by n matrix, can be achieved by finding a solution of

$$\mathbf{v}' = \mathbf{M}\mathbf{v} , \tag{4-3.2}$$

where $\mathbf{M}$ is the Jordan canonical form of $\mathbf{A}$. Recalling the form of $\mathbf{M}$, defined in formula (4-1.3), we see that $\mathbf{M}$ has some complex diagonal elements if $\mathbf{A}$ has any complex eigenvalues. Consequently, it is desirable to generalize the definition of a solution of a vector equation, this is done as follows.

Definition 4-3.1. *A solution of* $\mathbf{y}' = \mathbf{A}\mathbf{y}$ *on an interval* I *is an n-vector whose components are complex-valued functions with continuous first derivatives on* I *and which satisfies the equation.*

In view of this definition, it is clear that we should adopt the complex number system as the scalar field, and we do.

The direct sum of two vector spaces[3] can be used advantageously in this section. Given Y_1 and Y_2 as two finite-dimensional vector spaces, their *direct sum* $Y_1 \oplus Y_2$ is the set of all ordered pairs (a_1, a_2), where $a_1 \in Y_1$ and $a_2 \in Y_2$. It may be established, if addition and scalar multiplication are appropriately defined, that this set is a vector space and that its dimension is the sum of the dimensions of Y_1 and Y_2. It is of significance that a subspace of the direct sum consisting of all ordered pairs of the form $(a_1, 0)$ is isomorphic to Y_1. Similarly, the subspace containing all pairs of the form $(0, a_2)$ is isomorphic to Y_2.

Whether or not the reader is familiar with the algebraic concept of a direct sum, the following example stands on its own merit. The properties of a direct sum in this case evolve from the properties of matrix multiplication. Let $\mathbf{A}_1$ and $\mathbf{A}_2$ be two square matrices of orders n_1 and n_2, respectively, and let the vector space Y_i be the solution space of

$$\mathbf{y}' = \mathbf{A}_i\mathbf{y} \ , \quad i = 1, 2 \ . \tag{4-3.3}$$

If $\mathbf{Y}_i$ is a fundamental matrix for equation (4-3.3), then $\mathbf{y}_i \in Y_i$ if and only if

$$\mathbf{y}_i = \mathbf{Y}_i\mathbf{c}_i \tag{4-3.4}$$

for some vector $\mathbf{c}_i$ in $V_{n_i}(C)$. We may represent an element in the direct sum of Y_1 and Y_2 by

$$\begin{pmatrix} \mathbf{y}_1 \\ \mathbf{y}_2 \end{pmatrix} . \tag{4-3.5}$$

It may be observed here that an ordered pair is an ordered pair whether it be written in horizontal or vertical form. The vertical form is preferred here because the solutions of vector equations are usually written as column vectors. Because of its vertical form, the ordered pair (4-3.5) may be thought of as a partitioned column vector of dimension $n_1 + n_2$. Hence, we write

$$\begin{pmatrix} \mathbf{y}_1 \\ \mathbf{y}_2 \end{pmatrix} = \begin{pmatrix} \mathbf{Y}_1 & \mathbf{0} \\ \mathbf{0} & \mathbf{Y}_2 \end{pmatrix} \begin{pmatrix} \mathbf{c}_1 \\ \mathbf{c}_2 \end{pmatrix} ,$$

where $\mathbf{c}_1$ and $\mathbf{c}_2$ are the vectors appearing in formula (4-3.4). It is clear from this relation that

$$\begin{pmatrix} \mathbf{y}_1 \\ \mathbf{y}_2 \end{pmatrix} \in Y_1 \oplus Y_2 \quad \text{if and only if} \begin{pmatrix} \mathbf{c}_1 \\ \mathbf{c}_2 \end{pmatrix} \in V_{n_1+n_2}(C) \ .$$

This establishes the fact that $Y_1 \oplus Y_2$ is a vector space of dimension $n_1 + n_2$. It is equally clear that elements of the form

$$\begin{pmatrix} \mathbf{y}_1 \\ \mathbf{o} \end{pmatrix} \quad \text{and} \quad \begin{pmatrix} \mathbf{o} \\ \mathbf{y}_2 \end{pmatrix}$$

are, respectively, subspaces of the direct sum. The first of these subspaces is isomorphic to Y_1 and the second to Y_2.

[3] Halmos [21], Section 18.

Our understanding of the formation of a direct sum and its properties can now be applied to establish the following theorem. The notation that was introduced above is used in the theorem.

Theorem 4-3.1. *The solution space of*

$$\mathbf{y}' = \begin{pmatrix} \mathbf{A}_1 & \mathbf{0} \\ \mathbf{0} & \mathbf{A}_2 \end{pmatrix} \mathbf{y} \tag{4-3.6}$$

is the direct sum of the solution spaces of $\mathbf{y}' = \mathbf{A}_1\mathbf{y}$ *and* $\mathbf{y}' = \mathbf{A}_2\mathbf{y}$.

PROOF. Since $\mathbf{Y}_i$ is a fundamental matrix for equation (4-3.3),

$$\begin{pmatrix} \mathbf{Y}_1 & \mathbf{0} \\ \mathbf{0} & \mathbf{Y}_2 \end{pmatrix}' = \begin{pmatrix} \mathbf{A}_1\mathbf{Y}_1 & \mathbf{0} \\ \mathbf{0} & \mathbf{A}_2\mathbf{Y}_2 \end{pmatrix}$$

$$= \begin{pmatrix} \mathbf{A}_1 & \mathbf{0} \\ \mathbf{0} & \mathbf{A}_1 \end{pmatrix} \begin{pmatrix} \mathbf{Y}_1 & \mathbf{0} \\ \mathbf{0} & \mathbf{Y}_2 \end{pmatrix}.$$

Hence, the matrix

$$\mathbf{Y} = \begin{pmatrix} \mathbf{Y}_1 & \mathbf{0} \\ \mathbf{0} & \mathbf{Y}_2 \end{pmatrix}$$

is clearly a fundamental matrix for equation (4-3.6). The solution space of equation (4-3.6) is the column space of $\mathbf{Y}$. From our preliminary discussion it is possible to infer that the solution space is the direct sum of the column space of $\mathbf{Y}_1$ and the column space of $\mathbf{Y}_2$. This proves the theorem.

Corollary 4-3.1. *If* $\{\mathbf{A}_i : i = 1, 2, \ldots, r\}$ *is a set of square matrices, then the solution space of*

$$\mathbf{y}' = \begin{pmatrix} \mathbf{A}_1 & \mathbf{0} & \cdots & \mathbf{0} \\ \mathbf{0} & \mathbf{A}_2 & \cdots & \mathbf{0} \\ \vdots & \vdots & & \vdots \\ \mathbf{0} & \mathbf{0} & \cdots & \mathbf{A}_r \end{pmatrix} \mathbf{y} \tag{4-3.7}$$

is the direct sum of the solution spaces of the equations in the set

$$\{\mathbf{y}' = \mathbf{A}_i\mathbf{y} \ : \ i = 1, 2, \ldots, r\}.$$

Moreover, a fundamental matrix for (4-3.7) *is*

$$\begin{pmatrix} \mathbf{Y}_1 & \mathbf{0} & \cdots & \mathbf{0} \\ \mathbf{0} & \mathbf{Y}_2 & \cdots & \mathbf{0} \\ \vdots & \vdots & & \vdots \\ \mathbf{0} & \mathbf{0} & \cdots & \mathbf{Y}_r \end{pmatrix},$$

where $\mathbf{Y}_i$ *is a fundamental matrix for* $\mathbf{y}' = \mathbf{A}_i\mathbf{y}$.

REMARK. We apply the above results only in cases where each member of the set $\{\mathbf{A}_i\}$ is a constant matrix. It should be noted, however, that Theorem 4-3.1 is valid when each component of $\mathbf{A}_i$ is a continuous complex-valued function.

This result is now used to find a solution for equation (4-3.2).

Theorem 4-3.2. *If* $\mathbf{M}$ *is defined by relation* (4-1.3), *then a fundamental matrix for*

$$\mathbf{v}' = \mathbf{M}\mathbf{v} \tag{4-3.8}$$

is given by

$$\mathbf{V} = \begin{pmatrix} \mathbf{V}_1 & \mathbf{0} & \cdots & \mathbf{0} \\ \mathbf{0} & \mathbf{V}_2 & \cdots & \mathbf{0} \\ \cdot & \cdot & \cdot & \cdot \\ \cdot & \cdot & \cdot & \cdot \\ \cdot & \cdot & \cdot & \cdot \\ \mathbf{0} & \mathbf{0} & \cdots & \mathbf{V}_r \end{pmatrix}, \quad i = 1, 2, \ldots, r, \tag{4-3.9}$$

where $\mathbf{V}_i$ *is a fundamental matrix for*

$$\mathbf{v}' = \mathbf{M}_i\mathbf{v}, \quad i = 1, 2, \ldots, r. \tag{4-3.10}$$

The matrix $\mathbf{V}_i$ *is given by*

$$\mathbf{V}_i = e^{\lambda_i t}\mathbf{K}(\mathbf{e}_{n_i}(t)), \tag{4-3.11}$$

where

$$\tilde{\mathbf{e}}_{n_i}(t) = (1, t, t^2, \ldots, t^{n_i-1}). \tag{4-3.12}$$

PROOF. The matrix $\mathbf{M}_i$, of order n_i, was defined in Section 4-1 by

$$\mathbf{M}_i = \lambda_i\mathbf{I} + \mathbf{J}.$$

It is clear that λ_i is the only eigenvalue of $\mathbf{M}_i$ and that its multiplicity is n_i. A corresponding eigenvector is $\mathbf{d}_1$, and it may be noted, incidentally, that $e^{\lambda_i t}\mathbf{d}_1$ is a solution of equation (4-3.10). In order to find other solutions, we note that any vector $\mathbf{v}$ can be expressed as

$$\mathbf{v} = e^{\lambda_i t}\mathbf{h}.$$

If $\mathbf{v}$, in this form, is substituted into equation (4-3.10), we get

$$e^{\lambda_i t}\mathbf{h}' + \lambda_i e^{\lambda_i t}\mathbf{h} = (\lambda_i\mathbf{I} + \mathbf{J})e^{\lambda_i t}\mathbf{h},$$

which may be reduced to

$$\mathbf{h}' = \mathbf{J}\mathbf{h}. \tag{4-3.13}$$

Hence $\mathbf{v}$ is a solution of (4-3.10) if and only if $\mathbf{h}$ satisfies (4-3.13). The latter equation is the companion vector equation associated with the n_ith-order scalar equation

$$u^{[n_i]} = 0.$$

The vector $\mathbf{e}_{n_i}(t)$, defined by (4-3.12), is a fundamental vector for this equation. Hence, $\mathbf{K}(\mathbf{e}_{n_i}(t))$ is a fundamental matrix for equation (4-3.13). It follows that $\mathbf{V}_i$, defined by (4-3.11), is a fundamental matrix for equation (4-3.10). By using Corollary 4-3.1 we may conclude that the matrix $\mathbf{V}$ defined by (4-3.9) is a fundamental matrix for equation (4-3.8). This proves the theorem.

The main result of this section is now stated in the form of a theorem.

Theorem 4-3.3. *A fundamental matrix for*

$$\mathbf{y}' = \mathbf{A}\mathbf{y}$$

is given by

$$\mathbf{Y} = \mathbf{S}\mathbf{V} .$$

The matrix $\mathbf{V}$ *is defined by the relations* (4-3.9), (4-3.11), *and* (4-3.12). *The matrix* $\mathbf{S}$ *is such that* $\mathbf{S}^{-1}\mathbf{A}\mathbf{S} = \mathbf{M}$, *where* $\mathbf{M}$ *is the Jordan canonical form of* $\mathbf{A}$.

PROOF. The validity of the theorem is obvious, since the result follows from a direct application of Theorem 4-1.1.

Example 1. This example illustrates the results of this section. Consider

$$\mathbf{y}' = \mathbf{A}\mathbf{y} ,$$

where

$$\mathbf{A} = \begin{pmatrix} 1 & 0 & 0 & 0 & 1 \\ -1 & 1 & 2 & 1 & -1 \\ 0 & 0 & 1 & 0 & 1 \\ -1 & 0 & 1 & 2 & 1 \\ 0 & 0 & 0 & 0 & 2 \end{pmatrix} .$$

Let $\mathbf{S}$ and its inverse $\mathbf{S}^{-1}$ be defined by

$$\mathbf{S} = \begin{pmatrix} 1 & 0 & 1 & 0 & 1 \\ 0 & 1 & 0 & 1 & 0 \\ 0 & 0 & 1 & 0 & 1 \\ 1 & 0 & 0 & 1 & 1 \\ 0 & 0 & 0 & 0 & 1 \end{pmatrix} , \quad \mathbf{S}^{-1} = \begin{pmatrix} 1 & 0 & -1 & 0 & 0 \\ 1 & 1 & -1 & -1 & 1 \\ 0 & 0 & 1 & 0 & -1 \\ -1 & 0 & 1 & 1 & -1 \\ 0 & 0 & 0 & 0 & 1 \end{pmatrix} .$$

It may be verified that

$$\mathbf{S}^{-1}\mathbf{A}\mathbf{S} = \mathbf{M} ,$$

where

$$\mathbf{M} = \begin{pmatrix} 1 & 0 & 0 & 0 & 0 \\ 0 & 1 & 1 & 0 & 0 \\ 0 & 0 & 1 & 0 & 0 \\ 0 & 0 & 0 & 2 & 1 \\ 0 & 0 & 0 & 0 & 2 \end{pmatrix} .$$

The matrix $\mathbf{M}$ is in Jordan canonical form and

$$\mathbf{M}_1 = (1)\ ,\quad \mathbf{M}_2 = \begin{pmatrix} 1 & 1 \\ 0 & 1 \end{pmatrix},\quad \mathbf{M}_3 = \begin{pmatrix} 2 & 1 \\ 0 & 2 \end{pmatrix}.$$

Corresponding to these, we have

$$\mathbf{V}_1 = e^t(1)\ ,\quad \mathbf{V}_2 = e^t\begin{pmatrix} 1 & t \\ 0 & 1 \end{pmatrix},\quad \mathbf{V}_3 = e^{2t}\begin{pmatrix} 0 & t \\ 0 & 1 \end{pmatrix}.$$

The fundamental matrix $\mathbf{Y}$ for the given equation is

$$\mathbf{Y} = \mathbf{S}\begin{pmatrix} e^t & 0 & 0 & 0 & 0 \\ 0 & e^t & te^t & 0 & 0 \\ 0 & 0 & e^t & 0 & 0 \\ 0 & 0 & 0 & e^{2t} & te^{2t} \\ 0 & 0 & 0 & 0 & e^{2t} \end{pmatrix}.$$

Exercises

1. Find fundamental matrices for the following equations. (Answers are given below.)

(a) $\mathbf{y}' = \begin{pmatrix} -1 & 0 & 0 \\ 3 & 2 & 3 \\ 0 & 0 & -1 \end{pmatrix}\mathbf{y}\ ;$ (b) $\mathbf{y}' = \begin{pmatrix} 3 & -2 & 0 \\ 1 & 0 & 0 \\ -1 & 2 & 1 \end{pmatrix}\mathbf{y}\ ;$

(c) $y_1' = 3y_1 - y_2\ ,$
$y_2' = y_1 - y_3\ ,$
$y_3' = -y_1 + 2y_2 + 3y_3\ ;$

(d) $y_1' = -y_2 - y_3\ ,$
$y_2' = -2y_2 - 2y_3\ ,$
$y_3' = 2y_2 + 2y_3\ ;$

(e) $\mathbf{y}' = \begin{pmatrix} 2 & -4 & 2 \\ 1 & -2 & 1 \\ -1 & 2 & 0 \end{pmatrix}\mathbf{y}\ ;$ (f) $\mathbf{y}' = \begin{pmatrix} 0 & 1 & 0 \\ 0 & 0 & 1 \\ 0 & -2 & -2 \end{pmatrix}\mathbf{y}\ ;$

(g) $\mathbf{y}' = \begin{pmatrix} 0 & 1 \\ -a^2 & 0 \end{pmatrix}\mathbf{y}\ ;$ (h) $\mathbf{y}' = \begin{pmatrix} 1 & 1 \\ -2 & -1 \end{pmatrix}\mathbf{y}\ .$

2. Solve the following initial-value problems:

(a) $\mathbf{y}' = \begin{pmatrix} 3 & -2 & 0 \\ 1 & 0 & 0 \\ -1 & 2 & 1 \end{pmatrix}\mathbf{y} + \begin{pmatrix} 0 \\ e^t \\ 0 \end{pmatrix},$

$\mathbf{y}(0) = \mathbf{o}\ ;$

(b) $\mathbf{y}' = \begin{pmatrix} 4 & 2 & -2 \\ -5 & 3 & 2 \\ -2 & 4 & 1 \end{pmatrix}\mathbf{y},$

$\mathbf{y}(0) = \begin{pmatrix} 3 \\ 0 \\ 4 \end{pmatrix};$

(c) $\mathbf{y}' = \begin{pmatrix} 4 & 2 & -2 \\ -5 & 3 & 2 \\ -2 & 4 & 1 \end{pmatrix}\mathbf{y} + \begin{pmatrix} 0 \\ 1 \\ 1 \end{pmatrix},$

$\mathbf{y}(0) = \mathbf{o}\ .$

ANSWERS

1. (a) $\begin{pmatrix} 1 & -1 & 0 \\ -1 & 0 & 1 \\ 0 & 1 & 0 \end{pmatrix} \begin{pmatrix} e^{-t} & 0 & 0 \\ 0 & e^{-t} & 0 \\ 0 & 0 & e^{2t} \end{pmatrix}$;

(b) $\begin{pmatrix} 2 & 0 & 1 \\ 1 & 0 & 1 \\ 0 & 1 & 1 \end{pmatrix} \begin{pmatrix} e^{2t} & 0 & 0 \\ 0 & e^{t} & te^{t} \\ 0 & 0 & e^{t} \end{pmatrix}$;

(c) $\begin{pmatrix} 1 & -1 & 0 \\ 1 & -2 & 1 \\ -1 & 2 & 0 \end{pmatrix} \begin{pmatrix} e^{2t} & te^{2t} & t^2e^{2t} \\ 0 & e^{2t} & 2te^{2t} \\ 0 & 0 & 2e^{2t} \end{pmatrix}$;

(d) $\begin{pmatrix} 1 & -1 & 0 \\ 1 & -2 & 1 \\ -1 & 2 & 0 \end{pmatrix} \begin{pmatrix} 1 & 0 & 0 \\ 0 & 1 & t \\ 0 & 0 & 1 \end{pmatrix}$;

(e) $\begin{pmatrix} 2 & 0 & 1 \\ 1 & 0 & 1 \\ 0 & 1 & 1 \end{pmatrix} \begin{pmatrix} 1 & t & t^2 \\ 0 & 1 & 2t \\ 0 & 0 & 2 \end{pmatrix}$;

(f) $\begin{pmatrix} 1 & \bar{\mu} & \mu \\ 0 & -2 & -2 \\ 0 & 2\mu & 2\bar{\mu} \end{pmatrix} \begin{pmatrix} 1 & 0 & 0 \\ 0 & e^{-\mu t} & 0 \\ 0 & 0 & e^{-\bar{\mu} t} \end{pmatrix}$,

where $\mu = 1+i$;

(g) $\begin{pmatrix} e^{iat} & e^{-iat} \\ iae^{iat} & -iae^{-iat} \end{pmatrix}$; (h) $\begin{pmatrix} 1 & -1 \\ -1+i & 1+i \end{pmatrix} \begin{pmatrix} e^{it} & 0 \\ 0 & e^{-it} \end{pmatrix}$.

2. (a) $\begin{pmatrix} 2(t+1)e^{t} - 2e^{2t} \\ (2t+1)e^{t} - e^{2t} \\ 0 \end{pmatrix}$; (b) $\begin{pmatrix} 2e^{t} + e^{2t} \\ e^{t} + e^{2t} - 2e^{5t} \\ 4e^{t} + 2e^{2t} - 2e^{5t} \end{pmatrix}$;

(c) $\frac{1}{5}(e^{5t} - 1)\begin{pmatrix} 0 \\ 1 \\ 1 \end{pmatrix}$.

4-4. DIRECT SOLUTION

Section 4-3 implies that for a specific equation with coefficient matrix **A** if both the canonical form of **A** and the transformation matrix **S** are determined, then the solution of this equation can be written down by inspection. The technique developed below for finding a solution does not require the explicit determination of either the canonical form or the transformation matrix. For this reason it has certain practical advantages over the basic method of finding a solution. Assurance of success in the application of this new technique is provided by the results of Section 4-3.

Consider

$$\mathbf{y}' = \mathbf{A}\mathbf{y} \ , \tag{4-4.1}$$

where the matrix **A** has constant real components. From Section 4-3 we know that the solutions associated with each eigenvalue may be determined independently. We also know that if μ is an eigenvalue of multiplicity m then there are precisely m linearly independent solutions of (4-4.1) associated with μ and each of these solutions has the form

$$\mathbf{y} = e^{\mu t}\mathbf{h} \ , \tag{4-4.2}$$

where the components of the vector **h** are polynomials in t.

Suppose, then, that μ is an eigenvalue of **A** and that its multiplicity is m. For the case where the characteristic matrix $\mathbf{A}-\mu\mathbf{I}$ has rank $n-m$ the finding of solutions is easily disposed of, because **A** has m linearly independent eigenvectors associated with μ. If each of these in turn is substituted for **h** in formula (4-4.2), a set of m linearly independent solutions of equation (4-4.1) is obtained. In this case, therefore, the existence of a multiple eigenvalue creates no complication.

In the case where the rank of $\mathbf{A}-\mu\mathbf{I}$ is greater than $n-m$, there are fewer than m eigenvectors associated with μ. In a sense, there is a deficiency of eigenvectors and thus a corresponding deficiency of solutions of the simple type. We consider, therefore, the possibility of a solution of the form given by (4-4.2), where the vector **h** is a polynomial of degree k given by

$$\mathbf{h}_k = \mathbf{p}_0+\mathbf{p}_1 t + \cdots + \mathbf{p}_k t^k \ . \tag{4-4.3}$$

Substituting into (4-4.1), we get

$$e^{\mu t}(\mathbf{p}_1+2\mathbf{p}_2 t+ \cdots +k\mathbf{p}_k t^{k-1})+\mu e^{\mu t}(\mathbf{p}_0+\mathbf{p}_1 t+ \cdots +\mathbf{p}_k t^k) =$$
$$= \mathbf{A}e^{\mu t}(\mathbf{p}_0+\mathbf{p}_1 t+ \cdots +\mathbf{p}_k t^k) \ .$$

This relation may be reduced to

$$(\mathbf{A}-\mu\mathbf{I})(\mathbf{p}_0+\mathbf{p}_1 t+ \cdots +\mathbf{p}_k t^k) = \mathbf{p}_1+2\mathbf{p}_2 t+ \cdots +k\mathbf{p}_k t^{k-1} \ .$$

Since the last relation must be valid for all values of t in the fundamental interval, it may be replaced by the following set of relations, obtained by equating coefficients of like powers of t,

$$\begin{aligned} (\mathbf{A}-\mu\mathbf{I})\mathbf{p}_k &= \mathbf{o} \ , \\ (\mathbf{A}-\mu\mathbf{I})\mathbf{p}_{k-1} &= k\mathbf{p}_k \ , \\ (\mathbf{A}-\mu\mathbf{I})\mathbf{p}_{k-2} &= (k-1)\mathbf{p}_{k-1} \ , \\ &\ \ \vdots \\ (\mathbf{A}-\mu\mathbf{I})\mathbf{p}_0 &= \mathbf{p}_1 \ . \end{aligned} \tag{4-4.4}$$

A set of vectors $\{\mathbf{p}_k, \mathbf{p}_{k-1}, \ldots, \mathbf{p}_0\}$ satisfies the relations (4-4.4) if $\mathbf{p}_k$ is orthogonal to $\mathbf{A}-\mu\mathbf{I}$ and if each of the other vectors in the set, except possibly $\mathbf{p}_0$, belongs to the column space of $\mathbf{A}-\mu\mathbf{I}$. Moreover, if a solution set of vectors does exist for a specific value of k, say s, then a solution set exists when k is fixed at any one of the values $0, 1, 2, \ldots, s$. This implies the existence of $s+1$ solutions of (4-4.1) associated, respectively, with vectors

$$\mathbf{h}_0, \mathbf{h}_1, \mathbf{h}_2, \ldots, \mathbf{h}_s ,$$

where $\mathbf{h}_k$ is defined by (4-4.3). It is clear that this set of vectors is linearly independent and that the set of solutions of (4-4.1) determined by them is also linearly independent.

Each eigenvector of $\mathbf{A}$ (associated with the eigenvalue μ) is a potential generator of a set of solutions of the type described above. All such solutions, including the simple solutions where $\mathbf{h}$ is an eigenvector, must provide the full complement (m in number) of linearly independent solutions associated with μ. This follows from Section 4-3, and since, as was noted above, the eigenvalues can be treated independently a technique for solving equation (4-4.1) has been established.

The computational problem of finding solutions of (4-4.4) for $k = 0, 1, 2, \ldots, s$ may be facilitated by determining a set of vectors $\{\mathbf{q}_0, \mathbf{q}_1, \ldots, \mathbf{q}_s\}$ such that

$$\begin{aligned}
(\mathbf{A}-\mu\mathbf{I})\mathbf{q}_0 &= \mathbf{o} , \\
(\mathbf{A}-\mu\mathbf{I})\mathbf{q}_1 &= \mathbf{q}_0 , \\
(\mathbf{A}-\mu\mathbf{I})\mathbf{q}_2 &= \mathbf{q}_1 , \\
&\;\;\vdots \\
(\mathbf{A}-\mu\mathbf{I})\mathbf{q}_s &= \mathbf{q}_{s-1} .
\end{aligned} \tag{4-4.5}$$

It is assumed that this set of vectors is complete in the sense that $\mathbf{q}_s$ does not belong to the column space of $\mathbf{A}-\mu\mathbf{I}$. The first member of the set is, of course, an eigenvector of $\mathbf{A}$. The other members of the set are[4] *generalized eigenvectors* of $\mathbf{A}$. It is easily verified that a solution set for (4-4.4), where k is any natural number such that $0 \leqq k \leqq s$, is

$$\begin{aligned}
\mathbf{p}_k &= \mathbf{q}_0 , \\
\mathbf{p}_{k-1} &= k\mathbf{q}_1 , \\
\mathbf{p}_{k-2} &= k(k-1)\mathbf{q}_2 , \\
&\;\;\vdots \\
\mathbf{p}_0 &= k!\,\mathbf{q}_k .
\end{aligned} \tag{4-4.6}$$

[4] Brand [8], Section 3.

The following two examples illustrate the application of this method of finding a solution. In particular the first example is designed to reveal the advantage of finding solutions of (4-4.4) from solutions of (4-4.5).

Example 1. Find a fundamental set of solutions for

$$\mathbf{y}' = \mathbf{A}\mathbf{y} \ ,$$

where

$$\mathbf{A} = \begin{pmatrix} 2 & 1 & 0 & 0 \\ 0 & 2 & 1 & 0 \\ -1 & 0 & 3 & 1 \\ 1 & 1 & -1 & 1 \end{pmatrix} .$$

The characteristic matrix of **A** is given by

$$\mathbf{A} - \lambda\mathbf{I} = \begin{pmatrix} 2-\lambda & 1 & 0 & 0 \\ 0 & 2-\lambda & 1 & 0 \\ -1 & 0 & 3-\lambda & 1 \\ 1 & 1 & -1 & 1-\lambda \end{pmatrix} ,$$

and its characteristic function is

$$|\mathbf{A} - \lambda\mathbf{I}| = (2-\lambda)^4 \ .$$

It follows that 2 is an eigenvalue of multiplicity 4 and that the matrix $\mathbf{A} - 2\mathbf{I}$ is

$$\mathbf{A} - 2\mathbf{I} = \begin{pmatrix} 0 & 1 & 0 & 0 \\ 0 & 0 & 1 & 0 \\ -1 & 0 & 1 & 1 \\ 1 & 1 & -1 & -1 \end{pmatrix} .$$

This matrix is easily seen to be of rank 3. The matrix **A**, therefore, has one eigenvector $\mathbf{q}_0$ and three generalized eigenvectors $\mathbf{q}_1$, $\mathbf{q}_2$, and $\mathbf{q}_3$. These satisfy relations (4-4.5), that is,

$$(\mathbf{A} - 2\mathbf{I})\mathbf{q}_0 = \mathbf{o} \ ,$$
$$(\mathbf{A} - 2\mathbf{I})\mathbf{q}_1 = \mathbf{q}_0 \ ,$$
$$(\mathbf{A} - 2\mathbf{I})\mathbf{q}_2 = \mathbf{q}_1 \ ,$$
$$(\mathbf{A} - 2\mathbf{I})\mathbf{q}_3 = \mathbf{q}_2 \ .$$

It can be seen by inspection that

$$\mathbf{q}_0 = \begin{pmatrix} 1 \\ 0 \\ 0 \\ 1 \end{pmatrix} , \quad \mathbf{q}_1 = \begin{pmatrix} 0 \\ 1 \\ 0 \\ 0 \end{pmatrix} , \quad \mathbf{q}_2 = \begin{pmatrix} 1 \\ 0 \\ 1 \\ 0 \end{pmatrix} , \quad \mathbf{q}_3 = \begin{pmatrix} 0 \\ 1 \\ 0 \\ 1 \end{pmatrix} .$$

Using equations (4-4.3) and (4-4.6), we may easily infer that a set of fundamental solutions is

$$\mathbf{y}_i = e^{2t}\mathbf{h}_{i-1} \ , \quad i = 1, 2, 3, 4 \ ,$$

where

$$\mathbf{h}_0 = \mathbf{q}_0 ,$$
$$\mathbf{h}_1 = \mathbf{q}_0 t + \mathbf{q}_1 ,$$
$$\mathbf{h}_2 = \mathbf{q}_0 t^2 + 2\mathbf{q}_1 t + 2\mathbf{q}_2 ,$$
$$\mathbf{h}_3 = \mathbf{q}_0 t^3 + 3\mathbf{q}_1 t^2 + 6\mathbf{q}_2 t + 6\mathbf{q}_3 .$$

Hence, the solutions are

$$\mathbf{y}_1 = e^{2t}\begin{pmatrix} 1 \\ 0 \\ 0 \\ 1 \end{pmatrix}, \qquad \mathbf{y}_2 = e^{2t}\begin{pmatrix} t \\ 1 \\ 0 \\ t \end{pmatrix},$$

$$\mathbf{y}_3 = e^{2t}\begin{pmatrix} t^2+2 \\ 2t \\ 2 \\ t^2 \end{pmatrix}, \quad \mathbf{y}_4 = e^{2t}\begin{pmatrix} t^3+6t \\ 3t^2+6 \\ 6t \\ t^3+6 \end{pmatrix}.$$

Example 2. We find a fundamental set of solutions for Example 1 of Section 4-3. In this case the characteristic matrix is

$$\mathbf{A}-\lambda\mathbf{I} = \begin{pmatrix} 1-\lambda & 0 & 0 & 0 & 1 \\ -1 & 1-\lambda & 2 & 1 & -1 \\ 0 & 0 & 1-\lambda & 0 & 1 \\ -1 & 0 & 1 & 2-\lambda & 1 \\ 0 & 0 & 0 & 0 & 2-\lambda \end{pmatrix}.$$

The characteristic function is

$$|\mathbf{A}-\lambda\mathbf{I}| = (1-\lambda)^3(2-\lambda)^2 .$$

There are therefore two distinct eigenvalues, 1 and 2. We first consider the eigenvalue 1 for which

$$\mathbf{A}-\mathbf{I} = \begin{pmatrix} 0 & 0 & 0 & 0 & 1 \\ -1 & 0 & 2 & 1 & -1 \\ 0 & 0 & 0 & 0 & 1 \\ -1 & 0 & 1 & 1 & 1 \\ 0 & 0 & 0 & 0 & 1 \end{pmatrix}.$$

This matrix is seen to have rank 3, and by inspection the two vectors

$$\begin{pmatrix} 0 \\ 1 \\ 0 \\ 0 \\ 0 \end{pmatrix} \text{ and } \begin{pmatrix} 1 \\ 0 \\ 0 \\ 1 \\ 0 \end{pmatrix}$$

are seen to be eigenvectors. One sees that the second of these eigenvectors does not belong to the column space of $\mathbf{A}-\mathbf{I}$, and that there is consequently no generalized eigenvector associated with it. The first member of a fundamental set of solutions may, therefore, be specified by

$$\mathbf{y}_1 = e^t \begin{pmatrix} 1 \\ 0 \\ 0 \\ 1 \\ 0 \end{pmatrix} .$$

The first member of the above mentioned pair of eigenvectors does belong to the column space of $\mathbf{A}-\mathbf{I}$, and if it is represented by $\mathbf{q}_0$, a generalized eigenvector denoted by q_1 is defined by

$$(\mathbf{A}-\mathbf{I})\mathbf{q}_1 = \mathbf{q}_0 \ .$$

Hence,

$$\mathbf{q}_0 = \begin{pmatrix} 0 \\ 1 \\ 0 \\ 0 \\ 0 \end{pmatrix}, \quad \mathbf{q}_1 = \begin{pmatrix} 1 \\ 0 \\ 1 \\ 0 \\ 0 \end{pmatrix} .$$

No other generalized eigenvectors are associated with $\mathbf{q}_0$, since $\mathbf{q}_1$ does not belong to the column space of $\mathbf{A}-\mathbf{I}$. Therefore, we may list two more linearly independent solutions of the given equation,

$$\mathbf{y}_2 = e^t \begin{pmatrix} 0 \\ 1 \\ 0 \\ 0 \\ 0 \end{pmatrix}, \quad \mathbf{y}_3 = e^t(\mathbf{q}_0 t + \mathbf{q}_1) = e^t \begin{pmatrix} 1 \\ t \\ 1 \\ 0 \\ 0 \end{pmatrix} .$$

This completes the determination of the three solutions associated with the eigenvalue 1 of multiplicity 3.

We proceed to consider the eigenvalue 2 and note that

$$\mathbf{A}-2\mathbf{I} = \begin{pmatrix} -1 & 0 & 0 & 0 & 1 \\ -1 & -1 & 2 & 1 & -1 \\ 0 & 0 & -1 & 0 & 1 \\ -1 & 0 & 1 & 0 & 1 \\ 0 & 0 & 0 & 0 & 0 \end{pmatrix} .$$

This matrix has rank 4, and an eigenvector of $\mathbf{A}$ is given by

$$\mathbf{q}_0 = \begin{pmatrix} 0 \\ 1 \\ 0 \\ 1 \\ 0 \end{pmatrix} .$$

It may also be seen by inspection that

$$(\mathbf{A}-2\mathbf{I})\mathbf{q}_1 = \mathbf{q}_0 \ ,$$

where

$$\mathbf{q}_1 = \begin{pmatrix} 1 \\ 0 \\ 1 \\ 1 \\ 1 \end{pmatrix}.$$

The last two members of a fundamental set of solutions are therefore given by

$$\mathbf{y}_4 = e^{2t}\begin{pmatrix} 0 \\ 1 \\ 0 \\ 1 \\ 0 \end{pmatrix}, \quad \mathbf{y}_5 = e^{2t}(\mathbf{q}_0 t + \mathbf{q}_1) = e^{2t}\begin{pmatrix} 1 \\ t \\ 1 \\ t+1 \\ 1 \end{pmatrix}.$$

This completes the solution of the problem.

Exercises

1. Use the direct method to find solutions of the equations in Exercise 1 of Section 4-3

2. Find fundamental matrices for the following equations. (Answers are given below.)

(a) $$\mathbf{y}' = \begin{pmatrix} -1 & -1 & -1 & 2 \\ 0 & 1 & 0 & 0 \\ -1 & -1 & 0 & 1 \\ -1 & 0 & -1 & 2 \end{pmatrix}\mathbf{y};$$

(b) $$\mathbf{y}' = \begin{pmatrix} 0 & 1 & 0 & -1 \\ 0 & 0 & 0 & 1 \\ 1 & -1 & 0 & 1 \\ 0 & 0 & 0 & 1 \end{pmatrix}\mathbf{y};$$

(c) $$\mathbf{y}' = \begin{pmatrix} 1 & -1 & -1 & 1 \\ 1 & 2 & 1 & -1 \\ 0 & 0 & 1 & 0 \\ 1 & 0 & 0 & 1 \end{pmatrix}\mathbf{y};$$

(d) $$\mathbf{y}' = \begin{pmatrix} 1 & 0 & 0 & 1 \\ 1 & 3 & 1 & -1 \\ -1 & -1 & 2 & 1 \\ 0 & 1 & 1 & 2 \end{pmatrix}\mathbf{y}.$$

ANSWERS

2.

(a) $$\begin{pmatrix} 1 & 0 & 1 & 0 \\ 0 & 1 & 0 & 0 \\ 0 & 0 & 1 & 1 \\ 1 & 1 & 1 & 1 \end{pmatrix}\begin{pmatrix} e^t & te^t & 0 & 0 \\ 0 & e^t & 0 & 0 \\ 0 & 0 & 1 & t \\ 0 & 0 & 0 & 1 \end{pmatrix};$$

(b) $$\begin{pmatrix} 0 & 1 & 2 & 0 \\ 0 & 0 & 1 & 1 \\ 1 & 1 & 0 & 0 \\ 0 & 0 & 0 & 1 \end{pmatrix}\begin{pmatrix} 1 & t & t^2 & 0 \\ 0 & 1 & 2t & 0 \\ 0 & 0 & 2 & 0 \\ 0 & 0 & 0 & e^t \end{pmatrix};$$

(c) $$\begin{pmatrix} 1 & 0 & 1 & 0 \\ 0 & 1 & 0 & 0 \\ 0 & 0 & 1 & 1 \\ 1 & 1 & 1 & 1 \end{pmatrix}\begin{pmatrix} e^{2t} & 0 & 0 & 0 \\ 0 & e^t & te^t & 0 \\ 0 & 0 & e^t & 0 \\ 0 & 0 & 0 & e^t \end{pmatrix};$$

$$\text{(d)}\quad e^{2t}\begin{pmatrix} 1 & 0 & 1 & 0 \\ 0 & 1 & 0 & 0 \\ 0 & 0 & 1 & 1 \\ 1 & 1 & 1 & 1 \end{pmatrix}\begin{pmatrix} 1 & t & t^2 & t^3 \\ 0 & 1 & 2t & 3t^2 \\ 0 & 0 & 2 & 6t \\ 0 & 0 & 0 & 6 \end{pmatrix}.$$

4-5. REAL SOLUTIONS ASSOCIATED WITH COMPLEX EIGENVALUES

It was shown in Section 4-4 that

$$\mathbf{y}' = \mathbf{A}\mathbf{y} \tag{4-5.1}$$

has a solution

$$\mathbf{y} = e^{\mu t}\mathbf{h} , \tag{4-5.2}$$

where μ is an eigenvalue of $\mathbf{A}$, and the components of the vector $\mathbf{h}$ are polynomials in t. The components of $\mathbf{A}$ are assumed to be real so that if μ is real the components of $\mathbf{h}$ can be chosen as real-valued polynomials. On the other hand if μ is not real then the solution given by (4-5.2) is not real. In this case, let μ be written as

$$\mu = \alpha + i\beta , \quad \beta \neq 0 .$$

The complex conjugate of μ, $\bar{\mu} = \alpha - i\beta$, is easily seen to be an eigenvalue of $\mathbf{A}$, and the vector

$$\bar{\mathbf{y}} = e^{\bar{\mu}t}\bar{\mathbf{h}}$$

is clearly a solution of (4-5.1). Moreover, $\mathbf{y}$ and $\bar{\mathbf{y}}$ are linearly independent. Since the solutions of (4-5.1) form a vector space, the vectors

$$\mathbf{u} = \frac{1}{2}(\mathbf{y} + \bar{\mathbf{y}}) ,$$

$$\mathbf{v} = \frac{1}{2i}(\mathbf{y} - \bar{\mathbf{y}}) ,$$

belong to the solution space. These vectors are, respectively, the real and imaginary parts of $\mathbf{y}$. They are, therefore, real-valued, linearly independent solutions of equation (4-5.1). Hence, pairs of complex-valued solutions, associated with complex eigenvalues, are replaceable by an equivalent pair of real-valued solutions. The latter are merely the real and imaginary parts of the former.

If $\mathbf{h}$ is written as

$$\mathbf{h} = \mathbf{r} + i\mathbf{s} ,$$

the solution $\mathbf{y}$ can be written as

$$\mathbf{y} = e^{\alpha t}[(\mathbf{r}\cos\beta t - \mathbf{s}\sin\beta t) + i(\mathbf{r}\sin\beta t + \mathbf{s}\cos\beta t)] .$$

The corresponding real-valued solutions are then given by

$$\mathbf{u} = e^{\alpha t}(\mathbf{r}\cos\beta t - \mathbf{s}\sin\beta t) ,$$
$$\mathbf{v} = e^{\alpha t}(\mathbf{r}\sin\beta t + \mathbf{s}\cos\beta t) .$$

This completes the development of a technique for finding a set of n linearly independent, real vector solutions for $\mathbf{y}' = \mathbf{A}\mathbf{y}$.

Example 1. Find a fundamental set of real-valued solutions for

$$\mathbf{y}' = \begin{pmatrix} 0 & 8 & -12 & -8 \\ 0 & 0 & 1 & 1 \\ 0 & -7 & 12 & 8 \\ 1 & 7 & -12 & -8 \end{pmatrix} \mathbf{y} .$$

If $\mathbf{A}$ represents the coefficient matrix, then

$$|\mathbf{A} - \lambda\mathbf{I}| = \lambda^4 - 4\lambda^3 + 8\lambda^2 - 8\lambda + 4$$
$$= [\lambda - (1+i)]^2[\lambda - (1-i)]^2 .$$

The eigenvalues of $\mathbf{A}$ are, therefore,

$$1+i \quad \text{and} \quad 1-i ,$$

and each has multiplicity 2.

If the vectors $\mathbf{p}$ and $\mathbf{q}$ are defined by

$$\mathbf{p} = \begin{pmatrix} 14+2i \\ 1-7i \\ -17-6i \\ 25 \end{pmatrix} , \quad \mathbf{q} = \begin{pmatrix} 8-2i \\ 5+4i \\ 2i \\ 2 \end{pmatrix} ,$$

it may be verified that

$$[\mathbf{A} - (1+i)\mathbf{I}]\mathbf{p} = \mathbf{o}$$
$$[\mathbf{A} - (1+i)\mathbf{I}]\mathbf{q} = \mathbf{p} .$$

It follows that two solutions $\mathbf{y}_1$ and $\mathbf{y}_2$ are given by

$$\mathbf{y}_1 = e^{(1+i)t}\mathbf{p} , \quad \mathbf{y}_2 = e^{(1+i)t}(\mathbf{p}t + \mathbf{q}) .$$

The complex conjugates of these two provide a second pair of solutions that are associated with the eigenvalue $1-i$. The real and imaginary parts of $\mathbf{y}_1$ and $\mathbf{y}_2$ provide a set of four linearly independent real solutions. They are given by

$$\mathbf{u}_1 = e^t \begin{pmatrix} 14 \\ 1 \\ -17 \\ 25 \end{pmatrix} \cos t - e^t \begin{pmatrix} 2 \\ -7 \\ -6 \\ 0 \end{pmatrix} \sin t ;$$

$$\mathbf{v}_1 = e^t \begin{pmatrix} 14 \\ 1 \\ -17 \\ 25 \end{pmatrix} \sin t + e^t \begin{pmatrix} 2 \\ -7 \\ -6 \\ 0 \end{pmatrix} \cos t ;$$

$$\mathbf{u}_2 = e^t\begin{pmatrix} 14t+8 \\ t+5 \\ -17t \\ 25t+2 \end{pmatrix}\cos t - e^t\begin{pmatrix} 2t-2 \\ -7t+4 \\ -6t+2 \\ 0 \end{pmatrix}\sin t \ ;$$

$$\mathbf{v}_2 = e^t\begin{pmatrix} 14t+8 \\ t+5 \\ -17t \\ 25t+2 \end{pmatrix}\sin t + e^t\begin{pmatrix} 2t-2 \\ -7t+4 \\ -6t+2 \\ 0 \end{pmatrix}\cos t \ ;$$

Exercises

1. Find fundamental matrices for the following equations:

(a) $\mathbf{y}' = \begin{pmatrix} 0 & 1 \\ -a^2 & 0 \end{pmatrix}\mathbf{y}$; (b) $\mathbf{y}' = \begin{pmatrix} 1 & 1 \\ -2 & -1 \end{pmatrix}\mathbf{y}$;

(c) $\mathbf{y}' = \begin{pmatrix} 0 & 1 & 0 \\ 0 & 0 & 1 \\ 0 & -2 & -2 \end{pmatrix}\mathbf{y}$; (d) $\mathbf{y}' = \begin{pmatrix} 0 & 1 & 0 \\ 0 & 0 & 1 \\ 1 & -1 & 1 \end{pmatrix}\mathbf{y}$.

ANSWERS

1. (a) $\begin{pmatrix} \sin at & \cos at \\ a\cos at & -a\sin at \end{pmatrix}$; (b) $\begin{pmatrix} \sin t & \cos t \\ -\sin t+\cos t & -\sin t+\cos t \end{pmatrix}$;

(c) $e^{-t}\begin{pmatrix} e^t & -\sin t+\cos t & -\sin t-\cos t \\ 0 & -2\cos t & 2\sin t \\ 0 & 2\sin t+2\cos t & -2\sin t+\cos t \end{pmatrix}$;

(d) $\begin{pmatrix} e^t & \sin t & \cos t \\ e^t & \cos t & -\sin t \\ e^t & -\sin t & -\cos t \end{pmatrix}$.

4-6. THE *n*th-ORDER EQUATION

The equation

(4-6.1) $$Lu = 0 \ ,$$

where

(4-6.2) $$Lu = u^{[n]} + p_1 u^{[n-1]} + \cdots + p_n \mathbf{u}$$

and the coefficients $p_1, p_2, \ldots, p_n$ are constants, is called an *n*th-*order equation with constant coefficients.* Against the background of success of Chapter 2 in deducing the general theory of the *n*th-order equation from the theory of the first-order vector equation, it might be conjectured that the most convenient way to find solutions for a specific *n*th-order equation would be to find solutions for its companion vector equation. This turns out, however, not to be the case.

In fact, the easiest way to find a fundamental matrix for the vector equation associated with (4-6.1) is to find a fundamental vector for (4-6.1) and to determine its Wronskian matrix. It is appropriate, therefore, to give an outline of the standard method of finding solutions of equation (4-6.1). The outline is brief, since most elementary textbooks on differential equations and some calculus books give detailed treatments of this topic.

The operator L defined by (4-6.2) may be written as

$$L = D^n + p_1 D^{n-1} + \cdots + p_{n-1} D + p_n I \ , \tag{4-6.3}$$

where D^j represents the jth-order differential operator and I is the identity operator. Let L_1 and L_2 be two such operators and define their product $L_1 L_2$ by

$$(L_1 L_2)u = L_1(L_2 u) \ .$$

Because the coefficients are restricted to be constants, it can be shown that the operator $L_1 L_2$ is obtained by multiplying L_1 and L_2 together according to the rules for polynomial multiplication. This implies that

$$L_1 L_2 = L_2 L_1 \ .$$

It also implies that the operator L defined by (4-6.3) can be expressed in the factored form

$$L = (D-\lambda_1)^{n_1}(D-\lambda_2)^{n_2} \cdots (D-\lambda_r)^{n_r} \ .$$

The numbers $\lambda_1, \lambda_2, \ldots, \lambda_r$ are the distinct roots of the algebraic equation $f(\lambda) = 0$, where

$$f(\lambda) = \lambda^n + p_1 \lambda^{n-1} + \cdots + p_{n-1}\lambda + p_n \ .$$

The polynomial $f(\lambda)$ is called the *characteristic polynomial* of equation (4-6.1).

Since the factors of L are commutative, it is readily deduced that any solution of

$$(D-\lambda_j)^{n_j} u = 0 \tag{4-6.4}$$

is also a solution of (4-6.1). It can be verified that the functions

$$e^{\lambda_j t}, \ te^{\lambda_j t}, \ldots, t^{n_j - 1} e^{\lambda_j t}$$

form a fundamental set of solutions for (4-6.4). The complete set

$$\{e^{\lambda_j t}, te^{\lambda_j t}, \ldots, t^{n_j-1}e^{\lambda_j t} : j = 1, 2, \ldots, r\} \tag{4-6.5}$$

is easily seen, therefore, to be a fundamental set of solutions for equation (4-6.1).

If all the roots of $f(\lambda) = 0$ are real, then (4-6.5) provides a fundamental set of real solutions. In the event that λ_j is complex, we can write

$$\lambda_j = \alpha + i\beta$$

and conclude that, for some k,

$$\lambda_k = \alpha - i\beta \quad \text{and} \quad n_j = n_k \ .$$

Using the same argument that was applied in the previous section, we can deduce that the solution $t^s e^{\lambda_j t}$ and its complex conjugate $t^s e^{\lambda_k t}$ are replaceable by the two real solutions

$$t^s e^{\alpha t}\cos\beta t \quad \text{and} \quad t^s e^{\alpha t}\sin\beta t \ .$$

Hence, any complex-valued solutions in the set (4-6.5) are readily replaceable by real solutions. This completes the outline of the standard method for solving equation (4-6.1).

The vector equation equivalent to (4-6.1) is (see Section 3-4)

$$\mathbf{y}' = \mathbf{A}\mathbf{y} \ , \tag{4-6.6}$$

where

$$\mathbf{A} = \mathbf{J} - \mathbf{d}_n \tilde{\mathbf{p}} \ .$$

We have noted that the most direct method of finding a fundamental matrix for this equation is to form the Wronskian matrix of a fundamental vector for (4-6.1). However, the matrix **A** has special properties which are relevant to the solution of the differential equation.[5]

The matrix **A** is called the *companion matrix* of the polynomial $f(\lambda)$. Its characteristic function is given by

$$|\mathbf{A}-\lambda\mathbf{I}| = \begin{vmatrix} -\lambda & 1 & 0 & \cdots & 0 & 0 \\ 0 & -\lambda & 1 & \cdots & 0 & 0 \\ \cdot & \cdot & \cdot & \cdot & \cdot & \cdot \\ \cdot & \cdot & \cdot & \cdot & \cdot & \cdot \\ \cdot & \cdot & \cdot & \cdot & \cdot & \cdot \\ 0 & 0 & 0 & \cdots & -\lambda & 1 \\ -p_n & -p_{n-1} & -p_{n-2} & \cdots & -p_2 & (-p_1-\lambda) \end{vmatrix} .$$

The value of the determinant is unchanged if λ times its second column, λ^2 times its third column, . . ., and λ^{n-1} times its last column are added to its first column. In the latter form it is not difficult to see that the determinant has the value $(-1)^n f(\lambda)$. Hence, the eigenvalues are the roots of the algebraic equation $f(\lambda) = 0$.

The above evaluation of the characteristic function suggests that

$$(\mathbf{A}-\lambda\mathbf{I})\mathbf{e}(\lambda) = -f(\lambda)\mathbf{d}_n \ , \tag{4-6.7}$$

where $\mathbf{e}(\lambda)$ is defined by

$$\mathbf{e}(\lambda) = \begin{bmatrix} 1 \\ \lambda \\ \lambda^2 \\ \cdot \\ \cdot \\ \cdot \\ \lambda^{n-1} \end{bmatrix} .$$

---

[5] These properties have been discussed by Brand [8], and the treatment in the text was suggested by his treatment.

The right-hand side of relation (4-6.7) is the zero vector whenever λ is an eigenvalue. Consequently, it may be inferred that $\mathbf{e}(\lambda_j)$ is an eigenvector associated with the eigenvalue λ_j. Moreover, it is the only eigenvector associated with λ_j, since the rank of $\mathbf{A}-\lambda_j\mathbf{I}$ is $n-1$. This last fact can be inferred by observing that the cofactor of the lower left-hand corner element of $\mathbf{A}-\lambda\mathbf{I}$ is independent of λ and has the value $(-1)^{n-1}$.

An explicit representation of the generalized eigenvectors (see Section 4-4) can also be derived from relation (4-6.7). Repeated differentiation of that relation yields

$$\begin{aligned}(\mathbf{A}-\lambda\mathbf{I})\mathbf{e}'(\lambda)-\mathbf{e}(\lambda) &= -f'(\lambda)\mathbf{d}_n \ .\\ (\mathbf{A}-\lambda\mathbf{I})\mathbf{e}''(\lambda)-2\mathbf{e}'(\lambda) &= -f''(\lambda)\mathbf{d}_n \ ,\\ &\vdots\\ (\mathbf{A}-\lambda\mathbf{I})\mathbf{e}^{[k]}(\lambda)-k\mathbf{e}^{[k-1]}(\lambda) &= -f^{[k]}(\lambda)\mathbf{d}_n \ .\end{aligned} \tag{4-6.8}$$

Since the eigenvalue λ_j has multiplicity n_j,

$$f(\lambda_j)=f'(\lambda_j)=\cdots=f^{[n_j-1]}(\lambda_j)=0 \ .$$

It follows from (4-6.7) and (4-6.8) that

$$\begin{aligned}(\mathbf{A}-\lambda_j\mathbf{I})\mathbf{e}(\lambda_j) &= \mathbf{o} \ ,\\ (\mathbf{A}-\lambda_j\mathbf{I})\mathbf{e}'(\lambda_j) &= \mathbf{e}(\lambda_j) \ ,\\ (\mathbf{A}-\lambda_j\mathbf{I})\mathbf{e}''(\lambda_j) &= 2\mathbf{e}'(\lambda_j) \ ,\\ &\vdots\\ (\mathbf{A}-\lambda_j\mathbf{I})\mathbf{e}^{[n_j-1]}(\lambda_j) &= (n_j-1)\mathbf{e}^{[n_j-2]}(\lambda_j) \ .\end{aligned}$$

Therefore, the eigenvector and the generalized eigenvectors relative to λ_j are given by [see (4-4.5)]

$$\begin{aligned}\mathbf{q}_0 &= \mathbf{e}(\lambda_j) \ ,\\ \mathbf{q}_1 &= \mathbf{e}'(\lambda_j) \ ,\\ \mathbf{q}_2 &= \frac{1}{2!}\mathbf{e}''(\lambda_j) \ ,\\ &\vdots\\ \mathbf{q}_{n_j-1} &= \frac{1}{(n_j-1)!}\mathbf{e}^{[n_j-1]}(\lambda_j) \ .\end{aligned} \tag{4-6.9}$$

Hence, using the formulas developed in Section 4-4, we may infer that n_j independent solutions of equation (4-6.6) are given by

$$\text{(4-6.10)}\quad \mathbf{y}_k(t)=\left[t^k\mathbf{e}(\lambda_j)+\binom{k}{1}t^{k-1}\mathbf{e}'(\lambda_j)+\cdots+\binom{k}{k}\mathbf{e}^{[k]}(\lambda_j)\right]e^{\lambda_j t}\,,$$

$$k=0,1,\ldots,n_j-1\,.$$

By letting j assume the values $1, 2, \ldots, r$ we obtain a fundamental set of solutions for (4-6.6).

The fundamental set of solutions, given explicitly by formula (4-6.10), form the columns of a fundamental matrix for the differential equation. A simple representation of this matrix can be obtained. This is done for the special case where $\mathbf{A}$ has a single eigenvalue μ of multiplicity n. The treatment of this special case reveals the essence of the representation, and a second example indicates the nature of the representation in the general case.

Let $\mathbf{K}(\mathbf{e}(\lambda))$ be the Wronskian matrix of the vector $\mathbf{e}(\lambda)$. The rows of this matrix are easily seen to be the vectors

$$\tilde{\mathbf{e}}(\lambda),\ \tilde{\mathbf{e}}'(\lambda),\ \ldots,\ \tilde{\mathbf{e}}^{[n-1]}(\lambda)\,.$$

It may also be observed that

$$\text{(4-6.11)}\qquad \mathbf{K}(\mathbf{e}(\lambda))=(\delta_{ij}(j-1)!)\,\mathbf{B}_n(\lambda)\,,$$

where

$$\mathbf{B}_n(\lambda)=\begin{bmatrix} 1 & \lambda & \lambda^2 & \lambda^3 & \cdots & \lambda^{n-1}\\ 0 & 1 & \binom{2}{1}\lambda & \binom{3}{1}\lambda^2 & \cdots & \binom{n-1}{1}\lambda^{n-2}\\ 0 & 0 & 1 & \binom{3}{2}\lambda & \cdots & \binom{n-1}{2}\lambda^{n-3}\\ 0 & 0 & 0 & 1 & \cdots & \binom{n-1}{3}\lambda^{n-4}\\ \vdots & \vdots & \vdots & \vdots & \vdots & \vdots\\ 0 & 0 & 0 & 0 & \cdots & 1 \end{bmatrix}.$$

Since the nonzero components in the $(j+1)$st column of $\mathbf{B}_n(\lambda)$ are the terms in the expansion of $(\lambda+1)^j$, the matrix is called a *binomial matrix of order n.*

For the special case under consideration, a fundamental set of solutions is given by formula (4-6.10) with $n_j=n$ and $\lambda_j=\mu$. It is not difficult to see that the matrix $\mathbf{Y}(t)$ that has these solutions as its columns is given by

$$\mathbf{Y}(t)=e^{\mu t}\tilde{\mathbf{K}}(\mathbf{e}(\mu))\,\mathbf{B}_n(t)\,.$$

Using relation (4-6.11), this can be rewritten in either of two alternative forms,

$$\mathbf{Y}(t) = e^{\mu t}\tilde{\mathbf{K}}(\mathbf{e}(\mu))\left(\delta_{ij}\frac{1}{(j-1)!}\right)\mathbf{K}(\mathbf{e}(t)) \ ,$$

$$\mathbf{Y}(t) = e^{\mu t}\tilde{\mathbf{B}}_n(\mu)(\delta_{ij}(j-1)!)\mathbf{B}_n(t) \ .$$

This is the desired representation of the fundamental matrix in the special case where **A** has a single eigenvalue.

If we retain this restriction on **A**, then the relations (4-4.5) with $s = n-1$ can be adjoined to yield the matrix relation

$$(\mathbf{A}-\mu\mathbf{I})\mathbf{S} = \mathbf{S}\mathbf{J} \ , \tag{4-6.12}$$

where **S** is the n by n nonsingular matrix whose jth column is $\mathbf{q}_{j-1}$. From (4-6.12), it can be inferred that

$$\mathbf{S}^{-1}\mathbf{A}\mathbf{S} = \mathbf{M} \ ,$$

where $\mathbf{M} = \mu\mathbf{I}+\mathbf{J}$, the Jordan canonical form of **A**. Moreover, in view of (4-6.9), it is clear that

$$\mathbf{S} = \tilde{\mathbf{K}}(\mathbf{e}(\mu))\left(\delta_{ij}\frac{1}{(j-1)!}\right)$$
$$= \tilde{\mathbf{B}}_n(\mu) \ .$$

In the case where **A** has more than one eigenvalue, the matrix **S**, that transforms **A** into its canonical form, is similarly constituted. That is, the columns of **S** consist of the eigenvectors and the generalized eigenvectors. Also, **S** can be represented in terms of binomial matrices.

Example 1. Find a fundamental set of solutions for

$$u^{[4]} - 8u^{[3]} + 24u^{[2]} - 32u' + 16u = 0 \ .$$

Find, also, a fundamental matrix for the companion vector equation.

The characteristic polynomial is

$$f(\lambda) = \lambda^4 - 8\lambda^3 + 24\lambda^2 - 32\lambda + 16 = (\lambda-2)^4 \ .$$

A fundamental vector **u** for this fourth-order equation is therefore

$$\tilde{\mathbf{u}} = e^{2t}(1, t, t^2, t^3) \ .$$

The companion vector equation is

$$\mathbf{y}' = \begin{pmatrix} 0 & 1 & 0 & 0 \\ 0 & 0 & 1 & 0 \\ 0 & 0 & 0 & 1 \\ -16 & 32 & -24 & 8 \end{pmatrix}\mathbf{y} \ .$$

The coefficient matrix has the eigenvalue $\lambda = 2$ of multiplicity 4. Hence, the equation has a fundamental matrix given by

$$\mathbf{Y}(t)=e^{2t}\begin{pmatrix}1&0&0&0\\2&1&0&0\\2^2&2\cdot2&2&0\\2^3&3\cdot2^2&6\cdot2&6\end{pmatrix}\begin{pmatrix}1&t&t^2&t^3\\0&1&2t&3t^2\\0&0&1&3t\\0&0&0&1\end{pmatrix}.$$

Example 2. Find a fundamental set of solutions for

$$u^{[5]}-8u^{[4]}+25u^{[3]}-38u^{[2]}+28u'-8u=0\ ,$$

and find a fundamental matrix for its companion vector equation.
The characteristic polynomial is

$$f(\lambda)=(\lambda-1)^2(\lambda-2)^3\ .$$

A fundamental set of solutions is, therefore,

$$e^t,\ te^t,\ e^{2t},\ te^{2t},\ t^2e^{2t}\ .$$

The companion vector equation is

$$\mathbf{y}'=\begin{pmatrix}0&1&0&0&0\\0&0&1&0&0\\0&0&0&1&0\\0&0&0&0&1\\8&-28&38&-25&8\end{pmatrix}\mathbf{y}\ .$$

It may be verified that a fundamental matrix $\mathbf{Y}(t)$ is

$$\mathbf{Y}(t)=\begin{pmatrix}1&0&1&0&0\\1&1&2&1&0\\1&2&2^2&2\cdot2&2\\1&3&2^3&3\cdot2^2&6\cdot2\\1&4&2^4&4\cdot2^3&12\cdot2^2\end{pmatrix}\begin{pmatrix}1&t&0&0&0\\0&1&0&0&0\\0&0&1&t&t^2\\0&0&0&1&2t\\0&0&0&0&1\end{pmatrix}\begin{pmatrix}e^t&0&0&0&0\\0&e^t&0&0&0\\0&0&e^{2t}&0&0\\0&0&0&e^{2t}&0\\0&0&0&0&e^{2t}\end{pmatrix}.$$

Exercises

1. Find a fundamental set of solutions for each of the following differential equations Determine, also, a fundamental matrix for the companion vector equation.

(a) $u''-8u'+15u=0$;

(b) $u''+4u'+13u=0$;

(c) $u''-2u'+2u=0$;

(d) $u^{[3]}+6u^{[2]}+5u'-12u=0$;

(e) $u^{[3]}-6u^{[2]}+3u'+10u=0$;

(f) $u^{[4]}+2u^{[3]}+10u^{[2]}+18u'+9u=0$;

(g) $u^{[4]}+2u^{[2]}+u=0$;

(h) $u^{[4]}-2u^{[3]}+3u^{[2]}-2u'+2u=0$;

(i) $u^{[4]}-u=0$;

(j) $u^{[4]}-4u^{[3]}+6u^{[2]}-4u'+u=0$;

(k) $u^{[4]}+4u^{[3]}+8u^{[2]}+8u'+4u=0$.

2. Solve the following initial-value problems:

(a) $u''+u'-6u=0$, $u(0)=0$, $u'(0)=1$;

(b) $u''+u'-6u=e^t$, $u(0)=0$, $u'(0)=1$;

(c) $u''+u'-6u=e^{2t}$, $u(0)=0$, $u'(0)=0$.

3. Show that the Jordan canonical form of any real symmetric matrix is a diagonal matrix.

4. If $\mathbf{B}_n(t)$ is the binomial matrix defined in Section 4-6 show that

$$\tilde{\mathbf{B}}_n^{-1}(1) = \begin{Vmatrix} 1 & 0 & 0 & 0 & \cdots & 0 \\ -1 & 1 & 0 & 0 & \cdots & 0 \\ 1 & -2 & 1 & 0 & \cdots & 0 \\ -1 & 3 & -3 & 1 & \cdots & 0 \\ \cdot & \cdot & \cdot & \cdot & \cdot & \cdot \\ \cdot & \cdot & \cdot & \cdot & \cdot & \cdot \\ \cdot & \cdot & \cdot & \cdot & \cdot & \cdot \\ (-1)^{n-1} & \cdots & \cdots & \cdots & \cdots & 1 \end{Vmatrix},$$

Show also that a similar result holds for $\mathbf{B}_n(t)$.[6]

5. If $\mathbf{B}_n(\lambda)$ is the binomial matrix defined in Section 4-6, show that $\mathbf{B}_n^{-1}(\lambda) = \mathbf{B}_n(-\lambda)$.

6. Show that the binomial matrix $\mathbf{B}_n(t)$ satisfies the differential relation

$$\mathbf{B}_n'(t) = \mathbf{B}_n(t)\mathbf{A} ,$$

where

$$\mathbf{A} = \mathbf{J}(\delta_{ij}(j-1)) = \begin{Vmatrix} 0 & 1 & 0 & 0 & \cdots & 0 \\ 0 & 0 & 2 & 0 & \cdots & 0 \\ 0 & 0 & 0 & 3 & \cdots & 0 \\ \cdot & \cdot & \cdot & \cdot & \cdot & \cdot \\ \cdot & \cdot & \cdot & \cdot & \cdot & \cdot \\ 0 & 0 & 0 & 0 & \cdots & n-1 \\ 0 & 0 & 0 & 0 & \cdots & 0 \end{Vmatrix} .$$

7. Show that the matrix $\mathbf{A}$ defined in Exercise 6 commutes with $\mathbf{B}_n(t)$. Hence, infer that $\mathbf{B}_n(t)$ also satisfies

$$\mathbf{B}_n'(t) = \mathbf{A}\mathbf{B}_n(t) .$$

8. Find the vector equation for which $e^{\mu t}\tilde{\mathbf{K}}(\mathbf{e}(\mu))\mathbf{B}_n(t)$ is a fundamental matrix.

9. Show that[7]

$$\sum_{t=0}^{\gamma} \frac{\gamma!}{t!} = (-1)^{\gamma} \begin{vmatrix} 0! & 1 & 0 & 0 & 0 & 0 \\ 1! & -\binom{1}{0} & \binom{1}{1} & 0 & 0 & 0 \\ 2! & \binom{2}{0} & -\binom{2}{1} & \binom{2}{2} & 0 & 0 \\ \cdot & \cdot & \cdot & \cdot & \cdot & \cdot \\ \cdot & \cdot & \cdot & \cdot & \cdot & \cdot \\ \cdot & \cdot & \cdot & \cdot & \cdot & \cdot \\ (\gamma-1)! & (-1)^{\gamma-1}\binom{\gamma-1}{0} & \cdots & \cdots & -\binom{\gamma-1}{\gamma-2} & \binom{\gamma-1}{\gamma-1} \\ \gamma! & (-1)^{\gamma}\binom{\gamma}{0} & (-1)^{\gamma-1}\binom{\gamma}{1} & \cdots & \binom{\gamma}{\gamma-2} & -\binom{\gamma}{\gamma-1} \end{vmatrix} .$$

[6] The solution of this problem may be found in Cole [12], and in Riordan [42].
[7] This problem was proposed by Ghandi [18], page 1135.

4-7. STABILITY

In Chapter 3 it is shown that

$$\mathbf{y}' = \mathbf{A}\mathbf{y} \tag{4-7.1}$$

has solutions on any interval $[a, b]$ where the components of the coefficient matrix $\mathbf{A}$ are continuous. If these components are continuous everywhere, it is clear that a and b may be chosen arbitrarily and, hence, that solutions exist on $(-\infty, \infty)$. This is true, in particular, when $\mathbf{A}$ is a constant matrix. Since the concept of stability involves the behavior of solutions when t is large, we confine our attention to solutions of equation (4-7.1) on the interval $[0, \infty)$. Roughly speaking, *we have stability when neighboring solutions do not tend to diverge from each other as t becomes large*. Instability occurs when the solutions diverge. The solutions of equation (4-7.1) form a vector space. Consequently, if $\mathbf{y}_1$ and $\mathbf{y}_2$ are any two solutions, their difference $\mathbf{y} = \mathbf{y}_1 - \mathbf{y}_2$ is also a solution. It follows that the question of the "closeness" of $\mathbf{y}_1$ and $\mathbf{y}_2$ may be transferred to the question of the closeness of $\mathbf{y}$ and the zero or trivial solution. This justifies the definition given below for a stable differential equation.

The subsequent discussion applies to equation (4-7.1), where $\mathbf{A}$ is a real constant matrix.

Definition 4-7.1. *The vector differential equation* (4-7.1) *is* ***stable*** *when every solution* $\mathbf{y}$ *is such that* $\|\mathbf{y}(t)\|$ *remains bounded as t becomes large. It is* ***strictly stable*** *if*

$$\lim_{t\to\infty} \|\mathbf{y}(t)\| = 0 \text{ .}$$ [8]

Definition 4-7.2. *The maximum number of linearly independent eigenvectors associated with a given eigenvalue of a matrix is called the* ***index*** *of the eigenvalue.*

If μ is an eigenvalue of the matrix $\mathbf{A}$ and if k is the index of μ, then the rank of $\mathbf{A} - \mu\mathbf{I}$ is $n-k$. Hence, the index of μ is the dimension of the orthogonal complement of the row space of $\mathbf{A} - \mu\mathbf{I}$. It is easily proved (see Exercise 6 of Section 4-7) that if the Jordan canonical form of $\mathbf{A}$ is a diagonal matrix, then the index of each eigenvalue of $\mathbf{A}$ is equal to its multiplicity. On the other hand, if the canonical form is not diagonal, then some eigenvalue must have an index which is less than its multiplicity.

The following theorem establishes criteria for stability.

Theorem 4-7.1. *The equation* (4-7.1) *is stable if and only if the eigenvalues of* $\mathbf{A}$ *whose multiplicity and index are equal have nonpositive real parts and the other eigenvalues of* $\mathbf{A}$ *have negative real parts. The equation is strictly stable if and only if all the eigenvalues of* $\mathbf{A}$ *have negative real parts.*

---

[8] This definition is patterned after the definition given by Birkhoff and Rota [5], Section IV.5.

PROOF. Every solution of the differential equation can be written in the form $\mathbf{y} = \mathbf{Y}\mathbf{c}$, where $\mathbf{Y}$ is the fundamental matrix described in Theorems 4-3.2 and 4-3.3. It follows, therefore, that the equation is stable if and only if every component of $\mathbf{Y}$ is bounded. It is strictly stable if and only if every component of $\mathbf{Y}$ approaches zero as t becomes large. It can be inferred from the theorems cited that each component of $\mathbf{Y}$ has the form

$$h(t)e^{\mu t} ,$$

where $h(t)$ is a polynomial in t and μ is an eigenvalue of $\mathbf{A}$. If μ has multiplicity m and index k, then the degree of s of $h(t)$ must be such that

$$0 \leqq s \leqq m-k .$$

Moreover, if $k \neq m$, there is at least one component of $\mathbf{Y}$ for which $s \neq 0$.

If the eigenvalue μ is expressed as

$$\mu = \alpha + i\beta ,$$

with α and β real, then

$$|h(t)e^{\mu t}| = |h(t)|e^{\alpha t} .$$

It follows that every component of $\mathbf{Y}$ which has $e^{\mu t}$ as a factor is bounded if and only if

$$\text{(i)} \quad \alpha \leqq 0 , \quad \text{for } k = m ,$$

$$\text{(ii)} \quad \alpha < 0 , \quad \text{for } k < m .$$

In view of the initial discussion, this proves the first part of the theorem.

In order to establish the second part of the theorem, we need only observe that every component of $\mathbf{Y}$, which has $e^{\mu t}$ as a factor, approaches zero when t is large, if and only if $\alpha < 0$.

For the nth-order differential equation

$$Lu = 0 \tag{4-7.2}$$

we state the following definition of stability.

Definition 4-7.3. *The nth-order differential equation* (4-7.2) *is* ***stable*** *if every solution is bounded on* $[0, \infty]$. *It is* ***strictly stable*** *if every solution tends to zero as t becomes large.*

This definition, when $n = 1$, is consistent with Definition 4-7.1.

Theorem 4-7.2. *The nth-order differential equation* (4-7.2) *with constant coefficients is stable if and only if the simple zeros of its characteristic polynomial have nonpositive real parts and the multiple zeros have negative real parts. The equation is strictly stable if and only if all the zeros of the characteristic polynomial have negative real parts.*

PROOF. The Wronskian matrix of a fundamental vector for (4-7.2) is a fundamental matrix for the companion vector equation

(4-7.3) $$\mathbf{y}' = \mathbf{A}\mathbf{y} \ .$$

It can be inferred, therefore, that (4-7.2) is stable (strictly stable) if and only if (4-7.3) is stable (strictly stable). It was noted in Section 4-6 that the eigenvalues of **A** are identical with the zeros of the characteristic polynomial of (4-7.2). In addition, it was noted that every eigenvalue of **A** has index 1. This implies that the index of an eigenvalue of **A** is equal to its multiplicity only if the eigenvalue is simple. Therefore the application of Theorem 4-7.1 yields the desired result.

Exercises

1. Determine which of the equations in Exercise 1 of Section 4-3 are stable (or strictly stable).

2. Determine which of the equations in Exercise 1 of Section 4-5 are stable (or strictly stable).

3. Determine which of the equations in Exercise 1 of Section 4-6 are stable (or strictly stable).

4. Find the values of n for which $u^{[n]} + u = 0$ is stable.

5. The current i in a simple electric circuit satisfies the equation (see Section 4-8)

$$Li'' + Ri' + \frac{1}{C} i = 0 \ ,$$

where the nonnegative numbers C, R, and L represent, respectively, the capacitance, the resistance, and the inductance of the circuit.

(a) Show that the equation is stable.

(b) Show that the equation is strictly stable if $R > 0$.

(c) Under what condition is the solution oscillatory?

6. Prove that the Jordan canonical form of any matrix is diagonal if and only if the index of each eigenvalue is equal to its multiplicity.

4-8. NONHOMOGENEOUS EQUATIONS

Many physical systems can be described by linear differential equations. A familiar example of such a physical system is provided by the electric circuit shown in Figure 4-8.1. The resistance, inductance, capacity, and impressed electromotive force are represented by R, L, C, and E, respectively. If q represents the charge on the condenser, then q must satisfy

$$Lq'' + Rq' + \frac{1}{C} q = E \ .$$

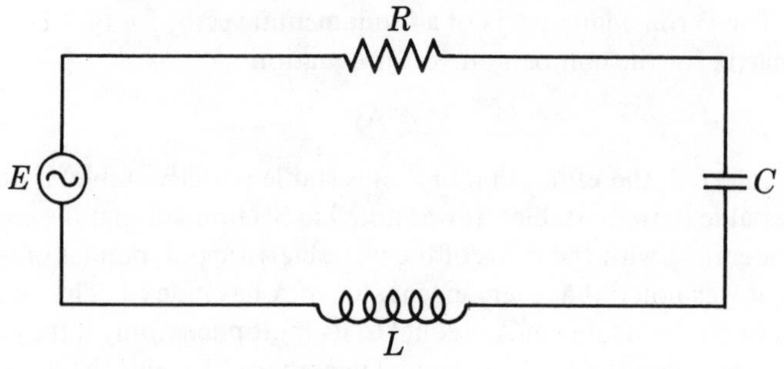

Figure 4-8.1

The current i is the derivative of q, and therefore must satisfy

$$Li'' + Ri' + \frac{1}{C}i = E' ,$$

(this is obtained by differentiating the previous equation).

Both of these equations are special cases of the general equation

$$Lu = r , \tag{4-8.1}$$

where the function r plays the role of an *input function.* A function u, which satisfies the equation, may be regarded as an *output function.* From this point of view, the equation acts as an operator which converts the input r into an output u. If the symbol G is used to represent this operator, we have

$$Gr = u .$$

It follows, therefore, that

$$L(Gr) = r \tag{4-8.2}$$

for every function r in $C[a, b]$. Since equation (4-8.1) does not have a unique solution, it must be recognized that G is not uniquely defined by relation (4-8.2). The formula, developed in Section 3 for solving a nonhomogeneous equation is an example of an operator of this type. Another example, which involves Green's function, is given in Chapter 6.

Many practical problems involve operators that have sinusoidal input functions. In the electric circuit example, E is a sinusoidal input function if the electromotive force is provided by an alternating current generator. Therefore, let us consider the problem of finding a particular solution of the nonhomogeneous equation

$$Lu = A\cos(\beta t + \gamma) , \tag{4-8.3}$$

where A, β, and γ are real constants. The easiest way to find a solution for this equation is to find a solution for the related equation

(4-8.4) $$Lu = ce^{i\beta t} ,$$

where the complex constant c is chosen so that $A\cos(\beta t+\gamma)$ is the real part of $ce^{i\beta t}$.

Before proceeding to find solutions of these equations, we may note that the replacement of equation (4-8.3) by equation (4-8.4) illustrates a useful computational device which is effective where linear operators are involved. Suppose that M is any linear operator and that we wish to determine Mx, where x is some real-valued function. It may be possible to find a real-valued function y such that the determination of $M(x+iy)$ is easier than the determination of Mx. Since M is linear we can write

$$M(x+iy) = Mx+iMy .$$

Consequently, the desired evaluation of Mx can be obtained by extracting the real part of $M(x+iy)$. For our example, the real part of any complex-valued solution of (4-8.4) is a solution of (4-8.3).

The function v defined by

$$v(t) = he^{i\beta t} ,$$

where h is a complex constant, is a solution of (4-8.4) if

$$L(he^{i\beta t}) = ce^{i\beta t} .$$

Since the left-hand side reduces to $hf(i\beta)e^{i\beta t}$, where f is the characteristic polynomial of L,

$$v(t) = \frac{c}{f(i\beta)}e^{i\beta t}$$

is a solution of (4-8.4). In view of the discussion given above, it follows that

$$u(t) = \operatorname{Re}\left[\frac{c}{f(i\beta)}e^{i\beta t}\right]$$

is a solution of (4-8.3). This solution can be rewritten as

(4-8.5) $$u(t) = Ag\cos(\beta t+\gamma+\delta) ,$$

where g is called the *gain factor* and δ the *phase lag*. It is easily verified that

$$g = |1/f(i\beta)| \quad \text{and} \quad \delta = \arg(1/f(i\beta)) .$$

Formula (4-8.5) breaks down if $f(i\beta) = 0$. In this case $e^{i\beta t}$ is a solution of the homogeneous equation corresponding to (4-8.3). In the terminology used for physical systems represented by the equation, we may say that the frequency of the input is the same as a natural frequency of the system. This phenomenon is known as *resonance*.[9]

Every solution y of equation (4-8.3) can be expressed as

$$y = u+w ,$$

[9] Birkhoff and Rota [5].

where u is defined by (4-8.5), and w is a solution of the homogeneous equation $Lu = 0$. If this homogeneous equation is strictly stable, then we may conclude that, when t is large,

$$y(t) \doteq u(t) \ . \tag{4-8.6}$$

The function w is frequently determined by a set of initial conditions. Referring to Formula (4-8.6), one sees that the output function associated with a given input function is ultimately independent of the initial conditions. When the output function y represents an electric current, u and w are, respectively, the *steady-state current* and the *transient current.*

Exercises

1. Find particular solutions of the following equations:

(a) $u'' + u' + u = \cos t$; (b) $u'' + u' + u = 3\sin t$;

(c) $u'' + 2u' + 5u = 5\cos(t - \pi/4)$; (d) $u'' + u = 2\sin 2t$;

(e) $u'' + 2u' + 2u = \cos 2t$; (f) $u'' + 2u' + 7u = 5\cos(2t - \pi/6)$.

2. Determine the gain factor and phase lag for the output which satisfies

$$u' + ku = A\cos(\beta t + \delta) \ .$$

5

Series Solutions

5-1. INTRODUCTION

Chapter 4 reveals that linear differential equations with constant coefficients can be solved by algebraic methods and that the solutions are expressible in terms of elementary functions. Except for a few special cases, these are the only differential equations whose solutions can be written in these simple terms. Other methods of expressing solutions must therefore be sought.

There are several reasons for attempting to find series solutions of differential equations. One of the most obvious of these is found by examining the form of the Taylor series for a function f, namely,

$$f(t) = f(t_0) + f'(t_0)(t-t_0) + \frac{1}{2!}f''(t_0)(t-t_0)^2 + \cdots \quad .$$

Each coefficient in this series is a simple constant times a derivative of f at the point t_0. The essence of a differential equation is a statement of some relationship involving the derivatives of the unknown function. For a linear equation this relationship is particularly simple and may be used to obtain a formula defining each derivative of a solution in terms of some of the lower-order derivatives. Since a set of initial conditions can be used to determine the lower-order derivatives at the point t_0, all the derivatives at t_0 can be determined from this formula. The Taylor series for the solution can therefore be written down, with the tentative assumption that the solution is indefinitely differentiable. The significant point, however, is that the series, once it is determined, can often be shown to converge to a solution of the equation without using the tentative assumptions on which the derivation is based.

To illustrate these remarks consider

$$u' - u = 0 \quad .$$

If a solution u of this equation has m derivatives, we must conclude that

$$u = u' = u^{[2]} = \cdots = u^{[m]} \quad .$$

If we prescribe the initial condition

$$u(0) = 1 \quad ,$$

then it must follow that

$$u^{[k]}(0) = 1 \quad , \quad k = 1, 2, \ldots, m \quad .$$

Under the assumption of indefinite differentiability for u, we have the explicit Taylor series

$$u(t) = 1+t+\frac{1}{2!}t^2+\cdots .$$

By application of elementary theorems pertaining to power series, we can demonstrate that this series converges for all values of t and that the exponential function to which it converges is a solution of the given equation. This demonstration is made quite independently of the derivation of the series.

It may be recalled that a similar example was presented in Section 4-1. There, it was shown by means of series representation that the matrix $e^{t\mathbf{A}}$ is a solution of the equation $\mathbf{y}' = \mathbf{A}\mathbf{y}$, where $\mathbf{A}$ is a constant matrix. We consider presently the case of a nonconstant $\mathbf{A}$ and show that series solutions exist with suitable restrictions on the components of $\mathbf{A}$.

The substitution

$$\tau = t-t_0$$

converts a power series expansion relative to the point t_0 into a power series expansion relative to the origin. We may therefore confine our attention to power series expansions of solutions relative to the origin. This simplifies the notation without any sacrifice of generality.

5-2. FORMAL SCALAR SERIES AND FORMAL SOLUTIONS OF A SECOND-ORDER EQUATION

If $\{a_j : j = 0, 1, 2, \ldots\}$ is any sequence of real numbers, the series

$$\sum_{j=0}^{\infty} a_j t^j$$

is a *formal power series* and is represented by $\mathscr{A}$. Since it is important to distinguish between the series itself and a possible function which the series may "represent," we use a script symbol for the former and an italic symbol a or $a(t)$ for the latter. For the present, we are concerned only with formal series and have no need of a symbol to designate any function associated with the series. Let addition and scalar multiplication for formal power series be defined by

$$\mathscr{A}+\mathscr{B} = \sum_{j=0}^{\infty} (a_j+b_j)t^j ,$$

$$\alpha\mathscr{A} = \sum_{j=0}^{\infty} \alpha a_j t^j ,$$

where α is any real number. It is easily verified that the set S of all formal power series forms a vector space over the field of real numbers. The zero element of S is the series for which every coefficient is zero.

The following definitions provide additional structure for the set S. The product of two series $\mathscr{A}$ and $\mathscr{B}$ is

$$\mathscr{A}\mathscr{B} = \sum_{j=0}^{\infty} \left(\sum_{i=0}^{j} a_j b_{j-i} \right) t^j .$$

The formal derivative $\mathscr{A}'$ of a series $\mathscr{A}$ is

$$\mathscr{A}' = \sum_{j=1}^{\infty} j a_j t^{j-1} .$$

The operation of differentiation can be repeated so that we have for the rth derivative

$$\mathscr{A}^{[r]} = \sum_{j=r}^{\infty} j(j-1) \cdots (j-r+1) a_j t^{j-r} .$$

At this point, it is instructive to derive a formal solution for a formal second-order equation. The derivation can be extended readily to cover the nth-order case. This is not done since the results for the scalar case can be inferred directly from those for the vector equation. The reason for treating the second-order case here is to enable us to present in its simplest form the general principle common to all the subsequent developments of this chapter.

Consider the formal second-order equation

$$\mathscr{U}'' + \mathscr{P}\mathscr{U}' + \mathscr{Q}\mathscr{U} = \mathscr{O} , \tag{5-2.1}$$

where $\mathscr{P}$ and $\mathscr{Q}$ are formal power series. A formal power series

$$\mathscr{U} = \sum_{j=0}^{\infty} u_j t^j$$

that satisfies the equation is a *formal solution*. We pose what may be called an initial-value problem by prescribing the first two coefficients of a solution. That is to say, if b_0 and b_1 are an arbitrary pair of real numbers, we impose on a solution $\mathscr{U}$ the condition that

$$\begin{aligned} u_0 &= b_0 , \\ u_1 &= b_1 . \end{aligned} \tag{5-2.2}$$

Replacing each symbol on the left-hand side of (5-2.1) by the series that it represents, we have

$$\begin{aligned} \mathscr{U}'' + \mathscr{P}\mathscr{U}' + \mathscr{Q}\mathscr{U} &= \\ &= \sum_{j=0}^{\infty} (j+2)(j+1) u_{j+2} t^j + \sum_{j=0}^{\infty} p_j t^j \sum_{i=0}^{\infty} (i+1) u_{i+1} t^i + \sum_{j=0}^{\infty} q_j t^j \sum_{i=0}^{\infty} u_i t^i \\ &= \sum_{j=0}^{\infty} \left[(j+2)(j+1) u_{j+2} + \sum_{i=0}^{j} (j-i+1) p_i u_{j-i+1} + \sum_{i=0}^{j} q_i u_{j-i} \right] t^j . \end{aligned}$$

The series $\mathscr{U}$ is a solution of equation (5-2.1) if and only if the last series above is the zero element of S, that is, if and only if the coefficient of t^j is zero for $j = 0, 1, 2, \ldots$. This condition may be rewritten as

$$(5\text{-}2.3) \qquad u_{j+2} = \frac{-1}{(j+1)(j+2)} \sum_{i=0}^{j} [(j-i+1)p_i u_{j-i+1} + q_i u_{j-i}] \ , \qquad j = 0, 1, 2, \ldots .$$

The first two coefficients of $\mathscr{U}$ are specified by the initial conditions (5-2.2), and it is clear that all the other coefficients are recursively defined by the repeated application of formula (5-2.3). We have therefore shown that the initial-value problem has a unique formal power series solution.

In this discussion, no convergence properties have been ascribed to any of the series. If the series $\mathscr{P}$ and $\mathscr{Q}$ do converge on some common interval to functions p and q, respectively, we may consider the differential equation

$$(5\text{-}2.4) \qquad u'' + pu' + qu = 0 \ .$$

In fact, it should be recognized that the discussion of equation (5-2.1) is primarily designed to provide information about the solutions of equation (5-2.4). We may anticipate a result that is established below and point out that if $\mathscr{P}$ and $\mathscr{Q}$ both converge on an interval $(-h, h)$, then the formal solution $\mathscr{U}$ also converges on this interval to a function u. Because of the isomorphism which exists between a set of converging power series and the set of functions to which they converge, it can easily be inferred that the function u must be a solution of equation (5-2.4). This conclusion is developed in more detail in Section 5-5 where we deal with solutions of a vector equation. At this point we merely want to indicate the general nature of the argument and to provide some motivation for the subsequent discussions.

Exercises

Find a formal solution for each initial-value problem.

1. $\mathscr{U}'' + t^2\mathscr{U}' - 4t\mathscr{U} = \mathscr{O}$.
   $u_0 = 1 \ , \quad u_1 = 0$.
2. $\mathscr{U}'' + (4+t+6t^2)\mathscr{U}' + (-3+4t-4t^2)\mathscr{U} = \mathscr{O}$,
   $u_0 = 1 \ , \quad u_1 = 0$.
3. $\mathscr{U}'' + 5t^3\mathscr{U} = \mathscr{O}$,
   $u_0 = 0 \ , \quad u_1 = 1$.

ANSWERS

1. $\mathscr{U} = 1 + \sum_{j=1}^{\infty} \frac{(-1)^j 4}{3^j j!(3j-4)(3j-1)} t^{3j}$.
2. $\mathscr{U} = 1 + \frac{3}{2}t^2 - \frac{8}{3}t^3 + \cdots$.
3. $\mathscr{U} = t + \sum_{j=1}^{\infty} \frac{(-1)^j}{j!6 \cdot 11 \cdot 16 \cdot \cdots \cdot (5j+1)} t^{5j+1}$.

5-3. FORMAL MATRIX SERIES AND FORMAL SOLUTIONS OF A MATRIX EQUATION

The formal power series introduced in Section 5-2 has real numbers as coefficients. It is clearly possible to generalize this concept of formal power series to the case of power series with matrices as coefficients. Thus, let a power series $\mathscr{A}$ be defined by

$$\mathscr{A} = \sum_{k=0}^{\infty} \mathbf{A}_k t^k \ ,$$

where $\{\mathbf{A}_k : k = 0, 1, 2, \ldots\}$ is an infinite sequence of real n by n matrices. The set of all such series is a vector space over the field of real numbers with the operations of addition and scalar multiplication defined by

$$\mathscr{A} + \mathscr{B} = \sum_{k=0}^{\infty} (\mathbf{A}_k + \mathbf{B}_k) t^k \ ,$$

$$\alpha\mathscr{A} = \sum_{k=0}^{\infty} \alpha\mathbf{A}_k t^k \ ,$$

where α is any real number. Additional operations that resemble scalar multiplication are

$$\mathbf{H}\mathscr{A} = \sum_{k=0}^{\infty} \mathbf{H}\mathbf{A}_k t^k \ ,$$

$$\mathscr{A}\mathbf{H} = \sum_{k=0}^{\infty} \mathbf{A}_k \mathbf{H} t^k \ ,$$

where $\mathbf{H}$ is any n by n real matrix. We define the product of two series by

$$\mathscr{A}\mathscr{B} = \sum_{k=0}^{\infty} \sum_{h=0}^{k} \mathbf{A}_h \mathbf{B}_{k-h} t^k \ ,$$

and the rth derivative of a series by

$$\mathscr{A}^{[r]} = \sum_{k=r}^{\infty} k(k-1) \cdots (k-r+1) \mathbf{A}_k t^{k-r}$$

$$= \sum_{k=0}^{\infty} (k+r)(k+r-1) \cdots (k+1) \mathbf{A}_{k+r} t^k \ .$$

Having specified the structure of a matrix series space, we are in a position to consider the formal matrix differential equation

$$\mathscr{Y}' = \mathscr{A}\mathscr{Y} \ , \tag{5-3.1}$$

where $\mathscr{A}$ is a formal matrix power series. We are interested in the question of the existence of a formal power series $\mathscr{Y}$ which satisfies equation (5-3.1). As in the earlier case, an initial-value problem is introduced by requiring a solution

$$\mathscr{Y} = \sum_{k=0}^{\infty} \mathbf{Y}_k t^k \ , \tag{5-3.2}$$

that satisfies the condition

$$\mathbf{Y}_0 = \mathbf{B} \ ,$$

where **B** is an arbitrary, constant, n by n matrix.

Substituting from (5-3.2) into (5-3.1), we have

$$\sum_{k=0}^{\infty} (k+1)\mathbf{Y}_{k+1} t^k = \sum_{k=0}^{\infty} \sum_{h=0}^{k} \mathbf{A}_h \mathbf{Y}_{k-h} t^k \ .$$

Hence, equating coefficients, we obtain

$$\mathbf{Y}_{k+1} = \frac{1}{k+1} \sum_{h=0}^{k} \mathbf{A}_h \mathbf{Y}_{k-h} \ , \quad k = 0, 1, 2, \ldots \ . \tag{5-3.3}$$

This formula determines each coefficient of $\mathscr{Y}$ in terms of coefficients with lower indices. Since the initial condition specifies that $\mathbf{Y}_0$ is equal to **B**, each coefficient of $\mathscr{Y}$ is uniquely determined. It can be inferred, therefore, that the initial-value problem has a unique formal series solution.

We may remark again, as we did in Section 5-2, that we have established the existence of a *formal* solution for a *formal* equation. Clearly, the ultimate aim is to determine whether or not the formal solution converges to a solution of $\mathbf{Y}' = \mathbf{AY}$ under the assumption that **A** is the matrix to which the formal series $\mathscr{A}$ in (5-3.1) converges.

Example 1. A simple (but not trivial) example is provided by considering the formal equation corresponding to $\mathbf{y}' = \mathbf{Ay}$, where **A** is any constant n by n matrix. The formal equation is

$$\mathscr{Y}' = \mathscr{A}\mathscr{Y} \ , \tag{5-3.4.}$$

where

$$\mathscr{A} = \mathbf{A} + \mathbf{0}t + \mathbf{0}t^2 + \cdots \ .$$

Since all the coefficients of $\mathscr{A}$, except the first, are zero, formula (5-3.3) becomes

$$\mathbf{Y}_{K+1} = \frac{1}{K+1} \mathbf{AY}_K \ .$$

Hence, if we impose the initial condition

$$\mathbf{Y}_0 = \mathbf{I} \ ,$$

we get

$$\mathbf{Y}_j = \frac{1}{j!} \mathbf{A}^j \ , \quad j = 0, 1, 2, \ldots \ .$$

Thus the formal solution of (5-3.4) is

$$\mathscr{Y} = \mathbf{I} + \mathbf{A}t + \frac{1}{2!}\mathbf{A}^2 t^2 + \frac{1}{3!}\mathbf{A}^3 t^3 + \cdots \ .$$

This result is consistent with the observation made in Section 4-1 concerning the matrix $e^{t\mathbf{A}}$.

Exercises

Find a formal solution for each of the following problems where **A** is any constant n by n matrix.

1. $\mathscr{Y}' = \mathscr{A}\mathscr{Y}$, $\mathbf{Y}_0 = \mathbf{I}$, where $\mathscr{A} = \mathbf{A}t$.

2. $\mathscr{Y}' = \mathscr{A}\mathscr{Y}$, $\mathbf{Y}_0 = \mathbf{I}$, where $\mathscr{A} = \mathbf{I}+\mathbf{A}t+\mathbf{A}^2t^2+\cdots$.

ANSWERS

1. $\mathscr{Y} = \mathbf{I}+\frac{1}{2}\mathbf{A}t^2+\frac{1}{4\cdot 2}\mathbf{A}^2t^4+\frac{1}{6\cdot 4\cdot 2}\mathbf{A}^3t^6+\cdots$.

2. $\mathscr{Y} = \mathbf{I}+\mathbf{I}t+\frac{1}{2!}(\mathbf{I}+\mathbf{A})t^2+\frac{1}{3!}(\mathbf{I}+\mathbf{A})(\mathbf{I}+2\mathbf{A})t^3+\cdots$.

5-4. SOME PROPERTIES OF MATRIX SERIES

In order to determine the relation between a formal solution of a formal equation and an actual solution of the corresponding matrix differential equation, we need to know and then to apply some basic convergence properties of series of matrices. Some of these properties are given in Chapter 1, but some additional properties are needed for the task at hand and are developed briefly in this section.

We continue to use the norm given by Definition 1-11.1, that is, the sum of the absolute values of all of the components of the matrix. Relative to this norm Theorem 1-11.1 establishes the fact that the set of all n by n real matrices is a complete metric space. Corollary 1-11.1 states that a sequence of matrices converges if and only if all of its component sequences converge. Since a series converges if and only if the sequence of its partial sums converges, Corollary 1-11.1 implies that a series of matrices converges if and only if all of its component series converge. We state this important fact in the form of a theorem using the notation $\mathbf{A}_k = (a_{k,ij})$.

Theorem 5-4.1. *The matrix series*

$$\sum_{k=0}^{\infty} \mathbf{A}_k$$

converges if and only if the component series

$$\sum_{k=0}^{\infty} a_{k,ij}$$

converges, $i, j = 1, 2, \ldots, n$.

PROOF. See preceding paragraph.

Having concluded that the convergence of a series of matrices is equivalent to the simultaneous convergence of n^2 series of scalars, we realize that many of the familiar facts about series of real numbers can be reformulated as facts about series of matrices. The following theorem is such a case.

Theorem 5-4.2. *If*

$$\sum_{k=0}^{8} \mathbf{A}_k$$

converges then

$$\lim_{k\to\infty} \mathbf{A}_k = \mathbf{0} \ .$$

It is convenient to introduce a partial ordering of a set of matrices by either of the two order relations defined below.

Definition 5-4.1. *Let* **A** *and* **B** *be two m by n real matrices.*

(i) **A** ***is less than*** **B**, $\mathbf{A} < \mathbf{B}$ (*or* $\mathbf{B} > \mathbf{A}$), *if every component of* $\mathbf{B} - \mathbf{A}$ *is positive.*

(ii) **A** *is* ***less than or equal*** *to* **B**, $\mathbf{A} \leqq \mathbf{B}$ (*or* $\mathbf{B} \geqq \mathbf{A}$), *if every component of* $\mathbf{B} - \mathbf{A}$ *is nonnegative.*

Theorem 5-4.3. Comparison Test. *If* $\mathbf{0} \leqq \mathbf{A}_k \leqq \mathbf{B}_k$ *for all sufficiently large k and if*

$$\sum_{k=0}^{\infty} \mathbf{B}_k$$

converges, then

$$\sum_{k=0}^{\infty} \mathbf{A}_k$$

converges.

PROOF. By application of Theorem 5-4.1, the proof follows directly from the comparison test for series of nonnegative real numbers.

Corollary 5-4.3. *If* $\mathbf{0} \leqq \mathbf{A}_k$ *and if*

$$\sum_{k=0}^{\infty} \| \mathbf{A}_k \|$$

converges, then

$$\sum_{k=0}^{\infty} \mathbf{A}_k$$

converges.

PROOF. Let the matrix $\mathbf{B}_k = (b_{k,ij})$ be defined by

$$b_{k,ij} = \| \mathbf{A}_k \| \ , \quad i = 1, 2, \ldots, m \ ; \ \ j = 1, 2, \ldots, n \ .$$

It is obvious that $\mathbf{A}_k \leqq \mathbf{B}_k$ and from Theorem 5-4.1 we conclude that

$$\sum_{k=0}^{\infty} \mathbf{B}_k$$

converges. Hence,

$$\sum_{k=0}^{\infty} \mathbf{A}_k$$

converges.

Theorem 5-4.4. Ratio Test. *If $\mathbf{A}_k \geqq \mathbf{0}$ and $\| \mathbf{A}_k \| > 0$, for all sufficiently large k, and if*

$$\lim_{k\to\infty} \frac{\| \mathbf{A}_{k+1} \|}{\| \mathbf{A}_k \|} = \lambda \ ,$$

then

$$\sum_{k=0}^{\infty} \mathbf{A}_k$$

converges if $\lambda < 1$ and diverges if $\lambda > 1$.

PROOF. If $\lambda < 1$, the ratio test for a series of positive real terms insures that

$$\sum_{k=0}^{\infty} \| \mathbf{A}_k \|$$

converges. Hence, Corollary 5-4.3 implies that

$$\sum_{k=0}^{\infty} \mathbf{A}_k$$

converges.

If $\lambda > 1$, then

$$\lim_{k\to\infty} \| \mathbf{A}_k \| \neq 0 \ .$$

This implies that

$$\sum_{k=0}^{\infty} \mathbf{A}_k$$

diverges and completes the proof of the theorem.

Theorem 5-4.5. Root Test. *If the components of $\mathbf{A}_k$, $k = 0, 1, 2, \ldots$, are nonnegative and if*

$$\limsup_{k\to\infty} \| \mathbf{A}_k \|^{1/k} = \lambda \ ,$$

then

$$\sum_{k=0}^{\infty} \mathbf{A}_k$$

converges if $\lambda < 1$ and diverges if $\lambda > 1$.

PROOF. If $\lambda < 1$, the root test for a series of positive real terms insures that

$$\sum_{k=0}^{\infty} \| \mathbf{A}_k \|$$

converges. Hence, by Corollary 5-4.3,

$$\sum_{k=0}^{\infty} \mathbf{A}_k$$

converges.

If $\lambda > 1$, then $\| \mathbf{A}_k \| > 1$ for an infinite set of values of k. It follows that

$$\lim_{k \to \infty} \mathbf{A}_k \neq \mathbf{0}$$

and, hence, that

$$\sum_{k=0}^{\infty} \mathbf{A}_k$$

diverges. This proves the theorem.

Up to this point the tests for convergence have been confined to series whose terms have nonnegative components. In order to achieve some relaxation of this restriction, we proceed as follows.

Definition 5-4.2. *If* $\mathbf{A} = (a_{ij})$ *is any matrix, a matrix called the* ***absolute of*** $\mathbf{A}$, abs($\mathbf{A}$), *is defined by* $\text{abs}(\mathbf{A}) = (| a_{ij} |)$.

It is easily verified that

$$\| \text{abs}(\mathbf{A}) \| = \| \mathbf{A} \|$$

and, if the dimensions of $\mathbf{A}$ and $\mathbf{B}$ are such that the product $\mathbf{AB}$ is defined,

$$\text{abs}(\mathbf{AB}) \leqq \text{abs}(\mathbf{A})\,\text{abs}(\mathbf{B}) \ .$$

Definition 5-4.3. *The series*

$$\sum_{k=0}^{\infty} \mathbf{A}_k$$

converges absolutely *if*

$$\sum_{k=0}^{\infty} \text{abs}(\mathbf{A}_k)$$

converges.

Theorem 5-4.6. *An absolutely convergent series of matrices converges.*

PROOF. The proof follows from the analogous theorem for a series of real numbers. Thus, if

$$\sum_{k=0}^{\infty} \text{abs}(\mathbf{A}_k)$$

converges, then (see Theorem 5-4.1)

$$\sum_{k=0}^{\infty} | a_{k,ij} |$$

converges for each pertinent pair of values of i and j. This implies that

$$\sum_{k=0}^{\infty} a_{k,ij}$$

converges and, hence, that

$$\sum_{k=0}^{\infty} \mathbf{A}_k$$

converges.

From Theorem 5-4.6, it is clear that the tests derived previously for series of matrices with nonnegative components can now be rephrased to apply to series whose terms are not so restricted. Thus, for example, it can be inferred from Theorem 5-4.5 that the series

$$\sum_{k=0}^{\infty} \mathbf{A}_k$$

converges if

$$\limsup_{k\to\infty} \| \mathbf{A}_k \|^{1/k} < 1 \ .$$

If $\mathbf{A}_k$ is a matrix whose components are functions defined on some interval I, then the series

$$\sum_{k=0}^{\infty} \mathbf{A}_k$$

converges on I if the series

$$\sum_{k=0}^{\infty} \mathbf{A}_k(t)$$

converges for every value of t in I. The formal power series

$$\sum_{k=0}^{\infty} \mathbf{A}_k t^k$$

can be considered to be a series of matrices of functions, if the indeterminate t is regarded as a real variable so that $\mathbf{A}_k t^k$ represents the scalar product of $\mathbf{A}_k$ and t^k.

Definition 5-4.4. *A series*

$$\sum_{k=0}^{\infty} \mathbf{B}_k$$

dominates *a series*

$$\sum_{k=0}^{\infty} \mathbf{A}_k$$

on an interval I if

$$\text{abs}(\mathbf{A}_k(t)) \leqq \mathbf{B}_k(t) \ , \quad k = 0, 1, 2, \ldots,$$

for all t in I. We say[1] *that a power series*

$$\sum_{k=0}^{\infty} \mathbf{B}_k t^k$$

majorizes *a power series*

$$\sum_{k=0}^{\infty} \mathbf{A}_k t^k \ ,$$

if

$$\text{abs}(\mathbf{A}_k) \leqq \mathbf{B}_k \ , \quad k = 0, 1, 2, \ldots \ .$$

Clearly, if the power series

$$\sum_{k=0}^{\infty} \mathbf{B}_k t^k$$

majorizes the power series

$$\sum_{k=0}^{\infty} \mathbf{A}_k t^k \ ,$$

then the former power series also dominates the latter power series for all nonnegative values of t.

It should be clear from the deductions of this section that series of matrices whose components are functions have many properties that are counterparts of the familiar properties of series of functions. Some of these properties are stated in the form of theorems; the proofs are left as exercises.

Theorem 5-4.7. Comparison Test. *If the series*

$$\sum_{k=0}^{\infty} \mathbf{B}_k(t)$$

converges uniformly on an interval I and if it dominates the series

$$\sum_{k=0}^{\infty} \mathbf{A}_k(t)$$

on I, then the latter series converges uniformly on I.

Theorem 5-4.8. Weierstrass M-Test. *If*

$$\sum_{k=0}^{\infty} \mathbf{M}_k$$

is a convergent series of constant matrices and if, for every t in I,

$$\text{abs}(\mathbf{A}_k(t)) \leqq \mathbf{M}_k \ , \quad k = 0, 1, 2, \ldots,$$

[1] Terminology of Birkhoff and Rota [5], page 60.

then

$$\sum_{k=0}^{\infty} \mathbf{A}_k(t)$$

converges uniformly on I.

Theorem 5-4.9. *If the series*

$$\sum_{k=0}^{\infty} \mathbf{A}_k$$

converges uniformly on I and if each component of $\mathbf{A}_k, k = 0, 1, 2, \ldots$, *is a continuous function on that interval, then the series converges to a continuous limit.*

Theorem 5-4.10. *The radius of convergence r of a power series*

$$\sum_{k=0}^{\infty} \mathbf{A}_k t^k$$

is given by either of the following formulas:

$$\text{(i)} \quad r^{-1} = \limsup_{k\to\infty} \| \mathbf{A}_k \|^{1/k} ,$$

$$\text{(ii)} \quad r^{-1} = \lim_{k\to\infty} \frac{\| \mathbf{A}_{k+1} \|}{\| \mathbf{A}_k \|} .$$

Theorem 5-4.11. *A power series and its formal derivative have the same radius of convergence.*

The following result is obtained by applying Theorem 5-4.7 to power series.

Theorem 5-4.12. *If*

$$\sum_{k=0}^{\infty} \mathbf{B}_k t^k$$

has radius of convergence h and if it majorizes the series

$$\sum_{k=0}^{\infty} \mathbf{A}_k t^k ,$$

then the latter series has a radius of convergence at least as large as h.

We use the usual terminology here and say that a function f is *analytic* at a point t_0 if it has a Taylor series which converges to f in some interval containing t_0. Similarly, we say that a matrix is *analytic* at t_0 if each of its components is analytic at that point. As we indicated earlier, we confine our discussion to functions and matrices which are analytic at the origin.

Exercises

1. Prove Theorem 5-4.7. Comparison Test.

2. Prove Theorem 5-4.8. Weierstrass *M*-Test.

3. Prove Theorem 5-4.9.

4. Prove Theorem 5-4.10.

5. Prove Theorem 5-4.11.

6. Prove Theorem 5-4.12.

7. Prove that

$$\sum_{k=0}^{\infty} \mathbf{A}^k = \mathbf{I}+\mathbf{A}+\mathbf{A}^2+\cdots$$

converges if $\|\mathbf{A}\| < 1$.

8. Show that the statement

$$\text{“the series } \sum_{k=0}^{\infty} \mathbf{A}^k \text{ diverges if } \|\mathbf{A}\| > 1\text{”}$$

is false by constructing a counterexample.

9(a) Show that if $\mathbf{I}-\mathbf{A}$ is nonsingular, then the partial sums of

$$\sum_{k=0}^{\infty} \mathbf{A}^k$$

are given by

$$\mathbf{S}_j = (\mathbf{I}-\mathbf{A}^{j+1})(\mathbf{I}-\mathbf{A})^{-1} .$$

(b) If $\mathbf{I}-\mathbf{A}$ is nonsingular and if $\|\mathbf{A}\| < 1$ show that

$$\sum_{k=0}^{\infty} \mathbf{A}^k$$

converges to $(\mathbf{I}-\mathbf{A})^{-1}$.

5-5. SOLUTIONS OF ANALYTIC VECTOR EQUATIONS

The vector equation

$$\mathbf{y}' = \mathbf{A}\mathbf{y} \tag{5-5.1}$$

is said to be analytic when the matrix **A** is analytic. In this section, we suppose that **A** is analytic with a power series expansion

$$\mathbf{A}(t) = \sum_{k=0}^{\infty} \mathbf{A}_k t^k ,$$

for which the radius of convergence is h, where $0 < h \leqq \infty$. A fundamental matrix for (5-5.1) is a solution of the matrix equation

$$\mathbf{Y}' = \mathbf{A}\mathbf{Y} . \tag{5-5.2}$$

If $\mathbf{C}$ is any nonsingular constant matrix, we may form an initial-value problem by associating the condition

$$\mathbf{Y}(0) = \mathbf{C} \tag{5-5.3}$$

with equation (5-5.2).

We know from the basic existence theorem that the initial-value problem (5-5.2) and (5-5.3) has a unique solution. We demonstrate that this solution is analytic by showing that the formal power series solution of the formal initial-value problem corresponding to (5-5.2) and (5-5.3) converges on the interval $(-h, h)$. Once convergence is established, it is easily argued that the matrix to which the series converges must be the solution in question. Convergence is established in Theorem 5-5.2, but the results of Theorem 5-5.1 are needed for the proof of the convergence theorem.

By replacing the analytic matrix $\mathbf{A}$ by its formal power series $\mathscr{A}$, we obtain the formal equation

$$\mathscr{Y}' = \mathscr{A}\mathscr{Y} \tag{5-5.4}$$

associated with equation (5-5.2). On the formal solution $\mathscr{Y}$ of this equation, we impose the condition

$$\mathbf{Y}_0 = \mathbf{C} \ . \tag{5-5.5}$$

This condition corresponds in an obvious sense to the initial condition (5-5.3).

Theorem 5-5.1. *If the formal power series $\mathscr{B}$ majorizes the formal series $\mathscr{A}$, then any solution of*

$$\mathscr{U}' = \mathscr{B}\mathscr{U} \ .$$

majorizes the solution of (5-5.4) *and* (5-5.5) *if its initial term satisfies the condition*

$$\mathbf{U}_0 \geqq \operatorname{abs}(\mathbf{C}) \ .$$

PROOF. In view of formula (5-3.3), the coefficients of the solution $\mathscr{Y}$ are given by

$$\begin{aligned}
\mathbf{Y}_0 &= \mathbf{C} \ , \\
\mathbf{Y}_1 &= \mathbf{A}_0\mathbf{Y}_0 \ , \\
\mathbf{Y}_2 &= \frac{1}{2}(\mathbf{A}_0\mathbf{Y}_1+\mathbf{A}_1\mathbf{Y}_0) \ , \\
&\ \ \vdots \\
\mathbf{Y}_{k+1} &= \frac{1}{k+1}(\mathbf{A}_0\mathbf{Y}_k+\mathbf{A}_1\mathbf{Y}_{k-1}+ \cdots +\mathbf{A}_k\mathbf{Y}_0) \ , \\
&\ \ \vdots
\end{aligned} \tag{5-5.6}$$

Similarly the coefficients for the majorizing equation are given by

$$\begin{aligned} \mathbf{U}_0 &\geqq \operatorname{abs}(\mathbf{C}) \ , \\ \mathbf{U}_1 &= \mathbf{B}_0 \mathbf{U}_0 \ , \\ \mathbf{U}_2 &= \frac{1}{2}(\mathbf{B}_0 \mathbf{U}_1 + \mathbf{B}_1 \mathbf{U}_0) \ , \\ &\ \ \vdots \\ \mathbf{U}_{k+1} &= \frac{1}{k+1}(\mathbf{B}_0 \mathbf{U}_k + \mathbf{B}_1 \mathbf{U}_{k-1} + \cdots + \mathbf{B}_k \mathbf{U}_0) \ , \\ &\ \ \vdots \end{aligned}$$

We observe at once that each coefficient matrix $\mathbf{U}_j$ has nonnegative components, i.e., $\mathbf{U}_j = \operatorname{abs}(\mathbf{U}_j)$, $j = 0, 1, 2, \ldots$. In order to execute an induction argument, we assume that

$$\operatorname{abs}(\mathbf{Y}_j) \leqq \mathbf{U}_j \ , \quad j = 0, 1, 2, \ldots, k \ .$$

On the basis of this assumption and the fact that $\mathscr{B}$ majorizes $\mathscr{A}$, we have

$$\begin{aligned} \operatorname{abs}(\mathbf{Y}_{k+1}) &\leqq \frac{1}{k+1}[\operatorname{abs}(\mathbf{A}_0)\operatorname{abs}(\mathbf{Y}_k) + \cdots + \operatorname{abs}(\mathbf{A}_k)\operatorname{abs}(\mathbf{Y}_0)] \\ &\leqq \frac{1}{k+1}[\mathbf{B}_0 \mathbf{U}_k + \cdots + \mathbf{B}_k \mathbf{U}_0] \\ &\leqq \mathbf{U}_{k+1} \ . \end{aligned}$$

Since $\operatorname{abs}(\mathbf{Y}_0) \leqq \mathbf{U}_0$, an induction argument establishes that $\operatorname{abs}(\mathbf{Y}_j) \leqq \mathbf{U}_j$. Hence the series $\mathscr{U}$ majorizes the series $\mathscr{Y}$, and the theorem is proved.

The convergence theorem will now be proved.

Theorem 5-5.2. *If the formal power series $\mathscr{A}$ has a radius of convergence h, then the formal solution of the formal initial-value problem* (5-5.4) *and* (5-5.5) *has a radius of convergence at least as large as h.*

PROOF. As in the previous theorem, let the formal solution of (5-5.4) and (5-5.5) be represented by $\mathscr{Y}$, the coefficients being defined by the relation (5-5.6). Since, by hypothesis,

$$\mathscr{A} = \sum_{k=0}^{\infty} \mathbf{A}_k t^k$$

has radius of convergence h, we may let τ be any point in $(0, h)$ and infer that the series

$$\sum_{k=0}^{\infty} \mathbf{A}_k \tau^k$$

converges. Hence, for some real positive number M, we have $\| \mathbf{A}_k \tau^k \| \leqq M$ or, equivalently,

$$\| \mathbf{A}_k \| \leqq M\tau^{-k} \ , \quad k = 0, 1, 2, \ldots \ . \tag{5-5.7}$$

Let $\mathbf{B}_k$ be the matrix in which each component is the real number $M\tau^{-k}$. It can be expressed as

$$\mathbf{B}_k = M\tau^{-k} \begin{pmatrix} 1 & 1 & \cdots & 1 \\ 1 & 1 & \cdots & 1 \\ \cdot & \cdot & \cdot & \cdot \\ \cdot & \cdot & \cdot & \cdot \\ \cdot & \cdot & \cdot & \cdot \\ 1 & 1 & \cdots & 1 \end{pmatrix} .$$

It is clear from (5-5.7) that $| a_{k,ij} | \leqq b_{k,ij}$; hence

$$\operatorname{abs}(\mathbf{A}_k) \leqq \mathbf{B}_k \ , \quad k = 0, 1, 2, \ldots \ .$$

It follows that the formal series

$$\mathscr{B} = \sum_{k=0}^{\infty} \mathbf{B}_k t^k$$

majorizes the formal series $\mathscr{A}$.

At this point it can be inferred from Theorem 5-5.1 that a solution $\mathscr{U}$ of the formal equation

$$\mathscr{U}' = \mathscr{B}\mathscr{U} \tag{5-5.8}$$

majorizes the solution $\mathscr{Y}$ of (5-5.4) and (5-5.5) if the initial term $\mathbf{U}_0$ of $\mathscr{U}$ is chosen so that

$$\mathbf{U}_0 \geqq \operatorname{abs}(\mathbf{Y}_0) \ .$$

The most convenient method of finding a formal solution of (5-5.8) is to observe that $\mathscr{B}$ converges on the interval $(-\tau, \tau)$ to the matrix

$$\mathbf{B} = M(1 - t/\tau)^{-1} \begin{pmatrix} 1 & 1 & \cdots & 1 \\ 1 & 1 & \cdots & 1 \\ \cdot & \cdot & \cdot & \cdot \\ \cdot & \cdot & \cdot & \cdot \\ \cdot & \cdot & \cdot & \cdot \\ 1 & 1 & \cdots & 1 \end{pmatrix} .$$

It may be verified that a solution of the matrix equation

$$\mathbf{U}' = \mathbf{B}\mathbf{U} \tag{5-5.9}$$

is given by

$$\mathbf{U} = u \begin{pmatrix} 1 & 1 & \cdots & 1 \\ 1 & 1 & \cdots & 1 \\ \cdot & \cdot & \cdot & \cdot \\ \cdot & \cdot & \cdot & \cdot \\ \cdot & \cdot & \cdot & \cdot \\ 1 & 1 & \cdots & 1 \end{pmatrix}, \tag{5-5.10}$$

where the common component u of the solution matrix satisfies the scalar equation

$$u' = nM(1-t/\tau)^{-1}u \ .$$

The solution of this equation is given by

$$u(t) = \alpha(1-t/\tau)^{-nM\tau} \ ,$$

where α is an arbitrary constant. The function u can be substituted into formula (5-5.10) to provide a matrix solution of equation (5-5.9). Moreover, the familiar power series expansion of $u(t)$ yields a corresponding power series expansion $\mathscr{U}$ of the matrix $\mathbf{U}$. This expansion is clearly a formal series solution of equation (5-5.8) and, if α is chosen as the largest component in the matrix abs($\mathbf{Y}_0$), we can infer from Theorem 5-5.1 that $\mathscr{U}$ majorizes $\mathscr{Y}$.

The radius of convergence of the expansion of the function u, and hence of the matrix series $\mathscr{U}$, is τ. It follows from Theorem 5-4.12 that the radius of convergence of $\mathscr{Y}$ is at least as great as τ. Since τ is an arbitrary point in $(0, h)$, the radius of convergence of $\mathscr{Y}$ is at least as great as h. This proves the theorem.

The final conclusion regarding the solution of the initial-value problem is contained in the following theorem.

Theorem 5-5.3. *The solution of the initial-value problem* (5-5.2) *and* (5-5.3) *is analytic and its power series expansion has a radius of convergence which is at least as large as the radius of convergence of the expansion of* **A**.

PROOF. We have shown that the solution $\mathscr{Y}$ of (5-5.4) and (5-5.5) converges on the interval $(-h, h)$. The matrix $\mathbf{Y}$ to which this series converges is analytic and, because of the isomorphism existing between power series and the functions to which they converge, we must conclude that $\mathbf{Y}$ is a solution of the initial-value problem (5-5.2) and (5-5.3). Since $\mathbf{C}$ was chosen nonsingular the matrix $\mathbf{Y}$ is a fundamental matrix for equation (5-5.1).

We terminate this section with an example of a matrix equation derived from the well-known Hermite equation. The example illustrates the preceding developments and also indicates that the results for matrix equations have direct application to the analysis of scalar differential equations.

Example 1. The equation

$$u'' - 2tu' + 2mu = 0 \,, \tag{5-5.11}$$

where t is the independent variable and m is a real constant, is known as the Hermite equation. The equivalent matrix equation is

$$\mathbf{Y}' = \mathbf{AY} \,, \tag{5-5.12}$$

where $\mathbf{A}(t) = \mathbf{A}_0 + \mathbf{A}_1 t$, and

$$\mathbf{A}_0 = \begin{pmatrix} 0 & 1 \\ -2m & 0 \end{pmatrix}, \quad \mathbf{A}_1 = \begin{pmatrix} 0 & 0 \\ 0 & 2 \end{pmatrix}.$$

The coefficients of a solution $\mathbf{Y}$ are determined by the recursive relation (5-3.3), which in this case reduces to

$$\mathbf{Y}_{k+1} = \frac{1}{k+1}(\mathbf{A}_0 \mathbf{Y}_k + \mathbf{A}_1 \mathbf{Y}_{k-1}) \,.$$

If we impose the initial condition

$$\mathbf{Y}_0 = \begin{pmatrix} 1 & 0 \\ 0 & 1 \end{pmatrix},$$

we can obtain

$$\mathbf{Y}_1 = \begin{pmatrix} 0 & 1 \\ -2m & 0 \end{pmatrix}, \qquad \mathbf{Y}_2 = \frac{1}{2!}\begin{pmatrix} -2m & 0 \\ 0 & -2(m-1) \end{pmatrix},$$

$$\mathbf{Y}_3 = \frac{1}{3!}\begin{pmatrix} 0 & -2(m-1) \\ 4m(m-2) & 0 \end{pmatrix}, \quad \mathbf{Y}_4 = \frac{1}{4!}\begin{pmatrix} 4m(m-2) & 0 \\ 0 & 4(m-1)(m-3) \end{pmatrix},$$

$$\vdots \qquad\qquad \vdots$$

$$\mathbf{Y}_{2k} = \frac{1}{(2k)!}\begin{pmatrix} (-2)^k m(m-2)\cdots(m-2(k-1)) & 0 \\ 0 & (-2)^k (m-1)(m-3)\cdots(m-1-2(k-1)) \end{pmatrix},$$

$$\mathbf{Y}_{2k+1} = \frac{1}{(2k+1)!}\begin{pmatrix} 0 & (-2)^k (m-1)(m-3)\cdots(m-(2k-1)) \\ (-2)^{k+1} m(m-2)\cdots(m-2k) & 0 \end{pmatrix}.$$

The coefficient matrix $\mathbf{A}$ is represented by a finite series which, therefore, has an infinite radius of convergence. It follows that the series

$$\mathbf{Y}_0 + \mathbf{Y}_1 t + \mathbf{Y}_2 t^2 + \cdots$$

converges for all values of t to a nonsingular matrix $\mathbf{Y}$ that is a solution of equation (5-5.12).

Because of the relation between (5-5.12) and (5-5.11), the matrix $\mathbf{Y}$ must be a Wronskian matrix of a fundamental vector for (5-5.11). The two functions comprising the first row of $\mathbf{Y}$ may be designated by u_1 and u_2. They have the following series representations:

$$u_1(t)=1-\frac{2m}{2!}t^2+\frac{2^2m(m-2)}{4!}t^4-\frac{2^3m(m-2)(m-4)}{6!}t^6+\cdots,$$

$$u_2(t)=t-\frac{2(m-1)}{3!}t^3+\frac{2^2(m-1)(m-3)}{5!}t^5-\frac{2^3(m-1)(m-3)(m-5)}{7!}t^7+\cdots.$$

If m is a nonnegative even integer, the series for u_1 terminates and becomes a polynomial. Similarly, when m is a nonnegative odd integer, u_2 is a polynomial. These are known as Hermite polynomials.

Exercises

Find a power series solution for each of the following initial-value problems and specify an interval on which the solution is valid.

1. $\mathbf{Y}'=\begin{pmatrix}0&0\\-1&0\end{pmatrix}\mathbf{Y}, \quad \mathbf{Y}(0)=\mathbf{I}.$

2. $\mathbf{Y}'=\begin{pmatrix}0&1\\-1&-t\end{pmatrix}\mathbf{Y}, \quad \mathbf{Y}(0)=\mathbf{I}.$

3. $\mathbf{Y}'=\mathbf{A}\mathbf{Y}, \quad \mathbf{Y}(0)=\mathbf{I},$ where

$$\mathbf{A}(t)=\begin{pmatrix}0&1\\ \dfrac{6}{1+t^2}&0\end{pmatrix}=\begin{pmatrix}0&1\\6&0\end{pmatrix}-\begin{pmatrix}0&0\\6&0\end{pmatrix}\{t^2-t^4+t^6-\cdots\}.$$

4. $\mathbf{Y}'=\begin{pmatrix}0&1&0\\0&0&1\\1&3t&0\end{pmatrix}\mathbf{Y}, \quad \mathbf{Y}(0)=\mathbf{I}.$

5. $\mathbf{Y}'=\begin{pmatrix}0&1\\-t&1\end{pmatrix}\mathbf{Y}, \quad \mathbf{Y}(0)=\mathbf{I}.$

ANSWERS

1. $$\mathbf{Y}=\begin{pmatrix}1&0\\0&1\end{pmatrix}+\begin{pmatrix}0&1\\-1&0\end{pmatrix}t-\frac{1}{2!}\begin{pmatrix}1&0\\0&1\end{pmatrix}t^2-\frac{1}{3!}\begin{pmatrix}0&1\\-1&0\end{pmatrix}t^3+\frac{1}{4!}\begin{pmatrix}1&0\\0&1\end{pmatrix}t^4+\cdots.$$

2. $$\mathbf{Y}(t)=\begin{pmatrix}1&0\\0&1\end{pmatrix}+\begin{pmatrix}0&1\\-1&0\end{pmatrix}t+\begin{pmatrix}-\frac{1}{2}&0\\0&-1\end{pmatrix}t^2+\begin{pmatrix}0&-\frac{1}{3}\\ \frac{1}{2}&0\end{pmatrix}t^3$$

$$+\begin{pmatrix} \frac{1}{4\cdot 2} & 0 \\ 0 & \frac{1}{3} \end{pmatrix} t^4 + \begin{pmatrix} 0 & \frac{1}{5\cdot 3} \\ -\frac{1}{4\cdot 2} & 0 \end{pmatrix} t^5 + \begin{pmatrix} -\frac{1}{6\cdot 4\cdot 2} & 0 \\ 0 & -\frac{1}{5\cdot 3} \end{pmatrix} t^6 + \cdots .$$

3. $$\mathbf{Y}(t) = \begin{pmatrix} 1 & 0 \\ 0 & 1 \end{pmatrix} + \begin{pmatrix} 0 & 1 \\ 6 & 0 \end{pmatrix} t + \begin{pmatrix} 3 & 0 \\ 0 & 3 \end{pmatrix} t^2 + \begin{pmatrix} 0 & 1 \\ 4 & 0 \end{pmatrix} t^3$$
$$+\begin{pmatrix} 1 & 0 \\ 0 & 0 \end{pmatrix} t^4 + \begin{pmatrix} 0 & 0 \\ -\frac{6}{5} & 0 \end{pmatrix} t^5 + \begin{pmatrix} -\frac{1}{5} & 0 \\ 0 & 0 \end{pmatrix} t^6 + \cdots .$$

4. $$\mathbf{Y}(t) = \mathbf{I} + \begin{pmatrix} 0 & 1 & 0 \\ 0 & 0 & 1 \\ 1 & 0 & 0 \end{pmatrix} t + \frac{1}{2!}\begin{pmatrix} 0 & 0 & 1 \\ 1 & 0 & 0 \\ 0 & 4 & 0 \end{pmatrix} t^2 + \frac{1}{3!}\begin{pmatrix} 1 & 0 & 0 \\ 0 & 4 & 0 \\ 0 & 0 & 7 \end{pmatrix} t^3$$
$$+\frac{1}{4!}\begin{pmatrix} 0 & 4 & 0 \\ 0 & 0 & 7 \\ 10 & 0 & 0 \end{pmatrix} t^4 + \frac{1}{5!}\begin{pmatrix} 0 & 0 & 7 \\ 10 & 0 & 0 \\ 0 & 7 & 0 \end{pmatrix} t^5 + \frac{1}{6!}\begin{pmatrix} 10 & 0 & 0 \\ 0 & 7 & 0 \\ 0 & 105 & 0 \end{pmatrix} t^6 + \cdots .$$

5. $$\mathbf{Y}(t) = \begin{pmatrix} 1 & 0 \\ 0 & 1 \end{pmatrix} + \begin{pmatrix} 0 & 1 \\ 0 & 1 \end{pmatrix} t + \frac{1}{2!}\begin{pmatrix} 0 & 1 \\ -1 & 1 \end{pmatrix} t^2 + \frac{1}{3!}\begin{pmatrix} -1 & 1 \\ -1 & -1 \end{pmatrix} t^3$$
$$+\frac{1}{4!}\begin{pmatrix} -1 & -1 \\ -1 & -4 \end{pmatrix} t^4 + \frac{1}{5!}\begin{pmatrix} -1 & -4 \\ 3 & -8 \end{pmatrix} t^5 + \frac{1}{6!}\begin{pmatrix} 3 & -8 \\ 8 & -3 \end{pmatrix} t^6 + \cdots .$$

5-6. SOLUTIONS OF ANALYTIC *n*th-ORDER EQUATIONS

The linear equation

$$u^{[n]} + p_1 u^{[n-1]} + \cdots + p_n u = 0 \tag{5-6.1}$$

is an *analytic equation* when each of the coefficients $p_1, p_2, \ldots, p_n$ is an analytic function on some common interval. As in the case of the vector equation, there is no loss in generality in assuming that this interval includes the origin. We therefore assume that

$$p_i(t) = \sum_{k=0}^{\infty} p_{ik} t^k , \quad i = 1, 2, \ldots, n ,$$

where the series converges to $p_i(t)$ on the interval $(-h, h)$. If the radius of convergence for the series representing $p_i(t)$ is h_i, then h can be chosen as any positive real number which is no greater than the least of the n numbers $h_1, h_2, \ldots, h_n$.

The vector equation equivalent to (5-6.1) is

$$\mathbf{y}' = \mathbf{A}\mathbf{y} \tag{5-6.2}$$

where, as in Chapter 3,

$$\mathbf{A} = \begin{pmatrix} 0 & 1 & 0 & \cdots & 0 \\ 0 & 0 & 1 & \cdots & 0 \\ \cdot & \cdot & \cdot & \cdot & \cdot \\ \cdot & \cdot & \cdot & \cdot & \cdot \\ \cdot & \cdot & \cdot & \cdot & \cdot \\ -p_n & -p_{n-1} & -p_{n-2} & \cdots & -p_1 \end{pmatrix}.$$

The first row of any fundamental matrix for (5-6.2) is a fundamental vector for (5-6.1). It is obvious that the matrix **A** has a power series expansion which converges to **A** on the interval $(-h, h)$. Hence, the results of Section 5-5 imply that (5-6.2) has a fundamental matrix **Y** determined by a power series which converges on the interval $(-h, h)$. In particular, therefore, the components of the first row of **Y** have power series expansions which are valid on $(-h, h)$. Thus, we have proved the following theorem.

Theorem 5-6.1. *If the coefficients of equation* (5-6.1) *are analytic with power series representations on the interval* $(-h, h)$, *then the solutions are analytic with power series representations on the same interval.*

PROOF. See preceding paragraph.

A fundamental set of solutions for equation (5-6.1) can be obtained, as indicated, by finding the power series expansion of a fundamental matrix for the vector equation (5-6.2). However, in practice, it is usually more convenient to obtain the solutions directly from the scalar equation. A set of initial conditions for (5-6.1) may be specified by

(5-6.3) $$\mathbf{k}(u(0)) = \mathbf{c}\ .$$

For a series solution

(5-6.4) $$u = \sum_{k=0}^{\infty} u_k t^k\ ,$$

this is equivalent to a specification of the first n coefficients $u_0, u_1, \ldots, u_{n-1}$.

If the series (5-6.4) is substituted into equation (5-6.1), a recurrence relation is obtained defining u_k in terms of coefficients with a lower index. Since the first n coefficients are determined by the initial conditions, the recurrence relation serves to determine all the other coefficients uniquely. The derivation of the general recurrence relation is straightforward. It is not useful, however, to reproduce it here since in any specific instance the formula may be derived directly from first principles. We illustrate this point by finding a solution of the Legendre equation.

Example 1. The Legendre equation is

(5-6.5) $$(1-t^2)u'' - 2tu' + m(m+1)u = 0\ ,$$

where m is some real constant. In the general discussion given previously, the restriction $p_0 = 1$ was imposed to facilitate the replacement of the scalar equation by the companion vector equation. This restriction is clearly unnecessary when the scalar equation is looked at directly. If the series (5-6.4) is substituted into the equation (5-6.5) after some simplification we get

$$\sum_{k=0}^{\infty} [(k+1)(k+2)u_{k+2} - (k-m)(k+m+1)u_k]t^k = 0 .$$

Hence, we have the recursive relation

$$u_{k+2} = \frac{(k-m)(k+m+1)}{(k+1)(k+2)} u_k , \quad k = 0, 1, 2, \ldots .$$

If we impose the initial conditions

$$u_0 = 1 \quad \text{and} \quad u_1 = 0 ,$$

then it is clear that every coefficient u_k with an odd index is zero, and that

$$u_2 = -\frac{m(m+1)}{2!},$$

$$u_4 = \frac{(m-2)m(m+1)(m+3)}{4!},$$

$$\vdots$$

$$u_{2j} = (-1)^j \frac{(m-2j+2)\cdots(m-2)m(m+1)(m+3)\cdots(m+2j-1)}{(2j)!} .$$

Thus we have a series solution for equation (5-6.5). The radius of convergence of the series is 1 since, if we multiply the equation by $1/(1-t^2)$ to put it into standard form, each coefficient has a power series expansion with radius of convergence 1.

If we impose the initial conditions

$$u_0 = 0 \quad \text{and} \quad u_1 = 1 ,$$

it is easily inferred that we obtain a series expansion for which all the even power terms have zero coefficients. The series solutions obtained in this way are infinite series except where m is a nonnegative integer. When m is a nonnegative even integer the even power series terminates and when m is a nonnegative odd integer the odd power series terminates. The resulting polynomials are known as Legendre polynomials.

Exercises

Find a fundamental set of power series solutions for each of the following equations. It may be noted that the equations in the Exercises of Section 5 are companion equations to the equations given here. It is suggested, however, that these equations be solved independently

1. $u''+u=0$.

2. $u''+tu'+u=0$.

3. $(1+t^2)u''-6u=0$.

4. $u'''-3tu'-u=0$.

5. $u''-u'+tu=0$.

Find a fundamental set of power series solutions for the equations in Exercises 6–8 and determine intervals in which the solutions are valid.

6. $u''+tu'+(2+t^2)u=0$.

7. $u''+tu'+(2+3t)u=0$.

8. $u''-tu=0$ (Airy's equation).

9. Find solutions of Airy's equation (see Exercise 8) in powers of $t-1$.

10. Tchebycheff's equation is

$$(1-t^2)u''-tu'+m^2u=0 ,$$

where m is a constant.

(a) Find a fundamental set of power series solutions for this equation.

(b) If m is a nonnegative integer, show that a polynomial solution exists.

11. Find power series solutions for

$$u''+(\sin t)u=0 .$$

ANSWERS

1. $u_1(t)=1-\dfrac{1}{2!}t^2+\dfrac{1}{4!}t^4-\dfrac{1}{6!}t^6+\cdots$,

$u_2(t)=t-\dfrac{1}{3!}t^3+\dfrac{1}{5!}t^5-\dfrac{1}{7!}t^7+\cdots$.

2. $u_1(t)=1-\dfrac{1}{2!}t^2+\dfrac{1}{4\cdot 2}t^4+\cdots+(-1)^k\dfrac{1}{2k(2k-2)\cdots 4\cdot 2}t^{2k}+\cdots$,

$u_2(t)=t-\dfrac{1}{3!}t^3+\dfrac{1}{5\cdot 3}t^5+\cdots+(-1)^k\dfrac{1}{(2k+1)(2k-1)\cdots 5\cdot 3}t^{2k+1}+\cdots$.

3. $u_1(t)=t+t^3$,

$u_2(t)=1+3t^2+t^4+\cdots+(-1)^k\dfrac{3}{(2k-3)(2k-1)}t^{2k}+\cdots$.

4. $u_1(t)=1+\dfrac{1}{3!}t^3+\dfrac{10}{6!}t^6+\cdots+\dfrac{1\cdot 10\cdots(9k-8)}{(3k)!}t^{3k}+\cdots$,

$u_2(t)=t+\dfrac{4}{4!}t^4+\dfrac{4\cdot 13}{7!}t^7+\cdots+\dfrac{4\cdot 13\cdots(9k-2)}{(3k+1)!}t^{3k+1}+\cdots$,

$$u_3(t)=\frac{1}{2}t^2+\frac{7}{5!}t^5+\frac{7\cdot 16}{8!}t^8+\cdots+\frac{7\cdot 16\cdots(9k-2)}{(3k+2)!}t^{3k+2}+\cdots .$$

5. $u_1(t)=1-\frac{1}{3!}t^3-\frac{1}{4!}t^4-\frac{1}{5!}t^5+\frac{3}{6!}t^6+\cdots,$

$$u_2(t)=t+\frac{1}{2!}t^2+\frac{1}{3!}t^3-\frac{1}{4!}t^4-\frac{4}{5!}t^5-\frac{8}{6!}t^6+\cdots .$$

6. $u_1(t)=1-t^2-\frac{1}{4}t^4-\frac{1}{12}t^6+\cdots,$

$$u_2(t)=t-\frac{1}{2}t^3-\frac{3}{40}t^5-\frac{41}{1680}t^7+\cdots .$$

7. $u_1(t)=1-t^2-\frac{1}{2}t^3+\frac{1}{3}t^4+\frac{11}{40}t^5+\cdots,$

$$u_2(t)=t-\frac{1}{2}t^3-\frac{1}{4}t^4+\frac{1}{8}t^5+\cdots .$$

8. $u_1(t)=1+\frac{1}{3\cdot 2}t^3+\frac{1}{6\cdot 5\cdot 3\cdot 2}t^6+\cdots,$

$$u_2(t)=t+\frac{1}{4\cdot 3}t^4+\frac{1}{7\cdot 6\cdot 4\cdot 3}t^7+\cdots .$$

10. $u_1(t)=1-\frac{m^2}{2!}t^2-\frac{(2^2-m^2)m^2}{4!}t^4-\frac{(4^2-m^2)(2^2-m^2)m^2}{6!}t^6-\cdots,$

$$u_2(t)=t+\frac{1-m^2}{3!}t^3+\frac{(3^2-m^2)(1-m^2)}{5!}t^5+\cdots .$$

11. $u_1(t)=1-\frac{1}{3!}t^3+\frac{1}{5!}t^5-\frac{4}{6!}t^6+\cdots,$

$$u_2(t)=t-\frac{2}{4!}t^4+\frac{4}{6!}t^6+\cdots .$$

5-7. SOLUTIONS AT A SINGULAR POINT

We have been concerned with

$$\mathbf{y}'=\mathbf{A}\mathbf{y} \tag{5-7.1}$$

when the matrix **A** is analytic at some point t_0. Such a point is commonly called an *ordinary point* for the differential equation. In Section 5-5, it was established that the solutions of equation (5-7.1) are analytic at an ordinary point.

If any component of **A** has a singularity at a point t_0, the equation is said to have a singularity at that point. The derivation of the nature of a solution of the equation in the neighborhood of a singular point is somewhat complicated and is not considered to be within the scope of this book. It is, however, a topic of considerable importance, and we may at least specify the basic types of singularities. We confine our attention to singularities at the point $t = 0$.

The simplest case involves equation (5-7.1), where

$$\mathbf{A}(t) = \frac{1}{t}\hat{\mathbf{A}}(t)$$

and $\hat{\mathbf{A}}(t)$ is analytic and not equal to $\mathbf{0}$ at $t = 0$. The components of **A**, therefore, have either simple poles or removable discontinuities at $t = 0$. In this case the equation is said to have a *singularity of the first kind* at the origin. If the components of **A** have essential singularities or poles of order higher than 1 at $t = 0$, then the equation is said to have a *singularity of the second kind* at the origin.[2]

The *n*th-order equation

$$u^{[n]} + p_1 u^{[n-1]} + \cdots + p_n u = 0 \tag{5-7.2}$$

has a singularity at $t = 0$, if any of the coefficients has a singularity at that point. We may associate a vector equation with this scalar equation by means of the following substitution:

$$\begin{aligned} y_1 &= u \ , \\ y_2 &= tu' \ , \\ &\ \ \vdots \\ y_n &= t^{n-1}u^{[n-1]} \ . \end{aligned} \tag{5-7.3}$$

The first $n-1$ of these relations imply that

$$\begin{aligned} y_1' &= \frac{1}{t}y_2 \ , \\ y_2' &= \frac{1}{t}y_2 + \frac{1}{t}y_3 \ , \\ y_3' &= 2\frac{1}{t}y_3 + \frac{1}{t}y_4 \ , \\ &\ \ \vdots \\ y_{n-1}' &= (n-2)\frac{1}{t}y_{n-1} + \frac{1}{t}y_n \ . \end{aligned} \tag{5-7.4}$$

[2] A discussion of the nature of solutions at singular points may be found in either Coddington and Levinson [11], Chapter IV, or Hartman [23], Appendix to Chapter IV.

If the last relation in (5-7.3) is differentiated, we get

$$y_n' = (n-1)t^{n-2}u^{[n-1]} + t^{n-1}u^{[n]} \ .$$

Under the assumption that u satisfies equation (5-7.2), this may be rewritten as

$$y_n' = (n-1)t^{n-2}u^{[n-1]} + t^{n-1}(-p_n u - p_{n-1}u' - \cdots - p_1 u^{[n-1]}) \ .$$

Finally, using relations (5-7.3), we have

$$(5\text{-}7.5) \quad y_n' = \frac{1}{t}\{-t^n p_n y_1 - t^{n-1}p_{n-1}y_2 - \cdots + [-tp_1 + (n-1)]y_n\} \ .$$

Thus, if u is a solution of (5-7.2), the functions $y_1, y_2, \ldots, y_n$ defined by (5-7.3) must satisfy the relations (5-7.4) and (5-7.5). That is to say, the vector **y** with these functions as components must satisfy the vector equation

$$(5\text{-}7.6) \qquad \mathbf{y}' = \frac{1}{t}\hat{\mathbf{A}}(t)\mathbf{y} \ ,$$

where

$$\hat{\mathbf{A}}(t) =$$

$$\begin{bmatrix} 0 & 1 & 0 & \cdots & 0 & 0 \\ 0 & 1 & 1 & \cdots & 0 & 0 \\ 0 & 0 & 2 & \cdots & 0 & 0 \\ \cdot & \cdot & \cdot & \cdot & \cdot & \cdot \\ \cdot & \cdot & \cdot & \cdot & \cdot & \cdot \\ \cdot & \cdot & \cdot & \cdot & \cdot & \cdot \\ 0 & 0 & 0 & \cdots & (n-2) & 1 \\ -t^n p_n & -t^{n-1}p_{n-1} & -t^{n-2}p_{n-2} & \cdots & -t^2 p_2 & [-tp_1 + (n-1)] \end{bmatrix}$$

Conversely, it is easily verified that the first component of any vector solution of (5-7.6) is a solution of (5-7.2). Clearly, therefore, the scalar equation and the vector equation are 'equivalent'.

The scalar equation (5-7.2) is said to have a *singularity of the first kind at* $t = 0$ if the corresponding vector equation (5-7.6) has a singularity of the first kind at $t = 0$. In terms of the coefficients of equation (5-7.2), this means that it has a singularity of the first kind at the origin if the equation is singular and if each of the functions

$$(5\text{-}7.7) \qquad t^k p_k(t) \ , \quad k = 1, 2, \ldots, n$$

is continuous or has a removable discontinuity at $t = 0$. Singularities of the first kind are also called *simple singularities*. If any of the functions (5-7.7) has a pole or other nonremovable singularity, then equation (5-7.2) is said to have a *singularity of the second kind* at the origin.

Many differential equations which are important in scientific applications have singularities of the first kind. Such equations have solutions which are expressible as

$$u(t) = t^{\nu} \sum_{k=0}^{\infty} u_k t^k , \tag{5-7.8}$$

where ν is some constant (real or complex). The proof of this fact may be found elsewhere[3] and is not given here. Techniques for determining the coefficients of such series solutions are found in most elementary texts on differential equations. An outline of the derivation of a solution for Bessel's equation follows.

Example 1. The differential equation

$$u'' + \frac{1}{t}u' + \left(1 - \frac{n^2}{t^2}\right) u = 0$$

is known as Bessel's equation. According to the criterion given previously, it has a singularity of the first kind at the origin. If the series in formula (5-7.8) is substituted into this equation, after some simplification we get

$$\sum_{k=0}^{\infty} [(\nu+k)^2 - n^2] u_k t^{\nu+k-2} + \sum_{k=2}^{\infty} u_k t^{\nu+k} = 0 .$$

Replacing k by $k-2$ in the second sum on the left-hand side, we may write this equation as

$$(\nu^2 - n^2) u_0 t^{\nu-2} + [(\nu+1)^2 - n^2] u_1 t^{\nu-1} + \sum_{k=2}^{\infty} \{[(\nu+k)^2 - n^2] u_k + u_{k-2}\} t^{\nu+k-2} = 0 . \tag{5-7.9}$$

The summation term in this equation is set equal to zero to yield the recursive relation

$$u_k = -\frac{u_{k-2}}{(\nu+k)^2 - n^2} , \quad k = 2, 3, 4, \ldots . \tag{5-7.10}$$

If we impose an initial condition on the solution by specifying that

$$u_0 = 1 ,$$

$$u_1 = 0 ,$$

then the recursive relation (5-7.10) requires that all coefficients with an odd index be zero. By requiring that ν satisfy the so-called *indicial equation*

$$\nu^2 - n^2 = 0 ,$$

we make the first term on the left-hand side of (5-7.9) zero. In particular, if $\nu = n$, then relation (5-7.10) becomes

$$u_k = -\frac{1}{(2n+k)k} u_{k-2} , \quad k = 2, 4, 6, \ldots ,$$

[3] Coddington and Levinson [11], and Hartman [23].

for all the coefficients of even index. The initial terms of the series solution, thus determined, are given by

$$u(t) = t^n \left[1 - \frac{1}{n+1}\left(\frac{t}{2}\right)^2 + \frac{1}{(n+1)(n+2)2!}\left(\frac{t}{2}\right)^4 - \frac{1}{(n+1)(n+2)(n+3)3!}\left(\frac{t}{2}\right)^6 + \cdots \right] .$$

If this solution is multiplied by the factor $1/[2^n\Gamma(n+1)]$, we obtain a solution $J_n(t)$, that is referred to as *Bessel's function of order n.* That is,

$$J_n(t) = \frac{1}{2^n\Gamma(n+1)} u(t) .$$

Using the familiar property of the gamma function that $x\Gamma(x) = \Gamma(x+1)$, we get

$$J_n(t) = \left(\frac{t}{2}\right)^n \left[\frac{1}{\Gamma(n+1)} - \frac{1}{\Gamma(n+2)}\left(\frac{t}{2}\right)^2 + \frac{1}{\Gamma(n+3)\Gamma(3)}\left(\frac{t}{2}\right)^4 - \frac{1}{\Gamma(n+4)\Gamma(4)}\left(\frac{t}{2}\right)^6 + \cdots \right] .$$

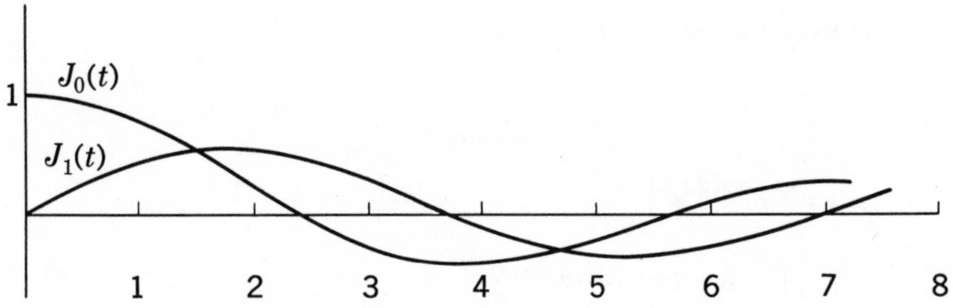

Figure 5-7.1

Tables of values of Bessel's function for a variety of values of n are available. Figure 5-7.1 shows the graphs of $J_0(t)$ and $J_1(t)$. It is clear that these two functions have properties in common with the sine and cosine functions. In particular, the Sturmian theory, developed in Chapter 9, can be applied to show that their oscillatory character persists for all values of t.

Exercises

1. Use the substitution (5-7.3) to transform Bessel's equation into a vector equation. Find a series solution for the vector equation from the known solution of the scalar equation.

2. Euler's differential equation is

$$t^n u^{[n]} + t^{n-1} p_1 u^{[n-1]} + \cdots + t p_{n-1} u' + p_n u = 0 ,$$

where $p_1, p_2, \ldots, p_n$ are constants.

(a) Show that Euler's equation is transformed into an equation with constant coefficients by means of the substitution $t = e^s$.

(b) Apply the transformation (5-7.3) to Euler's equation (after multiplying the equation by t^{-n}) and show that the resulting vector equation has the form $\mathbf{y}' = (1/t)\hat{\mathbf{A}}\mathbf{y}$, where $\hat{\mathbf{A}}$ is a constant matrix.

(c) Show that $\mathbf{y} = t^{\lambda}\mathbf{h}$ is a solution of the vector equation in part (b) if λ is an eigenvalue of $\hat{\mathbf{A}}$ and $\mathbf{h}$ is a corresponding eigenvector.

3. (a) Find a fundamental set of solutions for

$$t^2u'' - 2tu' + 2u = 0 .$$

(b) Transform the equation in part (a) into a vector equation by means of the relations (5-7.3). Use the results of Exercise 2(c) to find solutions of the vector equation.

4. Develop a recursive formula for finding solutions of equation (5-7.6) and apply it to the vector equation obtained in Exercise 1.

5. Find a fundamental set of power series solutions for the *hypergeometric equation*

$$t(t-1)u'' + [\gamma - (\alpha+\beta+1)t]u' - \alpha\beta u = 0$$

under the assumption that γ is not an integer.

ANSWER

5. $$u_1(t) = 1 + \frac{\alpha\beta}{\gamma}t + \frac{\alpha(\alpha+1)\beta(\beta+1)}{2!\,\gamma(\gamma+1)}t^2 + \cdots ,$$

$$u_2(t) = t^{1-\gamma}\left[1 + \frac{(\alpha-\gamma+1)(\beta-\gamma+1)}{(2-\gamma)}t + \frac{(\alpha-\gamma+1)(\alpha-\gamma+2)(\beta-\gamma+1)(\beta-\gamma+2)}{2!\,(2-\gamma)(3-\gamma)}t^2 + \cdots\right] .$$

6

The Two-Point Boundary Problem

6-1. INTRODUCTION

The initial-value problem (see Chapter 3) associated with the vector equation (of dimension n)

$$\mathbf{y}' = \mathbf{A}\mathbf{y} + \mathbf{f} \tag{6-1.1}$$

raises the question of the existence of a solution of equation (6-1.1) that also satisfies the initial condition

$$\mathbf{y}(t_0) = \mathbf{y}_0 \ . \tag{6-1.2}$$

This problem could be called a one-point boundary problem. It may be noted, incidentally, that if we replace (6-1.2) by

$$\mathbf{W}\mathbf{y}(t_0) = \mathbf{y}_0 \ ,$$

where $\mathbf{W}$ is a nonsingular, constant n by n matrix, we achieve only a trivial generalization of (6-1.2).

Motivation for our consideration of two-point boundary problems can be provided by citing physical examples, such as a vibrating string problem or a heat conduction problem, that can be described by linear equations. However, the mathematical significance of the two-point boundary problem stems from Green's Formula (3-6.6) and is, in fact, basically associated with the fundamental theorem of integral calculus. This theorem provides for an evaluation of the definite integral in terms of the antiderivative of the integrand evaluated at the end points of the interval of integration. Green's formula is obtained from the Lagrange identity by an application of this theorem.

Since we intend to classify the potential solutions of (6-1.1) according to their values at the end points of a fundamental interval $[a, b]$, the following discussion is relevant. Let the symbol V represent the space of all n-vectors with components in $C^1[a, b]$; this is the space of potential solutions of the differential equation. Each element $\mathbf{y}$ in V has a value at a and a value at b, and these may be written as a "vertical" ordered pair and interpreted as a partitioned $2n$-vector in $V_{2n}(R)$. In effect, this defines a mapping B from V onto $V_{2n}(R)$, where the mapping relation is

$$B(\mathbf{y}) = \begin{pmatrix} \mathbf{y}(a) \\ \mathbf{y}(b) \end{pmatrix} . \tag{6-1.3}$$

It is easily verified that the mapping is linear. For want of a better name, we call the vector on the right-hand side of relation (6-1.3) the *boundary vector* of $\mathbf{y}$. The mapping is obviously not one-to-one, but we can define inverse images of sets in $V_{2n}(R)$ in a familiar fashion. That is, if S is any set of elements in $V_{2n}(R)$, we use $B^{-1}(S)$ to represent the set of all elements in V whose images are in S. The following theorem is a natural consequence of the linearity of the mapping.

Theorem 6-1.1. *If S is a subspace of $V_{2n}(R)$, then $B^{-1}(S)$ is a subspace of V.*

PROOF. Let $\mathbf{y}_1$ and $\mathbf{y}_2$ be any two elements in $B^{-1}(S)$, and let α_1 and α_2 be any two scalars. The boundary vector of $\alpha_1\mathbf{y}_1+\alpha_2\mathbf{y}_2$ is given by

$$B(\alpha_1\mathbf{y}_1+\alpha_2\mathbf{y}_2) = \alpha_1 B(\mathbf{y}_1)+\alpha_2 B(\mathbf{y}_2) \ .$$

Since S is a subspace, this vector must be an element of S. It follows that $\alpha_1\mathbf{y}_1+\alpha_2\mathbf{y}_2$ is in $B^{-1}(S)$, and the theorem is proved (see Figure 6-1.1).

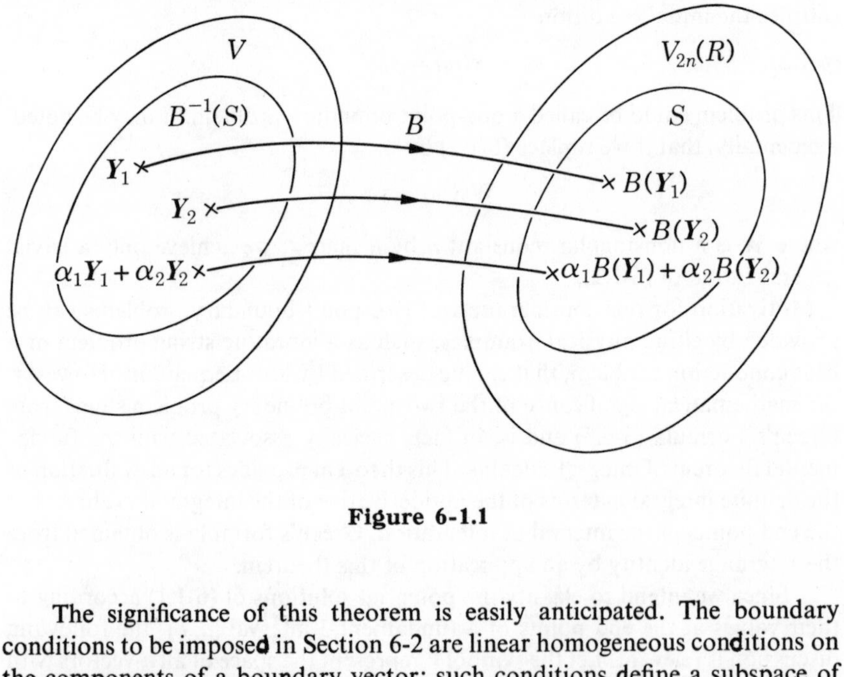

Figure 6-1.1

The significance of this theorem is easily anticipated. The boundary conditions to be imposed in Section 6-2 are linear homogeneous conditions on the components of a boundary vector; such conditions define a subspace of $V_{2n}(R)$. According to the theorem, therefore, these conditions define a subspace of V.

6-2. THE TWO-POINT HOMOGENEOUS BOUNDARY PROBLEM

The problem to be considered is

(6-2.1) $$\mathbf{y}' = \mathbf{A}\mathbf{y} \ ,$$

(6-2.2) $$\mathbf{W}^{[a]}\mathbf{y}(a)+\mathbf{W}^{[b]}\mathbf{y}(b)=\mathbf{o}\ ,$$

where $\mathbf{A}$ is an n by n matrix with continuous components on $[a, b]$ and $\mathbf{W}^{[a]}$ and $\mathbf{W}^{[b]}$ are m by n constant matrices. A solution of the problem is a solution of equation (6-2.1) whose values at a and b are such that the linear relation (6-2.2) is also satisfied. It is assumed that the m by $2n$ matrix

$$\mathbf{W}=(\mathbf{W}^{[a]}\,\mathbf{W}^{[b]})$$

has rank m. That this is not a restrictive hypothesis can be seen by considering the scalar relations

(6-2.3) $$\sum_{j=1}^{n}(w_{ij}{}^{[a]}y_j(a)+w_{ij}{}^{[b]}y_j(b))=0\ ,\quad i=1,2,\ldots,m\ ,$$

which correspond to (6-2.2). If the rank of $\mathbf{W}$ were less than the number of its rows, some of the relations in (6-2.3) would be linearly dependent on the others. Such dependent relations could clearly be discarded without altering the effect of the conditions. We assume, therefore, that the original set was linearly independent.

The case $m=n$, where $\mathbf{W}^{[a]}$ and $\mathbf{W}^{[b]}$ are square matrices, is the most important case but, for the present, we do not impose this restriction.

Theorem 6-2.1. *The solutions of the two-point homogeneous boundary problem* (6-2.1) *and* (6-2.2) *form a vector space.*

PROOF. The boundary condition (6-2.2) can be written as

(6-2.4) $$(\mathbf{W}^{[a]}\,\mathbf{W}^{[b]})\begin{pmatrix}\mathbf{y}(a)\\ \mathbf{y}(b)\end{pmatrix}=\mathbf{o}\ .$$

This restricts the boundary vector of an element $\mathbf{y}$ of V to a subspace of $V_{2n}(R)$. Theorem 6-1.1 insures that $\mathbf{y}$ is thereby restricted to a subspace of V. The solutions of equation (6-2.1) are known to form a subspace of V. The solutions of the boundary problem are the elements of V that belong to both of these subspaces. Since the intersection of two subspaces is a subspace, the theorem follows.

Definition 6-2.1. *The dimension of the solution space of a boundary problem is the* ***index of compatibility*** *of the problem. A boundary problem is* ***incompatible*** *if its index of compatibility is zero.*

Definition 6-2.2. *If* $\mathbf{Y}$ *is any fundamental matrix for the vector equation* (6-2.1) *the matrix* $\mathbf{D}$ *defined by*

(6-2.5) $$\mathbf{D}=\mathbf{W}^{[a]}\mathbf{Y}(a)+\mathbf{W}^{[b]}\mathbf{Y}(b)$$

is a ***characteristic matrix*** *for the boundary problem.*

It may be noted that the given boundary problem is not essentially altered if the end-point condition (6-2.2) is replaced by

$$\mathbf{B}\mathbf{W}^{[a]}\mathbf{y}(a)+\mathbf{B}\mathbf{W}^{[b]}\mathbf{y}(b) = \mathbf{o} \ ,$$

where $\mathbf{B}$ is any nonsingular, constant m by m matrix. Moreover, if $\mathbf{Y}$ is a fundamental matrix for equation (6-2.1), then so is $\mathbf{YC}$, where $\mathbf{C}$ is any nonsingular constant n by n matrix. This implies that $\mathbf{BDC}$ is a characteristic matrix. A characteristic matrix for a boundary problem is, therefore, far from unique. It is clear, however, that all characteristic matrices for a given boundary problem have the same rank.

Theorem 6-2.2. *If the boundary problem* (6-2.1) *and* (6-2.2) *has a characteristic matrix of rank r, then its index of compatibility is* $n-r$.

PROOF. If $\mathbf{Y}$ is a fundamental matrix for equation (6-2.1), every vector solution of that equation has the form $\mathbf{y} = \mathbf{Yc}$. This satisfies the end-point condition (6-2.2) if and only if

(6-2.6) $$\mathbf{Dc} = \mathbf{o} \ ,$$

where $\mathbf{D}$ is the characteristic matrix defined by formula (6-2.5). If the rank of $\mathbf{D}$ is r, then the equation (6-2.6) has $n-r$ linearly independent solutions for the vector $\mathbf{c}$. These solutions yield $n-r$ linearly independent solutions of the boundary problem. This proves the theorem.

Exercises

Find the index of compatibility for each of the following boundary problems, and determine the solution spaces.

1. $\mathbf{y}' = \begin{pmatrix} 1 & 1 \\ -1 & -1 \end{pmatrix} \mathbf{y} \ ,$

$$\begin{pmatrix} 1 & 0 \\ 0 & 1 \end{pmatrix} \mathbf{y}(0) + \begin{pmatrix} 0 & -1 \\ -1 & 0 \end{pmatrix} \mathbf{y}(1) = \mathbf{o} \ .$$

2. $\mathbf{y}' = \begin{pmatrix} 0 & 1 \\ 0 & 0 \end{pmatrix} \mathbf{y} \ ,$

$$\begin{pmatrix} 1 & 0 \\ 0 & 0 \end{pmatrix} \mathbf{y}(0) + \begin{pmatrix} 0 & 0 \\ 1 & 0 \end{pmatrix} \mathbf{y}(1) = \mathbf{o} \ .$$

3. $\mathbf{y}' = \begin{pmatrix} 0 & 1 & 0 \\ 0 & 0 & 1 \\ 0 & 0 & 0 \end{pmatrix} \mathbf{y} \ ,$

$$\begin{pmatrix} 0 & -1 & 0 \\ 1 & 0 & 0 \\ 0 & 0 & 1 \end{pmatrix} \mathbf{y}(0) + \begin{pmatrix} 1 & 0 & 0 \\ 0 & 0 & 0 \\ 0 & -1 & 0 \end{pmatrix} \mathbf{y}(1) = \mathbf{o} \ .$$

4. $\mathbf{y}' = \begin{pmatrix} 0 & 1 & 0 \\ 0 & 0 & 1 \\ 0 & 0 & 0 \end{pmatrix} \mathbf{y}$,

$$\begin{pmatrix} 1 & 0 & 0 \\ 0 & 0 & 0 \end{pmatrix} \mathbf{y}(0) + \begin{pmatrix} 0 & 0 & 0 \\ 1 & -1 & 0 \end{pmatrix} \mathbf{y}(1) = \mathbf{o} .$$

5. $\mathbf{y}' = \begin{pmatrix} 0 & 1 \\ -4 & 0 \end{pmatrix} \mathbf{y}$,

$$\begin{pmatrix} 1 & 0 \\ 0 & 0 \end{pmatrix} \mathbf{y}(0) + \begin{pmatrix} 0 & 0 \\ 1 & 0 \end{pmatrix} \mathbf{y}(\pi) = \mathbf{o} .$$

6-3. THE ADJOINT BOUNDARY PROBLEM

A brief review of the concept of an adjoint operator on the vector space $V_n(R)$ provides a useful background for the introduction of an adjoint boundary problem.[1]

It was observed in Section 1-6 that every linear functional f in $V_n(R)$ can be expressed as a linear combination of the components of the independent variable. That is for $\mathbf{x} \in V_n(R)$,

$$f(\mathbf{x}) = \sum_{i=1}^{n} y_i x_i$$

for some set of real numbers $\{y_i\}$. This implies that the functional values can be expressed as an inner product, namely

$$f(\mathbf{x}) = (\mathbf{x}, \mathbf{y}) ,$$

where $\mathbf{y}$ is the vector whose components form the set $\{y_i\}$. Let A be any linear operator mapping $V_n(R)$ into $V_n(R)$. The composite function formed from A and f is a functional g defined by

$$g(\mathbf{x}) = f(A\mathbf{x}) . \tag{6-3.1}$$

It is easily verified that g is a linear functional, so that it can be given the inner product representation

$$g(\mathbf{x}) = (\mathbf{x}, \mathbf{y}') , \tag{6-3.2}$$

where $\mathbf{y}'$ is some vector in $V_n(R)$. The vector $\mathbf{y}'$ is uniquely determined by f. Hence, we have effected a mapping of each $\mathbf{y}$ in $V_n(R)$ into a $\mathbf{y}'$ in $V_n(R)$. This mapping will be represented by

$$\mathbf{y}' = A^*\mathbf{y} . \tag{6-3.3}$$

It can be verified that A^* is a linear transformation. It is called the *adjoint* of the transformation A. Substituting from (6-3.3) into (6-3.2) and writing the right-hand side of (6-3.1) in inner product form, we conclude that

$$(A\mathbf{x}, \mathbf{y}) = (\mathbf{x}, A^*\mathbf{y}) . \tag{6-3.4}$$

[1] For more detail on this background the reader should consult Halmos [21].

This relation is valid for every $\mathbf{x}$ and $\mathbf{y}$ in $V_n(R)$ and may be regarded as the defining relation for A^*.

For the problem at hand, the vector space V (defined as in Section 6-1) is a domain for the differential operator. An inner product for this space is

$$(\mathbf{y}, \mathbf{z}) = \int_a^b \tilde{\mathbf{z}}(t)\mathbf{y}(t)\,dt \ .$$

Using this definition, we can write Green's formula (3-6.6) as

$$(6\text{-}3.5) \qquad (M\mathbf{y}, \mathbf{z}) - (\mathbf{y}, M^*\mathbf{z}) = \tilde{\mathbf{z}}(b)\mathbf{y}(b) - \tilde{\mathbf{z}}(a)\mathbf{y}(a) \ .$$

Here, we may recall, M is the differential operator defined by

$$M\mathbf{y} = \mathbf{y}' - \mathbf{A}\mathbf{y} \ ,$$

and M^* is its adjoint defined by

$$M^*\mathbf{z} = -\mathbf{z}' - \tilde{\mathbf{A}}\mathbf{z} \ .$$

Formula (6-3.5), which is valid for every pair of vectors $\mathbf{y}$ and $\mathbf{z}$ in V, may be compared with relation (6-3.4). The two relations are formally equivalent, if and only if the right-hand side of Green's formula is zero. We therefore adopt the rule that a boundary condition, adjoint to condition (6-2.2), should be defined so that when both conditions are applied

$$\tilde{\mathbf{z}}(b)\mathbf{y}(b) - \tilde{\mathbf{z}}(a)\mathbf{y}(a) = 0 \ .$$

This relation can also be written as

$$(6\text{-}3.6) \qquad (\tilde{\mathbf{z}}(a)\ \tilde{\mathbf{z}}(b))\begin{pmatrix} \mathbf{I} & \mathbf{0} \\ \mathbf{0} & -\mathbf{I} \end{pmatrix}\begin{pmatrix} \mathbf{y}(a) \\ \mathbf{y}(b) \end{pmatrix} = 0 \ .$$

The condition (6-2.4), which is equivalent to (6-2.3), restricts the boundary vector of $\mathbf{y}$ to be orthogonal to the rows of $(\mathbf{W}^{[a]}\,\mathbf{W}^{[b]})$. That is to say, the condition requires that the boundary vector of $\mathbf{y}$ should belong to the orthogonal complement of the row space of $(\mathbf{W}^{[a]}\,\mathbf{W}^{[b]})$. It follows, therefore, that relation (6-3.6) holds if

$$(\tilde{\mathbf{z}}(a)\ \tilde{\mathbf{z}}(b))\begin{pmatrix} \mathbf{I} & \mathbf{0} \\ \mathbf{0} & -\mathbf{I} \end{pmatrix}$$

is required to belong to the row space of $(\mathbf{W}^{[a]}\,\mathbf{W}^{[b]})$. This requirement can be written as

$$(6\text{-}3.7) \qquad (\tilde{\mathbf{z}}(a)\ \tilde{\mathbf{z}}(b))\begin{pmatrix} \mathbf{I} & \mathbf{0} \\ \mathbf{0} & -\mathbf{I} \end{pmatrix} = \tilde{\mathbf{a}}(\mathbf{W}^{[a]}\,\mathbf{W}^{[b]}) \ ,$$

where $\mathbf{a}$ is an arbitrary vector in $V_m(R)$. Hence, the following definition of the boundary problem, adjoint to the boundary problem (6-2.1) and (6-2.2), is clearly indicated:

$$(6\text{-}3.8) \qquad \tilde{\mathbf{z}}' = -\tilde{\mathbf{z}}\mathbf{A} \ , \quad \text{or} \quad \mathbf{z}' = -\tilde{\mathbf{A}}\mathbf{z} \ ,$$

$$\text{(6-3.9)} \qquad \begin{cases} \tilde{\mathbf{z}}(a) = \tilde{\mathbf{a}}\mathbf{W}^{[a]} \,, \\ \tilde{\mathbf{z}}(b) = -\tilde{\mathbf{a}}\mathbf{W}^{[b]} \,, \end{cases} \quad \text{or} \quad \begin{cases} \mathbf{z}(a) = \tilde{\mathbf{W}}^{[a]}\mathbf{a} \,, \\ \mathbf{z}(b) = -\tilde{\mathbf{W}}^{[b]}\mathbf{a} \,. \end{cases}$$

The two formulations of the boundary problem exhibited above are clearly equivalent. In the left-hand formulation, a solution appears as a row vector and in the right-hand formulation as the corresponding column vector. In later developments, we use whichever formulation is more convenient. A vector $\mathbf{z}$ is a solution of the boundary problem if it satisfies equation (6-3.8) and if any m-vector $\mathbf{a}$ exists such that relations (6-3.9) are satisfied.

The vector $\mathbf{a}$ in the adjoint boundary conditions plays the role of a parameter. We refer to this specification of boundary conditions as a *parametric representation.* The corresponding linear relation is easily obtained by eliminating the parametric vector. To accomplish this, let $\mathbf{W}_{\perp}$ be any $(2n-m)$ by $2n$ matrix whose rows form a basis for the orthogonal complement of the row space of the matrix $\mathbf{W}$. Obviously, $\mathbf{W}\tilde{\mathbf{W}}_{\perp} = \mathbf{0}$. Let $\mathbf{W}_{\perp}$ be expressed in the partitioned form

$$\mathbf{W}_{\perp} = (\mathbf{Q}^{[a]}\mathbf{Q}^{[b]}) \,,$$

where $\mathbf{Q}^{[a]}$ and $\mathbf{Q}^{[b]}$ are each $(2n-m)$ by n matrices. Multiplying both sides of relation (6-3.7) on the right by $\tilde{\mathbf{W}}_{\perp}$, we get

$$(\tilde{\mathbf{z}}(a)\; \tilde{\mathbf{z}}(b)) \begin{pmatrix} \mathbf{I} & \mathbf{0} \\ \mathbf{0} & -\mathbf{I} \end{pmatrix} \begin{pmatrix} \tilde{\mathbf{Q}}^{[a]} \\ \tilde{\mathbf{Q}}^{[b]} \end{pmatrix} = \tilde{\mathbf{o}} \,.$$

This can be simplified to yield

$$\text{(6-3.10)} \qquad \mathbf{Q}^{[a]}\mathbf{z}^{[a]} - \mathbf{Q}^{[b]}\mathbf{z}^{[b]} = \mathbf{o} \,.$$

The relation (6-3.10) is clearly equivalent to the two parametric conditions (6-3.9) and can be used to replace them if desired. It is conceivable also that one might wish to replace the end-point condition (6-2.2) by an equivalent pair of parametric conditions. These are easily seen to be

$$\mathbf{y}(a) = \tilde{\mathbf{Q}}^{[a]}\mathbf{c} \,,$$
$$\mathbf{y}(b) = \tilde{\mathbf{Q}}^{[b]}\mathbf{c} \,.$$

The relationship between a vector subspace and its orthogonal complement is a reciprocal one. This insures a reciprocal relationship between a given boundary condition and its adjoint. It follows, therefore, that the adjoint of the boundary problem (6-3.8) and (6-3.9) is the original boundary problem (6-2.1) and (6-2.2).

The following theorem develops a formula for solutions of the adjoint boundary problem. In this theorem and the subsequent developments of this section it is convenient to use the row vector rather than the column vector form of the adjoint problem.

Theorem 6-3.1. *The adjoint boundary problem* (6-3.8) *and* (6-3.9) *is compatible if and only if the rows of the characteristic matrix* $\mathbf{D}$ *are linearly dependent.*

PROOF. Let **D** be the characteristic matrix defined by formula (6-2.5), where **Y** is some specific fundamental matrix for equation (6-2.1). We have seen in Section 3-6 that $\mathbf{Y}^{-1}$ is a fundamental matrix for equation (6-3.8) and that every solution of the equation has the form

$$\tilde{\mathbf{z}} = \tilde{\mathbf{c}}\mathbf{Y}^{-1} . \tag{6-3.11}$$

A solution of this form satisfies (6-3.9) if and only if

$$\begin{aligned} \tilde{\mathbf{c}}\mathbf{Y}^{-1}(a) &= \tilde{\mathbf{a}}\mathbf{W}^{[a]} , \\ \tilde{\mathbf{c}}\mathbf{Y}^{-1}(b) &= -\tilde{\mathbf{a}}\mathbf{W}^{[b]} . \end{aligned} \tag{6-3.12}$$

Multiplying the first of these relations on the right by $\mathbf{Y}(a)$ and the second by $\mathbf{Y}(b)$ and subtracting the second result from the first, we get

$$\tilde{\mathbf{o}} = \tilde{\mathbf{a}}\mathbf{D} .$$

It follows that the adjoint problem has a nontrivial solution only if the rows of **D** are linearly dependent.

Conversely, if the rows of **D** are linearly dependent, a nonzero vector **a** exists that is orthogonal to **D** on the left. This vector, through the first of the pair of relations (6-3.12), yields an evaluation of $\tilde{\mathbf{c}}$. This, in turn, when substituted into (6-3.11) yields a solution $\tilde{\mathbf{z}}$, given by

$$\tilde{\mathbf{z}} = \tilde{\mathbf{a}}\,\mathbf{W}^{[a]}\,\mathbf{Y}(a)\,\mathbf{Y}^{-1} . \tag{6-3.13}$$

An alternative formula for $\tilde{\mathbf{z}}$ is obtained by using the second of the relations (6-3.12) to evaluate $\tilde{\mathbf{c}}$. It is

$$\tilde{\mathbf{z}} = -\tilde{\mathbf{a}}\,\mathbf{W}^{[b]}\,\mathbf{Y}(b)\,\mathbf{Y}^{-1} . \tag{6-3.14}$$

It follows from the derivation that these two evaluations of $\tilde{\mathbf{z}}$ are equal. This can, in fact, be checked by noting that the difference of the two evaluations is $\tilde{\mathbf{a}}\mathbf{D}\mathbf{Y}^{-1} = \tilde{\mathbf{o}}$. Since it is easily verified that $\tilde{\mathbf{z}}$ is a nontrivial solution of the boundary problem, we conclude that the problem is compatible. This proves the theorem.

Theorem 6-3.2. *The index of compatibility of the adjoint boundary problem is $m-r$, where r is the rank of a characteristic matrix.*

PROOF. Formula (6-3.13) reveals that each solution of the adjoint boundary problem has associated with it a unique parametric vector $\tilde{\mathbf{a}}$. The relationship is clearly linear, for if $\tilde{\mathbf{z}}_1$ and $\tilde{\mathbf{z}}_2$ are two solutions with corresponding parametric vectors $\tilde{\mathbf{a}}_1$ and $\tilde{\mathbf{a}}_2$, then

$$\alpha_1\tilde{\mathbf{z}}_1 + \alpha_2\tilde{\mathbf{z}}_2 = (\alpha_1\tilde{\mathbf{a}}_1 + \alpha_2\tilde{\mathbf{a}}_2)\,\mathbf{W}^{[a]}\,\mathbf{Y}(a)\,\mathbf{Y}^{-1} .$$

The dimension of the solution space of the boundary problem is, therefore, the same as the dimension of the space of associated parametric vectors. The latter space consists precisely of those vectors which are left-orthogonal to **D**. It follows that the index of compatibility of the problem is $m-r$, where r is the rank of **D**. This proves the theorem.

Corollary 6-3.2. *For the case where* $m = n$, *the boundary problem* (6-2.1) *and* (6-2.2) *and its adjoint* (6-3.8) *and* (6-3.9) *have the same index of compatibility.*

It should be clear that, if $\tilde{\mathbf{z}}_0$ is a solution of the boundary problem (6-3.8) and (6-3.9) and $\tilde{\mathbf{a}}_0$ is the corresponding parametric vector, then $\tilde{\mathbf{z}}_0$ is the unique solution of the initial-value problem

$$\tilde{\mathbf{z}}' = -\tilde{\mathbf{z}}\mathbf{A} ,$$

$$\tilde{\mathbf{z}}(a) = \tilde{\mathbf{a}}_0 \mathbf{W}^{[a]} .$$

From this point of view, it is easily appreciated that the space of parametric vectors which are left-orthogonal to **D** generates a corresponding solution space of the boundary problem. Obviously, the two spaces have the same dimension.

We may summarize at this point and recall that every vector **c** that belongs to the orthogonal complement of the row space of **D** yields, through the formula $\mathbf{y} = \mathbf{Yc}$, a solution of the boundary problem (6-2.1) and (6-2.2). Also, every vector $\tilde{\mathbf{a}}$ that belongs to the orthogonal complement of the column space of **D** yields, through $\tilde{\mathbf{z}} = \tilde{\mathbf{a}}\mathbf{W}^{[a]}\mathbf{Y}(a)\mathbf{Y}^{-1}$ a solution of the adjoint problem (6-3.8) and (6-3.9). Thus the matrix **D** that we have called a characteristic matrix of the given problem determines the solution space of both the given problem and its adjoint.

It must be recognized that the adjoint problem (6-3.8) and (6-3.9), when the boundary conditions are expressed in the form of (6-3.10), has a characteristic matrix which we may designate by **B** (see Exercise 8 of Section 6-3). Since problem (6-2.1) and (6-2.2) is the adjoint of the problem (6-3.8) and (6-3.9), an alternative description of the solution spaces of both problems is available through the matrix **B**.

We end this section by noting that the matrix boundary problem

$$\mathbf{Y}' = \mathbf{AY} ,$$

$$\mathbf{W}^{[a]}\mathbf{Y}(a) + \mathbf{W}^{[b]}\mathbf{Y}(b) = \mathbf{0} ,$$

is a generalization of the vector boundary problem (6-2.1) and (6-2.2). We have occasion to refer to solutions of this problem in Section 6-4 and we take the liberty of calling such solutions *matrix solutions of the boundary problem* (6-2.1) and (6-2.2). Similarly, when we refer to a *matrix solution of the adjoint problem* (6-3.8) and (6-3.9), we mean a solution of the problem

$$\mathbf{Z}' = -\mathbf{ZA} ,$$

$$\mathbf{Z}(a) = \mathbf{CW}^{[a]} , \quad \mathbf{Z}(b) = -\mathbf{CW}^{[b]} .$$

Here, the symbol **C** has been used for the parametric matrix because the symbol **A** appears in the differential equation.

Example 1. Consider the boundary problem

$$\mathbf{y}' = \begin{pmatrix} 0 & 1 & 0 \\ 0 & 0 & 1 \\ 0 & 0 & 1 \end{pmatrix} \mathbf{y} \,,$$

$$\begin{pmatrix} 1 & -1 & 0 \\ 0 & 0 & 0 \\ 1 & 0 & -1 \end{pmatrix} \mathbf{y}(0) + \begin{pmatrix} 0 & 0 & 0 \\ 1 & -1 & 0 \\ 0 & 0 & 0 \end{pmatrix} \mathbf{y}(1) = \mathbf{o} \,.$$

A fundamental matrix and its inverse are given by

$$\mathbf{Y}(t) = \begin{pmatrix} 1 & t & e^t \\ 0 & 1 & e^t \\ 0 & 0 & e^t \end{pmatrix}, \quad \mathbf{Y}^{-1}(t) = \begin{pmatrix} 1 & -t & t-1 \\ 0 & 1 & -1 \\ 0 & 0 & e^{-t} \end{pmatrix}.$$

A corresponding characteristic matrix is

$$\mathbf{D} = \begin{pmatrix} 1 & -1 & 0 \\ 0 & 0 & 0 \\ 1 & 0 & -1 \end{pmatrix} \begin{pmatrix} 1 & 0 & 1 \\ 0 & 1 & 1 \\ 0 & 0 & 1 \end{pmatrix} +$$

$$+ \begin{pmatrix} 0 & 0 & 0 \\ 1 & -1 & 0 \\ 0 & 0 & 0 \end{pmatrix} \begin{pmatrix} 1 & 1 & e \\ 0 & 1 & e \\ 0 & 0 & e \end{pmatrix} = \begin{pmatrix} 1 & -1 & 0 \\ 1 & 0 & 0 \\ 1 & 0 & 0 \end{pmatrix}.$$

The rank of $\mathbf{D}$ is 2 and the index of compatibility is $3-2=1$. The vector $\mathbf{d}_3$ is right-orthogonal to $\mathbf{D}$, hence

$$\mathbf{y}(t) = \mathbf{Y}(t)\mathbf{d}_3 = \begin{pmatrix} e^t \\ e^t \\ e^t \end{pmatrix}$$

is a solution, and the space spanned by this vector is the solution space.

The adjoint problem is

$$\tilde{\mathbf{z}}' = -\tilde{\mathbf{z}} \begin{pmatrix} 0 & 1 & 0 \\ 0 & 0 & 1 \\ 0 & 0 & 1 \end{pmatrix},$$

$$\tilde{\mathbf{z}}(0) = \tilde{\mathbf{a}} \begin{pmatrix} 1 & -1 & 0 \\ 0 & 0 & 0 \\ 1 & 0 & -1 \end{pmatrix}, \quad \tilde{\mathbf{z}}(1) = -\tilde{\mathbf{a}} \begin{pmatrix} 0 & 0 & 0 \\ 1 & -1 & 0 \\ 0 & 0 & 0 \end{pmatrix}.$$

The vector $\tilde{\mathbf{a}} = (0, 1, -1)$ is left-orthogonal to $\mathbf{D}$. Hence, [see formula (6-3.13)]

$$\tilde{\mathbf{z}}(t) = (0, 1, -1) \begin{pmatrix} 1 & -1 & 0 \\ 0 & 0 & 0 \\ 1 & 0 & -1 \end{pmatrix} \begin{pmatrix} 1 & 0 & 1 \\ 0 & 1 & 1 \\ 0 & 0 & 1 \end{pmatrix} \begin{pmatrix} 1 & -t & 1-t \\ 0 & 1 & -1 \\ 0 & 0 & e^{-t} \end{pmatrix}$$

$$= (-1, t, 1-t) \,,$$

is a solution of the adjoint problem. Since the index of compatibility is 1, this solution spans the solution space.

It is easily seen by inspection that the row space of

$$\mathbf{Q} = \begin{pmatrix} 0 & 0 & 0 & 0 & 0 & 1 \\ 0 & 0 & 0 & 1 & 1 & 0 \\ 1 & 1 & 1 & 0 & 0 & 0 \end{pmatrix},$$

is the orthogonal complement of the row space of **W**. Hence, we may replace the above adjoint boundary conditions by the equivalent set

$$\begin{pmatrix} 0 & 0 & 0 \\ 0 & 0 & 0 \\ 1 & 1 & 1 \end{pmatrix} \mathbf{z}(0) - \begin{pmatrix} 0 & 0 & 1 \\ 1 & 1 & 0 \\ 0 & 0 & 0 \end{pmatrix} \mathbf{z}(1) = \mathbf{o} .$$

It is easily verified that $\tilde{\mathbf{z}} = (-1, t, 1-t)$ satisfies these conditions.

Exercises

1–5. Write down the adjoint of each boundary problem in Exercises 1–5 of Section 6-2 and determine their solution spaces. In each case check the index of compatibility against the predicted index according to Theorem 6-3.2.

In Exercises 6 and 7 determine the solution spaces of the boundary problems and of their adjoints. Express the adjoint boundary conditions in both parametric and standard form.

6. $\mathbf{y}' = \begin{pmatrix} 0 & 1 \\ -2 & 3 \end{pmatrix} \mathbf{y}$,

$$\begin{pmatrix} 1 & -1 \\ 0 & 0 \end{pmatrix} \mathbf{y}(0) + \begin{pmatrix} 0 & 0 \\ 1 & -1 \end{pmatrix} \mathbf{y}(1) = \mathbf{o} .$$

7. $\mathbf{y}' = \begin{pmatrix} 0 & 1 & 0 \\ 0 & 0 & 1 \\ 0 & -1 & 0 \end{pmatrix} \mathbf{y}$,

$$\begin{pmatrix} 1 & 0 & 0 \\ 0 & 0 & 0 \\ 0 & 1 & 0 \end{pmatrix} \mathbf{y}(0) + \begin{pmatrix} 0 & 0 & 0 \\ 1 & 0 & 0 \\ 0 & 1 & 0 \end{pmatrix} \mathbf{y}(\pi) = \mathbf{o} .$$

8. In view of condition (6-3.10), the matrix

$$\mathbf{B} = \mathbf{Q}^{[a]}\tilde{\mathbf{Y}}^{-1}(a) - \mathbf{Q}^{[b]}\tilde{\mathbf{Y}}^{-1}(b)$$

is a characteristic matrix for the adjoint boundary problem. Find the relationship between the dimensions and ranks of the matrices **B** and **D**.

6-4. THE NONHOMOGENEOUS BOUNDARY PROBLEM AND GREEN'S MATRIX

The solution of a nonhomogeneous boundary problem is not in itself a topic of great significance. We shall see, however, that the solution can be obtained in the form of an integral transform. This transform, characterized by its kernel (Green's matrix), is of considerable significance. Green's matrix and its scalar counterpart, Green's function, play a large role in all subsequent developments of the text.

The boundary problem to be considered is

$$\mathbf{y}' = \mathbf{A}\mathbf{y}+\mathbf{f}\ , \tag{6-4.1}$$

$$\mathbf{W}^{[a]}\mathbf{y}(a)+\mathbf{W}^{[b]}\mathbf{y}(b) = \mathbf{o}\ , \tag{6-4.2}$$

where $\mathbf{W}^{[a]}$ and $\mathbf{W}^{[b]}$ are n by n square matrices. The more general boundary problem where the boundary relation, as well as the equation, is nonhomogeneous can be handled easily when a solution for (6-4.1) and (6-4.2) is known (see Exercise 10). Theorems 3-3.1 and 3-3.2 yield the fact that the vector

$$\mathbf{y}(t) = \mathbf{Y}(t)\int_a^t \mathbf{Y}^{-1}(s)\mathbf{f}(s)\,ds+\mathbf{Y}(t)\mathbf{c} \tag{6-4.3}$$

is a solution of the vector equation (6-4.1) for each $\mathbf{c}$ in $V_n(R)$. Moreover, every solution of that equation can be expressed in this form. Throughout this section, the symbol $\mathbf{Y}$ or $\mathbf{Y}(t)$ represents a specific fundamental matrix for the homogeneous equation $\mathbf{y}' = \mathbf{A}\mathbf{y}$.

Substituting from formula (6-4.3) into (6-4.2), we infer that $\mathbf{y}$ satisfies the boundary condition if $\mathbf{c}$ is chosen so that

$$\mathbf{W}^{[b]}\mathbf{Y}(b)\int_a^b \mathbf{Y}^{-1}(s)\mathbf{f}(s)\,ds+\mathbf{D}\mathbf{c} = \mathbf{o}\ ,$$

where

$$\mathbf{D} = \mathbf{W}^{[a]}\mathbf{Y}(a)+\mathbf{W}^{[b]}\mathbf{Y}(b)\ .$$

Our initial assumption on the dimension of $\mathbf{W}^{[a]}$ and $\mathbf{W}^{[b]}$ insures that $\mathbf{D}$ is a square matrix. At this point, we impose the additional hypothesis that $\mathbf{D}$ is *nonsingular*. Hence,

$$c = -\mathbf{D}^{-1}\mathbf{W}^{[b]}\mathbf{Y}(b)\int_a^b \mathbf{Y}^{-1}(s)\mathbf{f}(s)\,ds\ .$$

Substituting this evaluation of $\mathbf{c}$ into formula (6-4.3), we infer that a unique solution of the boundary problem is

$$\mathbf{y}(t) = \mathbf{Y}(t)\int_a^t \mathbf{Y}^{-1}(s)\mathbf{f}(s)\,ds-\mathbf{Y}(t)\mathbf{D}^{-1}\mathbf{W}^{[b]}\mathbf{Y}(b)\int_a^b \mathbf{Y}^{-1}(s)\mathbf{f}(s)\,ds\ . \tag{6-4.4}$$

In order to get a more convenient representation of the solution, we proceed as follows. Let the first term on the right-hand side of formula (6-4.4) be expressed as the sum of two terms by multiplying the factor $\mathbf{Y}(t)$ on the right by the identity matrix in the form $\mathbf{D}^{-1}(\mathbf{W}^{[a]}\mathbf{Y}(a)+\mathbf{W}^{[b]}\mathbf{Y}(b))$. That is,

$$\begin{aligned}\mathbf{Y}(t)\int_a^t \mathbf{Y}^{-1}(s)\mathbf{f}(s)\,ds &= \mathbf{Y}(t)\mathbf{D}^{-1}\mathbf{W}^{[a]}\mathbf{Y}(a)\int_a^t \mathbf{Y}^{-1}(s)\mathbf{f}(s)\,ds \\ &\quad +\mathbf{Y}(t)\mathbf{D}^{-1}\mathbf{W}^{[b]}\mathbf{Y}(b)\int_a^t \mathbf{Y}^{-1}(s)\mathbf{f}(s)\,ds\ .\end{aligned} \tag{6-4.5}$$

Let the second term on the right-hand side of formula (6-4.4) be expressed as the sum of two terms by separating the interval of integration into the two subintervals $[a, t]$ and $[t, b]$. It is clear that the first of these two terms is the negative of the second term on the right-hand side of (6-4.5). It follows that

$$\mathbf{y}(t) = \mathbf{Y}(t)\mathbf{D}^{-1}\mathbf{W}^{[a]}\mathbf{Y}(a)\int_a^t \mathbf{Y}^{-1}(s)\mathbf{f}(s)\,ds - \mathbf{Y}(t)\mathbf{D}^{-1}\mathbf{W}^{[b]}\mathbf{Y}(b)\int_t^b \mathbf{Y}^{-1}(s)\mathbf{f}(s)\,ds.$$

In this formula, the four factors preceding each integral may be moved inside the integral. Hence, the formula may be rewritten as

$$\mathbf{y}(t) = \int_a^b \mathbf{G}(t, s)\mathbf{f}(s)\,ds\ , \tag{6-4.6}$$

where $\mathbf{G}(t, s)$, the *Green's matrix*, is defined by

$$\mathbf{G}(t, s) = \begin{cases} \mathbf{Y}(t)\mathbf{D}^{-1}\mathbf{W}^{[a]}\mathbf{Y}(a)\mathbf{Y}^{-1}(s)\ , & s < t\ , \\ -\mathbf{Y}(t)\mathbf{D}^{-1}\mathbf{W}^{[b]}\mathbf{Y}(b)\mathbf{Y}^{-1}(s)\ , & s > t\ . \end{cases} \tag{6-4.7}$$

The preceding statements may be summed up by saying that *the nonhomogeneous boundary problem* (6-4.1) *and* (6-4.2), *has a unique solution given by formula* (6-4.6) *provided that the corresponding homogeneous boundary problem is incompatible.*

It should be noted that Green's matrix is independent of the choice of the fundamental matrix $\mathbf{Y}$. For, if that matrix is replaced by $\mathbf{YC}$ in formula (6-4.7) for Green's matrix, $\mathbf{D}^{-1}$ becomes $\mathbf{C}^{-1}\mathbf{D}^{-1}$ and the $\mathbf{C}$'s cancel out, thus leaving formula (6-4.7) unchanged. Similarly, it can be seen that Green's matrix is not altered if the given boundary condition is multiplied on the left by a nonsingular matrix $\mathbf{B}$.

We may look upon formula (6-4.6) as defining an operator $\mathscr{G}$ such that

$$\mathbf{y} = \mathscr{G}\mathbf{f}\ .$$

Because of the linear properties of the definite integral, it is easily inferred that $\mathscr{G}$ is a linear operator. This operator and the differential operator M, where

$$M\mathbf{y} = \mathbf{y}' - \mathbf{A}\mathbf{y}\ ,$$

are inverses of each other in the sense that, if the components of $\mathbf{f}$ belong to $C[a, b]$, then

$$M(\mathscr{G}\mathbf{f}) = \mathbf{f}\ .$$

Moreover, if the components of $\mathbf{y}$ belong to $C^1[a, b]$ and if $\mathbf{y}$ satisfies the condition (6-4.2), then

$$\mathscr{G}(M\mathbf{y}) = \mathbf{y}\ .$$

The fundamental characteristics of Green's matrix are revealed in the following theorems.

Theorem 6-4.1. *Green's matrix has the following properties.*

(i) *The components of* $\mathbf{G}(t, s)$, *regarded as functions of t with s fixed, have continuous first derivatives on* $[a, s)$ *and* $(s, b]$. *At the point* $t = s$, $\mathbf{G}$ *has an upward jump-discontinuity of 'unit' magnitude; that is,*

$$\mathbf{G}(s^+, s) - \mathbf{G}(s^-, s) = \mathbf{I} .$$

(ii) $\mathbf{G}$ *is a formal solution of the homogeneous boundary problem* (6-2.1) *and* (6-2.2). $\mathbf{G}$ *fails to be a true solution only because of the discontinuity at* $t = s$.

(iii) $\mathbf{G}$ *is the only n by n matrix with properties* (i) *and* (ii).

PROOF. The matrix $\mathbf{G}(t, s)$, defined by formula (6-4.7), may be written as

$$\mathbf{G}(t, s) = \begin{cases} \mathbf{Y}(t)\mathbf{H}_+ , & s < t , \\ \mathbf{Y}(t)\mathbf{H}_- , & s > t , \end{cases} \tag{6-4.8}$$

where the matrices $\mathbf{H}_+$ and $\mathbf{H}_-$ are free from t. Therefore, the components of $\mathbf{G}(t, s)$ have continuous first derivatives with respect to t on $[a, s)$ and $(s, b]$. In view of the fact that

$$\mathbf{H}_+ - \mathbf{H}_- = \mathbf{D}^{-1}(\mathbf{W}^{[a]}\mathbf{Y}(a) + \mathbf{W}^{[b]}\mathbf{Y}(b))\mathbf{Y}^{-1}(s) = \mathbf{Y}^{-1}(s) ,$$

it can be inferred that

$$\mathbf{G}(s^+, s) - \mathbf{G}(s^-, s) = \mathbf{Y}(s)\mathbf{Y}^{-1}(s) = \mathbf{I} .$$

This proves part (i) of the theorem.

The representation of $\mathbf{G}(t, s)$ exhibited in formula (6-4.8) reveals that it is a matrix solution of $\mathbf{y}' = \mathbf{A}\mathbf{y}$, except at the point $t = s$. Further,

$$\mathbf{W}^{[a]}\mathbf{G}(a, s) + \mathbf{W}^{[b]}\mathbf{G}(b, s) = \mathbf{W}^{[a]}\mathbf{Y}(a)\mathbf{H}_- + \mathbf{W}^{[b]}\mathbf{Y}(b)\mathbf{H}_+ .$$

Since $\mathbf{W}^{[a]}\mathbf{Y}(a) = \mathbf{D} - \mathbf{W}^{[b]}\mathbf{Y}(b)$, we have

$$\begin{aligned} \mathbf{W}^{[a]}\mathbf{G}(a, s) + \mathbf{W}^{[b]}\mathbf{G}(b, s) &= (\mathbf{D} - \mathbf{W}^{[b]}\mathbf{Y}(b))\mathbf{H}_- + \mathbf{W}^{[b]}\mathbf{Y}(b)\mathbf{H}_+ \\ &= \mathbf{D}\mathbf{H}_- + \mathbf{W}^{[b]}\mathbf{Y}(b)(\mathbf{H}_+ - \mathbf{H}_-) \\ &= \mathbf{D}\mathbf{H}_- + \mathbf{W}^{[b]}\mathbf{Y}(b)\mathbf{Y}^{-1}(s) \\ &= -\mathbf{D}\mathbf{D}^{-1}\mathbf{W}^{[b]}\mathbf{Y}(b)\mathbf{Y}^{-1}(s) + \mathbf{W}^{[b]}\mathbf{Y}(b)\mathbf{Y}^{-1}(s) \\ &= \mathbf{0} . \end{aligned}$$

Thus, $\mathbf{G}(t, s)$ satisfies the boundary condition (6-2.2). This completes the proof of part (ii) of the theorem.

For any specific value of s, let $\mathbf{H}(t, s)$ be a matrix with properties (i) and (ii). The matrix

$$\mathbf{X}(t, s) = \mathbf{H}(t, s) - \mathbf{G}(t, s) \tag{6-4.9}$$

must have a continuous first derivative with respect to t on $[a, s)$ and $(s, b]$. Since the discontinuities of $\mathbf{H}$ and $\mathbf{G}$ cancel each other, it is clear that $\mathbf{X}$ has a removable discontinuity at the point $t = s$. By defining $\mathbf{X}$ appropriately at this point, we insure that it is continuous for all t in $[a, b]$. Since the boundary condition is linear and since $\mathbf{X}$ is a linear combination of $\mathbf{H}$ and $\mathbf{G}$, we must conclude that

$$\mathbf{W}^{[a]}\mathbf{X}(a, s)+\mathbf{W}^{[b]}\mathbf{X}(b, s) = \mathbf{0} \ .$$

This implies that, for each s, $\mathbf{X}$ is a matrix solution of the homogeneous boundary problem (6-2.1) and (6-2.2). Since Green's matrix is defined under the assumption that the boundary problem (6-2.1) and (6-2.2) is incompatible, it follows that $\mathbf{X}$ is the zero matrix. Relation (6-4.9), therefore, implies that

$$\mathbf{H}(t, s) = \mathbf{G}(t, s) \ .$$

Consequently, Green's matrix is unique and is determined by properties (i) and (ii) (see Exercise 11). This completes the proof of the theorem.

In formula (6-4.7), defining Green's matrix, the left-hand factor is a fundamental matrix for equation (6-2.1), and the right-hand factor is a fundamental matrix for the corresponding adjoint equation. There is a strong suggestion, therefore, that the properties of Green's matrix, regarded as a function of s with t fixed, should be examined relative to the adjoint boundary problem.

Theorem 6-4.2. *Green's matrix has the following properties.*

(i) *The components of* $\mathbf{G}(t, s)$, *regarded as functions of s with t fixed, have continuous first derivatives on* $[a, t)$ *and* $(t, b]$. *At the point* $s = t$, $\mathbf{G}$ *has a downward jump-discontinuity of 'unit' magnitude; that is,*

$$\mathbf{G}(t, t^+)-\mathbf{G}(t, t^-) = -\mathbf{I} \ .$$

(ii) $\mathbf{G}$ *is a formal solution of the adjoint boundary problem* (6-3.8) *and* (6-3.9). *It fails to be a true solution because of the discontinuity at* $s = t$.

PROOF. The proof of part (i) is immediate. The continuity of the first derivative of each component of $\mathbf{G}$ follows from the continuity of the first derivatives of the components of $\mathbf{Y}^{-1}(s)$. The nature of the discontinuity of $\mathbf{G}$ at $s = t$ is easily inferred from the nature of the discontinuity described in Theorem 6-4.1.

If $\mathbf{G}$ is written as

$$\mathbf{G}(t, s) = \begin{cases} \mathbf{K}_-\mathbf{Y}^{-1}(s) \ , & s < t \ , \\ \mathbf{K}_+\mathbf{Y}^{-1}(s) \ , & s > t \ , \end{cases}$$

then it is obvious that it is a matrix solution of $\tilde{\mathbf{z}}' = -\tilde{\mathbf{z}}\mathbf{A}$, for all values of s in $[a, b]$ *except* $s = t$. By substituting $s = a$ and $s = b$ in formula (6-4.7), we obtain the two relations

$$\mathbf{G}(t, a) = \mathbf{Y}(t)\mathbf{D}^{-1}\mathbf{W}^{[a]} \ ,$$

$$\mathbf{G}(t, b) = -\mathbf{Y}(t)\mathbf{D}^{-1}\mathbf{W}^{[b]} \ .$$

Thus, **G** satisfies the boundary relations (6-3.9) with $\mathbf{Y}(t)\mathbf{D}^{-1}$ as the parametric matrix. This completes the demonstration of the fact that **G** is a formal solution of the adjoint boundary problem (6-3.8) and (6-3.9). As before, **G** fails to be a true solution because of its jump-discontinuity.

The nonhomogeneous boundary problem corresponding to the homogeneous adjoint problem (6-3.8) and (6-3.9) is

(6-4.10) $$\tilde{\mathbf{z}}' = -\tilde{\mathbf{z}}\mathbf{A}+\tilde{\mathbf{f}} ,$$

(6-4.11) $$\begin{cases} \tilde{\mathbf{z}}(a) = \tilde{\mathbf{a}}\mathbf{W}^{[a]} , \\ \tilde{\mathbf{z}}(b) = -\tilde{\mathbf{a}}\mathbf{W}^{[b]} . \end{cases}$$

The following theorem shows that $-\mathbf{G}$ serves as a kernel for an integral transform solution of this problem.

Theorem 6-4.3. *The vector*

(6-4.12) $$\tilde{\mathbf{z}}(s) = -\int_a^b \tilde{\mathbf{f}}(t)\mathbf{G}(t, s)\, dt ,$$

is a solution of the nonhomogeneous boundary problem (6-4.10) *and* (6-4.11), *if the corresponding homogeneous problem is incompatible.*

PROOF. The incompatibility of the homogeneous problem insures the existence of Green's matrix. If relation (6-4.12) is written as

$$\tilde{\mathbf{z}}(s) = -\int_a^s \tilde{\mathbf{f}}(t)\mathbf{G}(t, s)\, dt - \int_s^b \tilde{\mathbf{f}}(t)\mathbf{G}(t, s)\, dt ,$$

then the integrand of each integral has a continuous derivative with respect to t over its interval of integration. Hence, using $\mathbf{G}_s(t, s)$ to represent $\partial G(t, s)/\partial s$, we have

$$\begin{aligned}\tilde{\mathbf{z}}'(s) &= -\tilde{\mathbf{f}}(s)\mathbf{G}(s^-, s) - \int_a^s \tilde{\mathbf{f}}(t)\mathbf{G}_s(t, s)\, dt + \tilde{\mathbf{f}}(s)\mathbf{G}(s^+, s) - \int_s^b \tilde{\mathbf{f}}(t)\mathbf{G}_s(t, s)\, dt \\ &= \tilde{\mathbf{f}}(s)(\mathbf{G}(s^+, s) - \mathbf{G}(s^-, s)) - \int_a^b \tilde{\mathbf{f}}(t)\mathbf{G}_s(t, s)\, dt .\end{aligned}$$

Because of the unit discontinuity of **G** at $t = s$, the first term on the right-hand side of the above relation reduces to $\tilde{\mathbf{f}}(s)$. Since **G**, regarded as a function of s, is a formal solution of $\tilde{\mathbf{z}}' = -\tilde{\mathbf{z}}\mathbf{A}$, we may replace $\mathbf{G}_s(t, s)$ in the second term by $-\mathbf{G}(t, s)\mathbf{A}(s)$. Hence,

$$\begin{aligned}\tilde{\mathbf{z}}'(s) &= \tilde{\mathbf{f}}(s) + \int_a^b \tilde{\mathbf{f}}(t)\mathbf{G}(t, s)\mathbf{A}(s)\, dt \\ &= -\tilde{\mathbf{z}}(s)\mathbf{A}(s) + \tilde{\mathbf{f}}(s) .\end{aligned}$$

This proves that $\tilde{\mathbf{z}}$ satisfies equation (6-4.10).

The values of $\tilde{\mathbf{z}}$ at a and at b are given by

$$\tilde{\mathbf{z}}(a) = -\int_a^b \tilde{\mathbf{f}}(t)\mathbf{Y}(t)\mathbf{D}^{-1}\mathbf{W}^{[a]}\mathbf{Y}(a)\mathbf{Y}^{-1}(a)\,dt \ ,$$

$$\tilde{\mathbf{z}}(b) = \int_a^b \tilde{\mathbf{f}}(t)\mathbf{Y}(t)\mathbf{D}^{-1}\mathbf{W}^{[b]}\mathbf{Y}(b)\mathbf{Y}^{-1}(b)\,dt \ .$$

It follows that

$$\tilde{\mathbf{z}}(a) = \tilde{\mathbf{a}}\mathbf{W}^{[a]} \ ,$$

$$\tilde{\mathbf{z}}(b) = -\tilde{\mathbf{a}}\mathbf{W}^{[b]} \ ,$$

where the parametric vector $\tilde{\mathbf{a}}$ has the value

$$\tilde{\mathbf{a}} = -\int_a^b \tilde{\mathbf{f}}(t)\mathbf{Y}(t)\mathbf{D}^{-1}\,dt \ .$$

This completes the proof of the theorem.

A special case arises when one of the coefficient matrices in the boundary condition (6-4.2) is zero. Consider, for example, the case where $\mathbf{W}^{[b]} = \mathbf{0}$. This, effectively, reduces the two-point boundary problem to an initial-value problem. Green's matrix for this problem is

$$\mathbf{G}(t, s) = \begin{cases} \mathbf{Y}(t)\mathbf{D}^{-1}\mathbf{W}^{[a]}\mathbf{Y}(a)\mathbf{Y}^{-1}(s) \ , & s < t \ , \\ \mathbf{0} \ , & s > t \ . \end{cases}$$

Formula (6-4.6) can then be reduced to

$$\mathbf{y}(t) = \int_a^t \mathbf{G}(t, s)\mathbf{f}(s)\,ds \ .$$

It is appropriate to call this Green's matrix the Green's matrix for the initial-value problem (or a one-sided Green's matrix[2]).

Finally, it should be noted that Green's matrix is completely determined by a given incompatible homogeneous boundary problem. It is also a formal solution of this boundary problem. For these reasons it is common practice to refer to the Green's matrix for the homogeneous boundary problem.

Example 1. Find Green's matrix for the boundary problem

$$\mathbf{y}' = \begin{pmatrix} 0 & 1 \\ 0 & 0 \end{pmatrix} \mathbf{y} \ ,$$

$$\begin{pmatrix} 1 & 0 \\ 0 & 0 \end{pmatrix} \mathbf{y}(0) + \begin{pmatrix} 0 & 0 \\ 1 & 0 \end{pmatrix} \mathbf{y}(1) = \mathbf{o} \ .$$

---

[2]Terminology of Miller [35], Chapter III.

For this problem, a fundamental matrix **Y**, its inverse, and the corresponding characteristic matrix **D** are given by

$$\mathbf{Y}(t)=\begin{pmatrix}1 & t\\ 0 & 1\end{pmatrix},\quad \mathbf{Y}^{-1}(t)=\begin{pmatrix}1 & -t\\ 0 & 1\end{pmatrix},\quad \mathbf{D}=\begin{pmatrix}1 & 0\\ 1 & 1\end{pmatrix}.$$

Hence, substituting into formula (6-4.7), we have

$$\mathbf{G}(t,s)=\begin{cases}\begin{pmatrix}1 & t\\ 0 & 1\end{pmatrix}\begin{pmatrix}1 & 0\\ -1 & 1\end{pmatrix}\begin{pmatrix}1 & 0\\ 0 & 0\end{pmatrix}\begin{pmatrix}1 & 0\\ 0 & 1\end{pmatrix}\begin{pmatrix}1 & -s\\ 0 & 1\end{pmatrix}, & s<t\\ -\begin{pmatrix}1 & t\\ 0 & 1\end{pmatrix}\begin{pmatrix}1 & 0\\ -1 & 1\end{pmatrix}\begin{pmatrix}0 & 0\\ 1 & 0\end{pmatrix}\begin{pmatrix}1 & 1\\ 0 & 1\end{pmatrix}\begin{pmatrix}1 & -s\\ 0 & 1\end{pmatrix}, & s>t\end{cases}$$

$$=\begin{cases}\begin{pmatrix}(1-t) & -s(1-t)\\ -1 & s\end{pmatrix}, & s<t\\ -\begin{pmatrix}t & t(1-s)\\ 1 & (1-s)\end{pmatrix}, & s>t\,.\end{cases}$$

It may be verified by inspection that **G** satisfies the given boundary conditions and that

$$\mathbf{G}(s^+,s)-\mathbf{G}(s^-,s)=\mathbf{I}\,.$$

It is instructive to use this Green's matrix to find the solution of the following nonhomogeneous boundary problem:

$$\mathbf{y}'=\begin{pmatrix}0 & 1\\ 0 & 0\end{pmatrix}\mathbf{y}+\begin{pmatrix}t\\ 1\end{pmatrix},$$

$$\begin{pmatrix}1 & 0\\ 0 & 0\end{pmatrix}\mathbf{y}(0)+\begin{pmatrix}0 & 0\\ 1 & 0\end{pmatrix}\mathbf{y}(1)=\mathbf{o}\,.$$

Substituting into formula (6-4.6), we have

$$\mathbf{y}(t)=\int_0^t\begin{pmatrix}(1-t) & -s(1-t)\\ -1 & s\end{pmatrix}\begin{pmatrix}s\\ 1\end{pmatrix}ds+\int_t^1-\begin{pmatrix}t & t(1-s)\\ 1 & (1-s)\end{pmatrix}\begin{pmatrix}s\\ 1\end{pmatrix}ds$$

$$=\int_0^t\begin{pmatrix}0\\ 0\end{pmatrix}ds-\int_t^1\begin{pmatrix}t\\ 1\end{pmatrix}ds=\begin{pmatrix}t^2-t\\ t-1\end{pmatrix}.$$

It is easily verified that this is a solution of the given problem.

Exercises

Find Green's matrix for each of the following homogeneous boundary problems.

1. $\mathbf{y}'=\begin{pmatrix}0 & 1\\ 0 & 0\end{pmatrix}\mathbf{y}\,,$

$$\begin{pmatrix}1 & 0\\ 0 & 0\end{pmatrix}\mathbf{y}(0)+\begin{pmatrix}0 & 0\\ 0 & 1\end{pmatrix}\mathbf{y}(1)=\mathbf{o}\,.$$

2. $\mathbf{y}' = \begin{pmatrix} 0 & 1 \\ 0 & 0 \end{pmatrix} \mathbf{y}\,,$

$$\begin{pmatrix} 1 & -1 \\ 0 & 0 \end{pmatrix} \mathbf{y}(0) + \begin{pmatrix} 0 & 0 \\ 1 & 1 \end{pmatrix} \mathbf{y}(1) = \mathbf{o}\,.$$

3. $\mathbf{y}' = \begin{pmatrix} 0 & 1 \\ -1 & 0 \end{pmatrix} \mathbf{y}\,,$

$$\begin{pmatrix} 1 & 0 \\ 0 & 0 \end{pmatrix} \mathbf{y}(0) + \begin{pmatrix} 0 & 0 \\ 0 & 1 \end{pmatrix} \mathbf{y}(\pi) = \mathbf{o}\,.$$

4. $\mathbf{y}' = \begin{pmatrix} 0 & 1 \\ -2 & 3 \end{pmatrix} \mathbf{y}\,,$

$$\begin{pmatrix} 1 & 0 \\ 0 & 0 \end{pmatrix} \mathbf{y}(0) + \begin{pmatrix} 0 & 0 \\ -e^{-2} & e^{-2} \end{pmatrix} \mathbf{y}(1) = \mathbf{o}\,.$$

5. $\mathbf{y}' = \begin{pmatrix} 0 & 1 & 0 \\ 0 & 0 & 1 \\ 0 & 0 & 0 \end{pmatrix} \mathbf{y}\,,$

$$\begin{pmatrix} 0 & -1 & 0 \\ 1 & 0 & 0 \\ 0 & 0 & 1 \end{pmatrix} \mathbf{y}(0) + \begin{pmatrix} 1 & 0 & 0 \\ 0 & 0 & 0 \\ 0 & -1 & 0 \end{pmatrix} \mathbf{y}(1) = \mathbf{o}\,.$$

Solve the following nonhomogeneous boundary problems by using the Green's matrices determined in the preceding exercises.

6. $\mathbf{y}' = \begin{pmatrix} 0 & 1 \\ 0 & 0 \end{pmatrix} \mathbf{y} + \begin{pmatrix} 0 \\ 2 \end{pmatrix},$

$$\begin{pmatrix} 1 & 0 \\ 0 & 0 \end{pmatrix} \mathbf{y}(0) + \begin{pmatrix} 0 & 0 \\ 0 & 1 \end{pmatrix} \mathbf{y}(1) = \mathbf{o}\,.$$

7. $\mathbf{y}' = \begin{pmatrix} 0 & 1 \\ 0 & 0 \end{pmatrix} \mathbf{y}(0) + \begin{pmatrix} 0 \\ 2 \end{pmatrix},$

$$\begin{pmatrix} 1 & -1 \\ 0 & 0 \end{pmatrix} \mathbf{y}(0) + \begin{pmatrix} 0 & 0 \\ 1 & 1 \end{pmatrix} \mathbf{y}(1) = \mathbf{o}\,.$$

8. $\mathbf{y}' = \begin{pmatrix} 0 & 1 \\ -1 & 0 \end{pmatrix} \mathbf{y} + \begin{pmatrix} 0 \\ \sin t + \cos t \end{pmatrix},$

$$\begin{pmatrix} 1 & 0 \\ 0 & 0 \end{pmatrix} \mathbf{y}(0) + \begin{pmatrix} 0 & 0 \\ 0 & 1 \end{pmatrix} \mathbf{y}(\pi) = \mathbf{o}\,.$$

9. In view of condition (6-3.10), the matrix

$$\mathbf{B} = \mathbf{Q}^{[a]}\tilde{\mathbf{Y}}^{-1}(a) - \mathbf{Q}^{[b]}\tilde{\mathbf{Y}}^{-1}(b)$$

is the characteristic matrix for the adjoint boundary problem. Find the relationship between the dimensions and ranks of the matrices **B** and **D**.

10. Find a formula involving Green's matrix for the solution of the nonhomogeneous problem

$$\mathbf{y}' = \mathbf{A}\mathbf{y}+\mathbf{f} \ ,$$
$$\mathbf{W}^{[a]}\mathbf{y}(a)+\mathbf{W}^{[b]}\mathbf{y}(b) = \mathbf{b} \ .$$

Assume that the corresponding homogeneous problem is incompatible.

11. Derive the formula for Green's matrix from properties (i) and (ii) of Theorem 6-4.1.

6-5. THE *n*th-ORDER BOUNDARY PROBLEM

The boundary problem associated with an *n*th-order equation has played a significant role in the development of the theory of differential equations. This boundary problem is easily reduced to a vector boundary problem. Consequently, the results of the first four sections of this chapter could be used to establish many facts that we intend to develop below. Instead of following this procedure, we give the *n*th-order problem an independent treatment. The importance of the problem justifies this approach. We note, moreover, that the extra effort involved in providing this independent treatment is negligible. For, by following the pattern established in the treatment of the vector problem, we can obtain the corresponding results for the scalar problem with ease.

The linear operator L is defined, as in Section 3-7, by

$$Lu = \sum_{j=0}^{n} p_j u^{[n-j]} \ ,$$

where

$$p_j \in C^{[n-j]}[a, b] \ , \quad \text{and} \quad p_0(t) \neq 0 \text{ on } [a, b] \ .$$

The auxiliary conditions to be applied to $Lu = 0$ are

$$\text{(6-5.1)} \qquad \sum_{j=1}^{n} (w_{ij}^{[a]} u^{[j-1]}(a) + w_{ij}^{[b]} u^{[j-1]}(b)) = 0 \ , \quad i = 1, 2, \ldots, m \ .$$

Using matrix notation for the auxiliary conditions, we can write the boundary problem as

$$\text{(6-5.2)} \qquad Lu = 0 \ ,$$

$$\text{(6-5.3)} \qquad \mathbf{W}^{[a]}\mathbf{k}(u(a)) + \mathbf{W}^{[b]}\mathbf{k}(u(b)) = \mathbf{o} \ .$$

We assume that the m by $2n$ matrix

$$\mathbf{W} = (\mathbf{W}^{[a]}\,\mathbf{W}^{[b]})$$

has rank m. This is equivalent to assuming that the m conditions (6-5.1) are linearly independent.

If we impose the restriction that

$$p_0 = 1$$

and if the matrix $\mathbf{A}$ is defined by formula (3-4.8), then the vector boundary problem

(6-5.4) $$\mathbf{y}' = \mathbf{A}\mathbf{y} \ ,$$

(6-5.5) $$\mathbf{W}^{[a]}\mathbf{y}(a) + \mathbf{W}^{[b]}\mathbf{y}(b) = \mathbf{o} \ ,$$

is the *companion boundary problem* of the boundary problem (6-5.2) and (6-5.3). It should be obvious that the first component of any solution of (6-5.4) and (6-5.5) is a solution of (6-5.2) and (6-5.3), and the Wronskian vector of any solution of (6-5.2) and (6-5.3) is a solution of (6-5.4) and (6-5.5). Specific mention of the relationship between these two problems is made from time to time, but it is instructive to the reader to keep the correspondence in mind at all times.

The space $C^n[a, b]$ contains potential solutions of the boundary problem (6-5.2) and (6-5.3). Here, as in Section 6-1, we define a mapping B of this space into $V_{2n}(R)$ by

$$B(u) = \begin{pmatrix} \mathbf{k}(u(a)) \\ \mathbf{k}(u(b)) \end{pmatrix} .$$

The vector on the right-hand side of this relation (or its transpose) is the *boundary vector* of the function u. If the condition (6-5.3) is written as

$$(\mathbf{W}^{[a]}\,\mathbf{W}^{[b]}) \begin{pmatrix} \mathbf{k}(u(a)) \\ \mathbf{k}(u(b)) \end{pmatrix} = \mathbf{o} \ ,$$

it may be inferred that this restricts the boundary vector of u to a subspace of $V_{2n}(R)$. It follows as in Theorem 6-1.1, therefore, that the condition (6-5.3) restricts u to a subspace of $C^n[a, b]$. Hence the solutions of the boundary problem (6-5.2) and (6-5.3) form a vector space.

If $\mathbf{u}$ is any fundamental vector for Equation (6-5.2), we say that the matrix

$$\mathbf{D} = \mathbf{W}^{[a]}\mathbf{K}(\mathbf{u}(a)) + \mathbf{W}^{[b]}\mathbf{K}(\mathbf{u}(b)) \ ,$$

is a *characteristic matrix* for the boundary problem. (It is also a characteristic matrix for the companion boundary problem (6-5.4) and (6-5.5) if $p_0 = 1$.) It is easily inferred that all the characteristic matrices have the same rank.

Theorem 6-5.1. *If the boundary problem* (6-5.2) *and* (6-5.3) *has a characteristic matrix of rank r, then its index of compatibility is* $n-r$.

PROOF. If $\mathbf{u}$ is a fundamental vector for equation (6-5.2), every solution of that equation has the form

$$u = \tilde{\mathbf{u}}\mathbf{c} \ .$$

We recall that

$$\mathbf{k}(u) = \mathbf{K}(\mathbf{u})\mathbf{c} \ .$$

Hence u satisfies relation (6-5.3) if and only if

$$[\mathbf{W}^{[a]}\mathbf{K}(\mathbf{u}(a)) + \mathbf{W}^{[b]}\mathbf{K}(\mathbf{u}(b))]\mathbf{c} = \mathbf{o} \ ,$$

or if and only if

(6-5.6) $$\mathbf{D}\mathbf{c} = \mathbf{o} \ .$$

If the rank of $\mathbf{D}$ is r, then equation (6-5.6) has precisely $n-r$ linearly independent solutions, and these determine precisely $n-r$ linearly independent solutions of the boundary problem. This proves the theorem.

Exercises

Find the index of compatibility and the solution space of each of the following boundary problems and compare the results with those for Exercises 2–5 of Section 6-2.

1. $u'' = 0$,
$u(0) = 0$, $u(1) = 0$.

2. $u''' = 0$,
$-u'(0)+u(1) = 0$, $u(0) = 0$, $u''(0)-u'(1) = 0$.

3. $u''' = 0$,
$u(0) = 0$, $u(1)-u'(1) = 0$.

4. $u''+4u = 0$,
$u(0) = 0$, $u(\pi) = 0$.

Find the index of compatibility and the solution space of each of the following boundary problems.

5. $u''' = 0$,
$u(0) = 0$, $u(1) = 0$, $u'(0)+u'(1) = 0$.

6. $u''' = 0$,
$u(0) = 0$, $u'(1) = 0$, $u'(0)-2u(1) = 0$.

7. $u''-3u'+2u = 0$,
$u(0)-u(1) = 0$, $u'(0)-u'(1) = 0$.

Find the values of the parameter λ for which the following boundary problems are compatible.

8. $u''+\lambda^2 u = 0$,
$u(0) = 0$, $u(\pi) = 0$.

9. $u''+\lambda^2 u = 0$,
$u'(0) = 0$, $u'(\pi) = 0$.

10. $u''+\lambda^2 u = 0$,
$u(0)+u'(0) = 0$, $u(1) = 0$.

6-6. THE *n*th-ORDER ADJOINT BOUNDARY PROBLEM

Definition 6-6.1. *The inner product of two functions u and v in $C^n[a, b]$ is defined by*

$$(u, v) = \int_a^b u(t)v(t)\,dt \ .$$

Green's formula is obtained by integrating the Lagrange identity [relation (3-7.3)]. By using the inner product notation, we may write Green's formula as

$$(6\text{-}6.1)\quad (Lu, v)-(u, L^*v) = \tilde{\mathbf{k}}(v(b))\mathbf{P}(b)\mathbf{k}(u(b))-\tilde{\mathbf{k}}(v(a))\mathbf{P}(a)\mathbf{k}(u(a)) \ .$$

As in Section 6-3, we attempt to impose a condition on the boundary vector of v so that, when that condition and the condition (6-5.3) are both satisfied, the right-hand side of Green's formula is zero. The stipulation of a zero value for the right-hand side of Green's formula may be written as

$$(6\text{-}6.2)\quad (\tilde{\mathbf{k}}(v(a))\ \tilde{\mathbf{k}}(v(b)))\begin{pmatrix} \mathbf{P}(a) & \mathbf{0} \\ \mathbf{0} & -\mathbf{P}(b) \end{pmatrix}\begin{pmatrix} \mathbf{k}(u(a)) \\ \mathbf{k}(u(b)) \end{pmatrix} = 0 \ .$$

Since the condition (6-5.3) requires that the boundary vector of u should be orthogonal to the row space of the matrix $(\mathbf{W}^{[a]}\mathbf{W}^{[b]})$, the relation (6-6.2) is satisfied if we impose on v the condition that the vector

$$(\tilde{\mathbf{k}}(v(a))\ \tilde{\mathbf{k}}(v(b)))\begin{pmatrix} \mathbf{P}(a) & \mathbf{0} \\ \mathbf{0} & -\mathbf{P}(b) \end{pmatrix}$$

belong to the row space of $(\mathbf{W}^{[a]}\mathbf{W}^{[b]})$. This condition is expressed by

$$(6\text{-}6.3)\quad (\tilde{\mathbf{k}}(v(a))\ \tilde{\mathbf{k}}(v(b)))\begin{pmatrix} \mathbf{P}(a) & \mathbf{0} \\ \mathbf{0} & -\mathbf{P}(b) \end{pmatrix} = \tilde{\mathbf{a}}(\mathbf{W}^{[a]}\mathbf{W}^{[b]}) \ ,$$

where the vector $\tilde{\mathbf{a}}$ is any vector in $V_m(R)$. The conditions (6-6.3), which may also be written in the form of (6-6.5) below, are the *adjoint boundary conditions.* The boundary problem

$$(6\text{-}6.4)\quad L^*v = 0 \ ,$$

$$(6\text{-}6.5)\quad \begin{cases} \tilde{\mathbf{k}}(v(a))\mathbf{P}(a) = \tilde{\mathbf{a}}\mathbf{W}^{[a]} \ , \\ \tilde{\mathbf{k}}(v(b))\mathbf{P}(b) = -\tilde{\mathbf{a}}\mathbf{W}^{[b]} \ , \end{cases}$$

is, therefore, the *adjoint of the boundary problem* (6-5.2) and (6-5.3).

A function v in $C^n[a, b]$ is a solution of problem (6-6.4) and (6-6.5), if it satisfies equation (6-6.4) and if, for some vector $\tilde{\mathbf{a}}$, it satisfies the two conditions (6-6.5). It is clear that a solution always exists in conjunction with a unique parametric vector $\tilde{\mathbf{a}}$. The nature of the one-to-one correspondence between a solution v and its parametric vector $\tilde{\mathbf{a}}$ is revealed by noting that v is a solution of the initial-value problem

$$L^*(v) = 0 \ ,$$
$$\tilde{\mathbf{k}}(v(a)) = \tilde{\mathbf{a}}\mathbf{W}^{[a]}\mathbf{P}^{-1}(a) \ .$$

It is readily verified that the solutions of the problem (6-6.4) and (6-6.5) form a vector space. For, if v_1 and v_2 are two solutions of the problem, the function $\alpha_1 v_1+\alpha_2 v_2$ satisfies the equation (6-6.4). Moreover, if $\tilde{\mathbf{a}}_1$ and $\tilde{\mathbf{a}}_2$ are the parametric vectors associated with v_1 and v_2, respectively, then

$$\mathbf{k}(\alpha_1 v_1(a) + \alpha_2 v_2(a))\mathbf{P}(a) = (\alpha_1 \mathbf{a}_1 + \alpha_2 \mathbf{a}_2)\mathbf{W}^{[a]} ,$$

$$\mathbf{k}(\alpha_1 v_1(b) + \alpha_2 v_2(b))\mathbf{P}(b) = -(\alpha_1 \mathbf{a}_1 + \alpha_2 \mathbf{a}_2)\mathbf{W}^{[b]} .$$

Hence, $\alpha_1 v_1 + \alpha_2 v_2$ satisfies the boundary conditions (6-6.5) with $\alpha_1 \tilde{\mathbf{a}}_1 + \alpha_2 \tilde{\mathbf{a}}_2$ as the parametric vector.

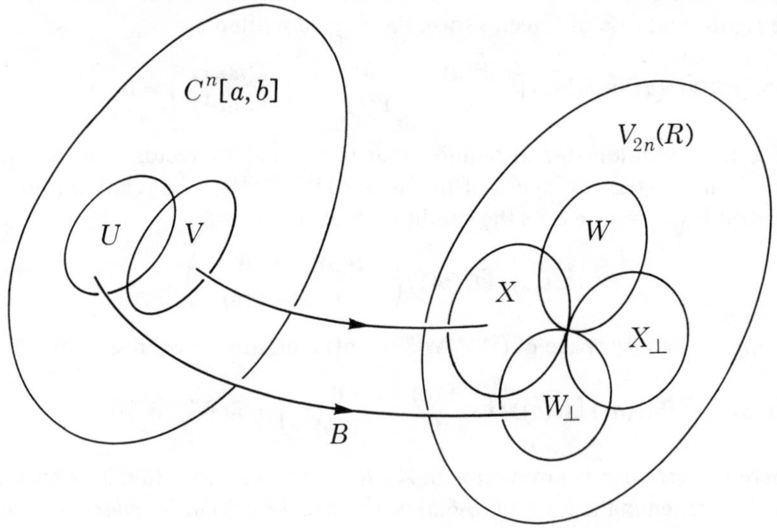

Figure 6-6.1

Figure 6-6.1 may provide some additional insight into the nature of the relationship between condition (6-5.3) and its adjoint condition (6-6.5). Let W represent the row space of the matrix $\mathbf{W}$, and let $W_\perp$ be the orthogonal complement of W. Let X represent the row space of the matrix

$$\mathbf{W}\begin{pmatrix} \mathbf{P}^{-1}(a) & \mathbf{0} \\ \mathbf{0} & -\mathbf{P}^{-1}(b) \end{pmatrix},$$

and let $X_\perp$ represent the orthogonal complement of X. Let a subspace U of $C^n[a, b]$ be defined by

$$B(U) = W_\perp .$$

That is, U contains those functions whose boundary vectors are in $W_\perp$. It follows that U contains the functions which satisfy Equation (6-5.3). Let a subspace V of $C^n[a, b]$ be defined by

$$B(V) = X .$$

Since relation (6-6.3) can be written as

$$(6\text{-}6.6)\qquad (\tilde{\mathbf{k}}(v(a))\;\tilde{\mathbf{k}}(v(b))) = \tilde{\mathbf{a}}\mathbf{W}\begin{pmatrix} \mathbf{P}^{-1}(a) & \mathbf{0} \\ \mathbf{0} & -\mathbf{P}^{-1}(b) \end{pmatrix},$$

we infer that V contains those functions whose boundary vectors are in X and which, therefore, satisfy condition (6-6.5).

Let $\mathbf{Q}$ be any matrix whose rows, considered as vectors, form a basis for the subspace $X_\perp$, and let $\mathbf{Q}$ be written in the partitioned form

$$\mathbf{Q} = (\mathbf{Q}^{[a]}\;\mathbf{Q}^{[b]}) ,$$

where each of $\mathbf{Q}^{[a]}$ and $\mathbf{Q}^{[b]}$ is a $(2n-m)$ by n submatrix. Since a function v is in V if and only if its boundary vector is orthogonal to every element of $X_\perp$, it is clear that V is defined by

$$(\mathbf{Q}^{[a]}\;\mathbf{Q}^{[b]})\begin{pmatrix} \mathbf{k}(v(a)) \\ \mathbf{k}(v(b)) \end{pmatrix} = \mathbf{o} ,$$

or by its equivalent

$$(6\text{-}6.7)\qquad \mathbf{Q}^{[a]}\mathbf{k}(v(a)) + \mathbf{Q}^{[b]}\mathbf{k}(v(b)) = \mathbf{o} .$$

It may be noted that

$$(6\text{-}6.8)\qquad \mathbf{W}\begin{pmatrix} \mathbf{P}^{-1}(a) & \mathbf{0} \\ \mathbf{0} & -\mathbf{P}^{-1}(b) \end{pmatrix}\tilde{\mathbf{Q}} = \mathbf{0}$$

follows directly from the definition of $\mathbf{Q}$. Hence, the multiplication of relation (6-6.6) on the right by $\tilde{\mathbf{Q}}$ eliminates the parametric vector $\tilde{\mathbf{a}}$ and yields relation (6-6.7).

Note, also, that if $\mathbf{C}$ is any nonsingular $(2n-m)$ by $(2n-m)$ matrix, the replacement of $\mathbf{Q}$ by $\mathbf{CQ}$ merely effects a change of basis for the subspace $X_\perp$. It also replaces relation (6-6.7) by the equivalent condition

$$\mathbf{C}[\mathbf{Q}^{[a]}\mathbf{k}(v(a)) + \mathbf{Q}^{[b]}\mathbf{k}(v(b))] = \mathbf{o} .$$

In the classical derivation of an adjoint boundary condition, the above result is achieved through the so-called boundary-form formula.[3] The use of orthogonal complements $W_\perp$ and $X_\perp$ rather than simple complements of W and X dispenses with the need for the boundary-form formula here.

Theorem 6-6.1.[4] *The boundary condition* (6-6.7) *is the adjoint of condition* (6-5.3) *if and only if the matrix* $\mathbf{Q}$ *satisfies relation* (6-6.8).

PROOF. The proof has already been given. It consists of observing that the rows of $\mathbf{Q}$ form a basis for $X_\perp$ if and only if they are $2n-m$ in number, linearly independent, and orthogonal to the basis vectors of X.

[3] Coddington and Levinson [11], pages 286–288.
[4] This result is equivalent to Theorem 3.1 in Coddington and Levinson [11], page 289.

Corollary 6-6.1. *If $m = n$, the boundary condition* (6-5.3) *is self-adjoint if and only if*

$$\mathbf{W}\begin{pmatrix} \mathbf{P}^{-1}(a) & \mathbf{0} \\ \mathbf{0} & -\mathbf{P}^{-1}(b) \end{pmatrix}\tilde{\mathbf{W}} = \mathbf{0} .$$

The condition for self-adjointness may also be written as

$$\mathbf{W}^{[a]}\mathbf{P}^{-1}(a)\tilde{\mathbf{W}}^{[a]} = \mathbf{W}^{[b]}\mathbf{P}^{-1}(b)\tilde{\mathbf{W}}^{[b]} .$$

The following theorem develops a formula for the solution of the adjoint boundary problem. It also suggests that the compatibility index of the adjoint problem is determined by the rank of the characteristic matrix of the given problem. This fact is proved in Theorem 6-6.3.

Theorem 6-6.2. *The adjoint problem* (6-6.4) *and* (6-6.5) *is compatible if and only if the rows of the characteristic matrix* **D** *are linearly dependent.*

PROOF. Let **u** and **v** be fundamental vectors for equations (6-5.2) and (6-6.4), respectively, chosen (see Corollary 3-7.3) so that

$$\tilde{\mathbf{K}}(\mathbf{v})\mathbf{P}\mathbf{K}(\mathbf{u}) = \mathbf{I} . \tag{6-6.9}$$

Every solution of $L^*v = 0$ has the form

$$v = \tilde{\mathbf{v}}\mathbf{c} = \tilde{\mathbf{c}}\mathbf{v} . \tag{6-6.10}$$

Since $\mathbf{k}(v) = \mathbf{K}(\mathbf{v})\mathbf{c}$, this solution satisfies the boundary condition (6-6.5) if and only if

$$\begin{aligned} \tilde{\mathbf{c}}\tilde{\mathbf{K}}(\mathbf{v}(a))\mathbf{P}(a) &= \tilde{\mathbf{a}}\mathbf{W}^{[a]} , \\ \tilde{\mathbf{c}}\tilde{\mathbf{K}}(\mathbf{v}(b))\mathbf{P}(b) &= -\tilde{\mathbf{a}}\mathbf{W}^{[b]} . \end{aligned} \tag{6-6.11}$$

Multiplying the first of these relations on the right by $\mathbf{K}(\mathbf{u}(a))$ and the second by $\mathbf{K}(\mathbf{u}(b))$ and subtracting, and referring to (6-6.9) we get

$$\tilde{\mathbf{0}} = \tilde{\mathbf{a}}\mathbf{D} ,$$

where **D** is the characteristic matrix. Thus, problem (6-6.4) and (6-6.5) has a nontrivial solution only if the rows of **D** are linearly dependent.

Conversely, if the rows of **D** are linearly dependent, a nonzero vector $\tilde{\mathbf{a}}$ exists that is orthogonal to **D** on the left. This vector, through the first of the relations (6-6.11), provides a determination of $\tilde{\mathbf{c}}$ that, when substituted into (6-6.10), yields the solution

$$v = \tilde{\mathbf{a}}\mathbf{W}^{[a]}\mathbf{K}(\mathbf{u}(a))\mathbf{v} . \tag{6-6.12}$$

An alternative formula for the same solution is obtained by using the second of the relations (6-6.11) for the determination of $\tilde{\mathbf{c}}$. It is

$$v = -\tilde{\mathbf{a}}\mathbf{W}^{[b]}\mathbf{K}(\mathbf{u}(b))\mathbf{v} . \tag{6-6.13}$$

The solution v, defined above, is not the zero solution. For, if we suppose $v = 0$, we must infer that $\mathbf{k}(v) = \mathbf{o}$. Because of the boundary condition, this implies that

$$\tilde{\mathbf{o}} = \tilde{\mathbf{a}}\mathbf{W}^{[a]} \quad \text{and} \quad \tilde{\mathbf{o}} = \tilde{\mathbf{a}}\mathbf{W}^{[b]} .$$

These two relations together imply that $\tilde{\mathbf{a}}$ is orthogonal to $(\mathbf{W}^{[a]}\mathbf{W}^{[b]})$ thus contradicting the hypothesis that the rows of $\mathbf{W}$ are linearly independent. This proves the theorem.

By using relation (6-6.9), we may replace formulas (6-6.12) and (6-6.13) by

$$v = \tilde{\mathbf{a}}\mathbf{W}^{[a]}\mathbf{P}^{-1}(a)\tilde{\mathbf{K}}^{-1}(\mathbf{v}(a))\mathbf{v} ,$$

$$v = -\tilde{\mathbf{a}}\mathbf{W}^{[b]}\mathbf{P}^{-1}(b)\tilde{\mathbf{K}}^{-1}(\mathbf{v}(b))\mathbf{v} .$$

These formulas have the advantage of not involving the fundamental vector $\mathbf{u}$.

Theorem 6-6.3. *The index of compatibility of the adjoint boundary problem is $m-r$, where r is the rank of a characteristic matrix.*

PROOF. We have seen that each solution of

$$\tilde{\mathbf{a}}\mathbf{D} = \tilde{\mathbf{o}} \tag{6-6.14}$$

determines, through formula (6-6.12), a unique solution of the boundary problem (6-6.4) and (6-6.5). The developments of Theorem 6-6.2 reveal the correspondence between v and $\tilde{\mathbf{a}}$. It follows that the index of compatibility of the problem (6-6.4) and (6-6.5) is the dimension of the solution space of equation (6-6.14). This proves the theorem.

Corollary 6-6.3. *If $m = n$, the boundary problem* (6-5.2) *and* (6-5.3) *and its adjoint* (6-6.4) *and* (6-6.5) *have the same index of compatibility.*

Example 1. The boundary problem

$$u'' - 3u' + 2u = 0 ,$$

$$u(0) - u'(0) = 0 , \quad u(1) - u'(1) = 0 ,$$

has the characteristic matrix

$$\mathbf{D} = \begin{pmatrix} 0 & -1 \\ 0 & -e^2 \end{pmatrix}$$

if we use $\tilde{\mathbf{u}} = (e^t, e^{2t})$ as a fundamental vector. The vector $\mathbf{d}_1$ is orthogonal to $\mathbf{D}$ on the right, and we infer that $u = e^t$ spans the solution space of the boundary problem.

The boundary conditions may be written as

$$\begin{pmatrix} 1 & -1 \\ 0 & 0 \end{pmatrix}\mathbf{k}(u(0)) + \begin{pmatrix} 0 & 0 \\ 1 & -1 \end{pmatrix}\mathbf{k}(u(1)) = \mathbf{o} ,$$

and the concomitant matrix is (see Example 1 of Section 3-7)

$$\mathbf{P} = \begin{pmatrix} -3 & 1 \\ -1 & 0 \end{pmatrix} .$$

Therefore, the adjoint boundary problem is

$$v'' + 3v' + 2v = 0 ,$$

$$\tilde{\mathbf{k}}(v(0))\mathbf{P} = \tilde{\mathbf{a}}\begin{pmatrix} 1 & -1 \\ 0 & 0 \end{pmatrix} , \quad \tilde{\mathbf{k}}(v(1))\mathbf{P} = -\tilde{\mathbf{a}}\begin{pmatrix} 0 & 0 \\ 1 & -1 \end{pmatrix} .$$

The vector $\tilde{\mathbf{v}} = (-e^{-t}, e^{-2t})$ is a fundamental vector for the adjoint equation, and it may be verified that $\tilde{\mathbf{K}}(v)\mathbf{PK}(\mathbf{u}) = \mathbf{I}$. Noting that $\tilde{\mathbf{a}} = (-1, e^{-2})$ is orthogonal to $\mathbf{D}$ on the left, through formula (6-6.12) we have a solution v of the adjoint boundary problem given by

$$v = (-1, e^{-2})\begin{pmatrix} 1 & -1 \\ 0 & 0 \end{pmatrix}\begin{pmatrix} 1 & 1 \\ 1 & 2 \end{pmatrix}\begin{pmatrix} -e^{-t} \\ e^{-2t} \end{pmatrix}$$

$$= e^{-2t} .$$

The function v spans the solution space of the adjoint boundary problem.

By use of Theorem 6-6.1, it may be verified that we can write the adjoint boundary conditions as

$$\begin{pmatrix} 2 & 1 \\ 0 & 0 \end{pmatrix}\mathbf{k}(v(0)) + \begin{pmatrix} 0 & 0 \\ 2 & 1 \end{pmatrix}\mathbf{k}(v(1)) = \mathbf{o} ,$$

or

$$2v(0) + v'(0) = 0 , \quad 2v(1) + v'(1) = 0 .$$

Exercises

1-7. For each of the Exercises 1–7 of Section 6-5, write the adjoint boundary problem, determine the index of compatibility, and find the solution space.

8. If the boundary condition for the adjoint problem (6-6.4) and (6-6.5) is written as (6-6.7), then the matrix

$$\mathbf{B} = \mathbf{Q}^{[a]}\mathbf{K}(\mathbf{v}(a)) + \mathbf{Q}^{[b]}\mathbf{K}(\mathbf{v}(b))$$

is the characteristic matrix for the adjoint problem. If the ranks of $\mathbf{B}$ and $\mathbf{D}$ are represented by $r_{\mathbf{B}}$ and $r_{\mathbf{D}}$, respectively, show that $r_{\mathbf{B}} - r_{\mathbf{D}} = n - m$.

9. Express the boundary condition (6-5.3) in parametric form.

6-7. THE *n*th-ORDER NONHOMOGENEOUS BOUNDARY PROBLEM AND GREEN'S FUNCTION

The problem to be considered here is

(6-7.1) $$Lu = f ,$$

(6-7.2) $$\mathbf{W}^{[a]}\mathbf{k}(u(a)) + \mathbf{W}^{[b]}\mathbf{k}(u(b)) = \mathbf{o} .$$

If, as usual, a fundamental vector for $Lu = 0$ is represented by $\mathbf{u}$, then a particular solution $\hat{u}$ of equation (6-7.1) is given by (see Section 3-5)

$$\hat{u}(t) = \tilde{\mathbf{u}}(t) \int_a^t \mathbf{K}^{-1}(\mathbf{u}(s))\mathbf{d}_n f(s) p_0^{-1}(s)\, ds \ .$$

We need the Wronskian vector of this particular solution, and for its derivation it is convenient to replace $\tilde{\mathbf{u}}(t)$ by $\tilde{\mathbf{d}}_1 \mathbf{K}(\mathbf{u}(t))$ and write

$$\hat{u}(t) = \tilde{\mathbf{d}}_1 \mathbf{K}(\mathbf{u}(t)) \int_a^t \mathbf{K}^{-1}(\mathbf{u}(s))\mathbf{d}_n f(s) p_0^{-1}(s)\, ds \ .$$

Recalling the fact that

$$\frac{d}{dt}\int_a^t g(s)\, ds = g(t) \ ,$$

we have

$$\hat{u}'(t) = \tilde{\mathbf{d}}_1 \mathbf{K}(\mathbf{u}(t))\mathbf{K}^{-1}(\mathbf{u}(t))\mathbf{d}_n f(t) p_0^{-1}(t) + \tilde{\mathbf{d}}_1 \mathbf{K}'(\mathbf{u}(t)) \int_a^t \mathbf{K}^{-1}(\mathbf{u}(s))\mathbf{d}_n f(s) p_0^{-1}(s)\, ds$$

$$= 0 + \tilde{\mathbf{d}}_2 \mathbf{K}(\mathbf{u}(t)) \int_a^t \mathbf{K}^{-1}(\mathbf{u}(s))\mathbf{d}_n f(s) p_0^{-1}\, ds \ .$$

Similarly,

$$\hat{u}''(t) = \tilde{\mathbf{d}}_3 \mathbf{K}(\mathbf{u}(t)) \int_a^t \mathbf{K}^{-1}(\mathbf{u}(s))\mathbf{d}_n f(s) p_0^{-1}(s)\, ds \ ,$$

$$\vdots$$

$$\hat{u}^{[n-1]}(t) = \tilde{\mathbf{d}}_n \mathbf{K}(\mathbf{u}(t)) \int_a^t \mathbf{K}^{-1}(\mathbf{u}(s))\mathbf{d}_n f(s) p_0^{-1}(s)\, ds \ .$$

The jth derivative of u can, therefore, be expressed as

$$\hat{u}^{[j]}(t) = \tilde{\mathbf{u}}^{[j]}(t) \int_a^t \mathbf{K}^{-1}(\mathbf{u}(s))\mathbf{d}_n f(s) p_0^{-1}(s)\, ds \ .$$

Hence,

$$\mathbf{k}(\hat{u}(t)) = \mathbf{K}(\mathbf{u}(t)) \int_a^t \mathbf{K}^{-1}(\mathbf{u}(s))\mathbf{d}_n f(s) p_0^{-1}(s)\, ds \ . \tag{6-7.3}$$

Every solution of equation (6-7.1) has the form

$$u(t) = \hat{u}(t) + \tilde{\mathbf{u}}(t)\mathbf{c} \ . \tag{6-7.4}$$

This satisfies the boundary condition (6-7.2) if

$$\mathbf{W}^{[a]}(\mathbf{k}(\hat{u}(a)) + \mathbf{K}(\mathbf{u}(a))\mathbf{c}) + \mathbf{W}^{[b]}(\mathbf{k}(\hat{u}(b)) + \mathbf{K}(\mathbf{u}(b))\mathbf{c}) = \mathbf{o} \ .$$

Using formula (6-7.3), we may reduce this to

$$\mathbf{D}\mathbf{c} + \mathbf{W}^{[b]}\mathbf{K}(\mathbf{u}(b)) \int_a^b \mathbf{K}^{-1}(\mathbf{u}(s))\mathbf{d}_n f(s) p_0^{-1}(s)\, ds = \mathbf{o} \ ,$$

where

$$\mathbf{D} = \mathbf{W}^{[a]}\mathbf{K}(\mathbf{u}(a)) + \mathbf{W}^{[b]}\mathbf{K}(\mathbf{u}(b)) \ .$$

The hypothesis that the characteristic matrix $\mathbf{D}$ is nonsingular is imposed, and hence

$$\mathbf{c} = -\mathbf{D}^{-1}\mathbf{W}^{[b]}\mathbf{K}(\mathbf{u}(b))\int_a^b \mathbf{K}^{-1}(\mathbf{u}(s))\mathbf{d}_n f(s)p_0^{-1}(s)\,ds\ .$$

Substituting this evaluation of $\mathbf{c}$ into (6-7.4), we obtain the following expression for the unique solution of problem (6-7.1) and (6-7.2):

$$(6\text{-}7.5)\quad u(t) = \tilde{\mathbf{u}}(t)\int_a^t \mathbf{K}^{-1}(\mathbf{u}(s))\mathbf{d}_n f(s)p_0^{-1}(s)\,ds$$
$$-\tilde{\mathbf{u}}(t)\mathbf{D}^{-1}\mathbf{W}^{[b]}\mathbf{K}(\mathbf{u}(b))\int_a^b \mathbf{K}^{-1}(\mathbf{u}(s))\mathbf{d}_n f(s)p_0^{-1}(s)\,ds\ .$$

We may reduce this expression to a more convenient form by the technique employed in Section 6-4. The identity matrix

$$\mathbf{D}^{-1}[\mathbf{W}^{[a]}\mathbf{K}(\mathbf{u}(a))+\mathbf{W}^{[b]}\mathbf{K}(\mathbf{u}(b))]$$

is inserted between $\tilde{\mathbf{u}}(t)$ and the integral symbol in the first term on the right-hand side of relation (6-7.5). The second term on the right-hand side of the same relation is broken into two parts by separating the interval of integration into the two subintervals $[a, t]$ and $[t, b]$. At this point, the right-hand side of (6-7.5) consists of four terms and two of these cancel each other. Thus formula (6-7.5) becomes

$$u(t) = \tilde{\mathbf{u}}(t)\mathbf{D}^{-1}\mathbf{W}^{[a]}\mathbf{K}(\mathbf{u}(a))\int_a^t \mathbf{K}^{-1}(\mathbf{u}(s))\mathbf{d}_n f(s)p_0^{-1}(s)\,ds -$$
$$-\tilde{\mathbf{u}}(t)\mathbf{D}^{-1}\mathbf{W}^{[b]}\mathbf{K}(\mathbf{u}(b))\int_t^b \mathbf{K}^{-1}(\mathbf{u}(s))\mathbf{d}_n f(s)p_0^{-1}(s)\,ds\ .$$

The formula for the solution of problem (6-7.1) and (6-7.2) may therefore be rewritten as

$$(6\text{-}7.6)\qquad u(t) = \int_a^b G(t,s)f(s)\,ds\ ,$$

where

$$(6\text{-}7.7)\quad (Gt,s) = \begin{cases} \tilde{\mathbf{d}}_1\mathbf{K}(\mathbf{u}(t))\mathbf{D}^{-1}\mathbf{W}^{[a]}\mathbf{K}(\mathbf{u}(a))\mathbf{K}^{-1}(\mathbf{u}(s))\mathbf{d}_n p_0^{-1}(s)\ , & s < t\ , \\ -\tilde{\mathbf{d}}_1\mathbf{K}(\mathbf{u}(t))\mathbf{D}^{-1}\mathbf{W}^{[b]}\mathbf{K}(\mathbf{u}(b))\mathbf{K}^{-1}(\mathbf{u}(s))\mathbf{d}_n p_0^{-1}(s)\ , & s > t\ . \end{cases}$$

Since formula (6-7.7) for Green's function may appear cumbersome at first sight, a few remarks are in order. If $p_0 = 1$, the vector boundary problem (6-5.4) and (6-5.5) and the scalar boundary problem (6-5.2) and (6-5.3) are equivalent. Hence, the Wronskian matrix $\mathbf{K}(\mathbf{u}(t))$ is a fundamental matrix for the vector equation (6-5.4). Using this in formula (6-4.7), we can infer that Green's matrix for the problem (6-5.4) and (6-5.5) is given by

$$\mathbf{G}(t,s) = \begin{cases} \mathbf{K}(\mathbf{u}(t))\mathbf{D}^{-1}\mathbf{W}^{[a]}\mathbf{K}(\mathbf{u}(a))\mathbf{K}^{-1}(\mathbf{u}(s))\ , & s < t\ , \\ -\mathbf{K}(\mathbf{u}(t))\mathbf{D}^{-1}\mathbf{W}^{[b]}\mathbf{K}(\mathbf{u}(b))\mathbf{K}^{-1}(\mathbf{u}(s))\ , & s > t\ . \end{cases}$$

Clearly, therefore, Green's function given by (6-7.7) is the upper right-hand corner component of Green's matrix for the problem (6-5.4) and (6-5.5).

By an argument similar to the one used in Section 6-4, we can show here that Green's function is independent of the choice of the fundamental vector **u**.

Formula (6-7.7) can be made less cumbersome by letting **v** represent the fundamental vector for $L^*v = 0$ such that

$$\tilde{\mathbf{K}}(\mathbf{v})\mathbf{P}\mathbf{K}(\mathbf{u}) = \mathbf{I} \ . \tag{6-7.8}$$

From this and recalling the form of the matrix **P** we have

$$\begin{aligned} \mathbf{K}^{-1}(\mathbf{u}(s))\mathbf{d}_n &= \tilde{\mathbf{K}}(\mathbf{v}(s))\mathbf{P}(s)\mathbf{d}_n \\ &= \tilde{\mathbf{K}}(\mathbf{v}(s))\mathbf{d}_1 p_0(s) \\ &= \mathbf{v}(s)p_0(s) \ . \end{aligned}$$

Hence an alternative representation of Green's function is given by

$$G(t,s) = \begin{cases} \tilde{\mathbf{u}}(t)\mathbf{D}^{-1}\mathbf{W}^{[a]}\mathbf{K}(\mathbf{u}(a))\mathbf{v}(s) \ , & s < t \ , \\ -\tilde{\mathbf{u}}(t)\mathbf{D}^{-1}\mathbf{W}^{[b]}\mathbf{K}(\mathbf{u}(b))\mathbf{v}(s) \ , & s > t \ . \end{cases} \tag{6-7.9}$$

This formula has more than an aesthetic advantage over formula (6-7.7), since it reveals the symmetric nature of Green's function relative to the fundamental vectors **u** and **v**, respectively.

The advantage of the present representation of Green's function compared to the classical representation in terms of determinants is apparent in the proof of the following theorem.

Theorem 6-7.1. *Regarded as a function of t with s fixed, Green's function has the following properties:*

(i) *Together with its first $n-1$ derivatives, it is continuous on* $[a, s)$ *and* $(s, b]$. *At the point $t = s$, the function and its first $n-2$ derivatives have removable discontinuities while the $(n-1)$st derivative has an upward jump of $p_0^{-1}(s)$.*

(ii) *G is a formal solution of the homogeneous boundary problem* (6-5.2) *and* (6-5.3). *It fails to be a true solution because of the discontinuity at $t = s$.*

(iii) *G is the only function with properties* (i) *and* (ii).

PROOF. Green's function can clearly be written as

$$G(t,s) = \begin{cases} \tilde{\mathbf{u}}(t)\mathbf{h}_+ \ , & s < t \ , \\ \tilde{\mathbf{u}}(t)\mathbf{h}_- \ , & s > t \ , \end{cases} \tag{6-7.10}$$

where the vectors $\mathbf{h}_+$ and $\mathbf{h}_-$ are free from t. Hence,

$$\mathbf{k}_1(G(t,s)) = \begin{cases} \mathbf{K}(\mathbf{u}(t))\mathbf{h}_+ \ , & s < t \ , \\ \mathbf{K}(\mathbf{u}(t))\mathbf{h}_- \ , & s > t \ , \end{cases}$$

where the subscript 1 on $\mathbf{k}$ indicates differentiation with respect to the first variable. Since

$$\begin{aligned}\mathbf{h}_+ - \mathbf{h}_- &= \mathbf{D}^{-1}[\mathbf{W}^{[a]}\mathbf{K}(\mathbf{u}(a)) + \mathbf{W}^{[b]}\mathbf{K}(\mathbf{u}(b))]\mathbf{K}^{-1}(\mathbf{u}(s))\mathbf{d}_n p_0^{-1}(s) \\ &= \mathbf{K}^{-1}(\mathbf{u}(s))\mathbf{d}_n p_0^{-1}(s) \ ,\end{aligned}$$

we can infer that

$$\begin{aligned}\mathbf{k}_1(G(s^+, s)) - \mathbf{k}_1(G(s^-, s)) &= \mathbf{K}(\mathbf{u}(s))\mathbf{K}^{-1}(\mathbf{u}(s))\mathbf{d}_n p_0^{-1}(s) \\ &= \mathbf{d}_n p_0^{-1}(s) \ .\end{aligned}$$

This proves that G and each of its first $n-2$ derivatives has a removable discontinuity at $t = s$ and that the $(n-1)$st derivative has an upward jump of $p_0^{-1}(s)$.

The representation of G in formula (6-7.10) reveals that it is a solution of $Lu = 0$, except at $t = s$. Further, following the pattern established in Theorem 6-4.1,

$$\begin{aligned}\mathbf{W}^{[a]}\mathbf{k}_1(G(a,s)) + \mathbf{W}^{[b]}\mathbf{k}_1(G(b,s)) &= \mathbf{W}^{[a]}\mathbf{K}(\mathbf{u}(a))\mathbf{h}_- + \mathbf{W}^{[b]}\mathbf{K}(\mathbf{u}(b))\mathbf{h}_+ \\ &= \{\mathbf{D} - \mathbf{W}^{[b]}\mathbf{K}(\mathbf{u}(b))\}\mathbf{h}_- + \mathbf{W}^{[b]}\mathbf{K}(\mathbf{u}(b))\mathbf{h}_+ \\ &= \mathbf{D}\mathbf{h}_- + \mathbf{W}^{[b]}\mathbf{K}(\mathbf{u}(b))\{\mathbf{h}_+ - \mathbf{h}_-\} \\ &= \mathbf{D}\mathbf{h}_- + \mathbf{W}^{[b]}\mathbf{K}(\mathbf{u}(b))\mathbf{K}^{-1}(\mathbf{u}(s))\mathbf{d}_n p_0^{-1}(s) \\ &= \mathbf{D}\mathbf{h}_- - \mathbf{D}\mathbf{h}_- \\ &= \mathbf{o} \ .\end{aligned}$$

Thus, G satisfies the boundary condition (6-5.3) and the proof of part (ii) is complete. Since the proof of part (iii) is entirely similar to the proof of the corresponding part of Theorem 6-4.1, we may consider the proof of this theorem completed.

The properties of Green's function relative to the adjoint boundary problem are established in the following theorem.

Theorem 6-7.2. *Regarded as a function of s with t fixed, Green's function has the following properties:*

(i) *Together with its first $n-1$ derivatives, it is continuous on $[a, t)$ and $(t, b]$. At the point $s = t$, the function and its first $n-2$ derivatives have removable discontinuities while the $(n-1)$st derivative has a jump of $(-1)^n p_0^{-1}(t)$.*

(ii) *G is a formal solution of the homogeneous boundary problem* (6-6.4) *and* (6-6.5). *It fails to be a true solution because of the discontinuity at $t = s$.*

PROOF. Formula (6-7.9) may be abbreviated to

$$G(t,s) = \begin{cases} \tilde{\mathbf{h}}_- \mathbf{v}(s) \ , & s < t \ , \\ \tilde{\mathbf{h}}_+ \mathbf{v}(s) \ , & s > t \ , \end{cases} \qquad (6\text{-}7.11)$$

by making the appropriate definition for the vectors $\mathbf{h}_-$ and $\mathbf{h}_+$. It follows that

$$\tilde{\mathbf{k}}_2(G(t,s)) = \begin{cases} \tilde{\mathbf{h}}_-\tilde{\mathbf{K}}(\mathbf{v}(s)) , & s < t , \\ \tilde{\mathbf{h}}_+\tilde{\mathbf{K}}(\mathbf{v}(s)) , & s > t , \end{cases} \tag{6-7.12}$$

Hence, we may write

$$\begin{aligned} \tilde{\mathbf{k}}_2(G(t,t^+)) - \tilde{\mathbf{k}}_2(G(t,t^-)) &= \{\tilde{\mathbf{h}}_+ - \tilde{\mathbf{h}}_-\tilde{\mathbf{K}}\}(\mathbf{v}(t)) \\ &= -\tilde{\mathbf{u}}(t)\tilde{\mathbf{K}}(\mathbf{v}(t)) \\ &= -\tilde{\mathbf{d}}_1\mathbf{K}(\mathbf{u}(t))\tilde{\mathbf{K}}(\mathbf{v}(t)) . \end{aligned}$$

From relation (6-7.8), we have

$$\tilde{\mathbf{K}}(\mathbf{v}(t)) = \mathbf{K}^{-1}(\mathbf{u}(t))\mathbf{P}^{-1}(t) ,$$

so that

$$-\tilde{\mathbf{d}}_1\mathbf{K}(\mathbf{u}(t))\mathbf{K}(\mathbf{v}(t)) = -\tilde{\mathbf{d}}_1\mathbf{P}^{-1}(t) .$$

The structure of $\mathbf{P}^{-1}(t)$, described in Corollary 3-7.2, is such that

$$\tilde{\mathbf{d}}_1\mathbf{P}^{-1}(t) = (-1)^{n-1}\tilde{\mathbf{d}}_n p_0^{-1}(t) .$$

It follows that

$$\tilde{\mathbf{k}}_2(G(t,t^+)) - \tilde{\mathbf{k}}_2(G(t,t^-)) = (-1)^n\tilde{\mathbf{d}}_n p_0^{-1}(t) .$$

This completes the proof of part (i).

It is obvious from the representation (6-7.11) that G is a solution of $L^*v = 0$ except at the point $s = t$. At the boundary points, we have from formula (6-7.12), using relation (6-7.8),

$$\begin{aligned} \tilde{\mathbf{k}}_2(G(t,a))\mathbf{P}(a) &= \tilde{\mathbf{h}}_-\tilde{\mathbf{K}}(\mathbf{v}(a))\mathbf{P}(a) \\ &= \tilde{\mathbf{u}}(t)\mathbf{D}^{-1}\mathbf{W}^{[a]} , \\ \tilde{\mathbf{k}}_2(G(t,b))\mathbf{P}(b) &= \tilde{\mathbf{h}}_+\tilde{\mathbf{K}}(\mathbf{v}(b))\mathbf{P}(b) \\ &= -\tilde{\mathbf{u}}(t)\mathbf{D}^{-1}\mathbf{W}^{[b]} . \end{aligned}$$

This demonstrates that G satisfies the boundary condition (6-6.5) with $\tilde{\mathbf{u}}(t)\mathbf{D}^{-1}$ playing the role of the parametric vector. The proof of the theorem is therefore complete.

The next theorem shows that the nonhomogeneous adjoint boundary problem has a solution that can be expressed in integral form with Green's function as the kernel. The problem in question is

$$L^*v = f , \tag{6-7.13}$$

$$\begin{cases} \tilde{\mathbf{k}}(v(a))\mathbf{P}(a) = \tilde{\mathbf{a}}\mathbf{W}^{[a]} , \\ \tilde{\mathbf{k}}(v(b))\mathbf{P}(b) = -\tilde{\mathbf{a}}\mathbf{W}^{[b]} . \end{cases} \tag{6-7.14}$$

In the course of proving this theorem we need to use the following, easily verified fact. If $g(t, s)$ is a function of two variables which is continuous except for a possible jump discontinuity along the line $t = s$, then

$$g(s^+, s) - g(s^-, s) = -(g(s, s^+) - g(s, s^-)) \ . \tag{6-7.15}$$

Theorem 6-7.3. *The function*

$$v(s) = \int_a^b G(t, s) f(t)\, dt$$

is a solution of the adjoint boundary problem (6-7.13) *and* (6-7.14).

PROOF. Since the discontinuity of G at $t = s$ is removable we may write

$$v'(s) = \int_a^b \frac{\partial}{\partial s} G(t, s) f(t)\, dt \ .$$

The discontinuity of the integrand in the last relation is again removable and we have

$$v''(s) = \int_a^b \frac{\partial^2}{\partial s^2} G(t, s) f(t)\, dt \ .$$

Continuing in this way, we get

$$v^{[j]}(s) = \int_a^b \frac{\partial^j}{\partial s^j} G(t, s) f(t)\, dt \ , \quad j = 1, 2, \ldots, n-1 \ . \tag{6-7.16}$$

when $j = n-1$, the integrand has a nonremovable discontinuity. Hence, in order to obtain $v^{[n]}$ we write $v^{[n-1]}$ as

$$v^{[n-1]}(s) = \int_a^s \frac{\partial^{n-1}}{\partial s^{n-1}} G(t, s) f(t)\, dt + \int_s^b \frac{\partial^{n-1}}{\partial s^{n-1}} G(t, s) f(t)\, dt \ .$$

This yields

$$v^{[n]}(s) = \left(\frac{\partial^{n-1}}{\partial s^{n-1}} G(s^-, s) - \frac{\partial^{n-1}}{\partial s^{n-1}} G(s^+, s) \right) f(s) + \int_a^b \frac{\partial^n}{\partial s^n} G(t, s) f(t)\, dt \ .$$

Using the transformation equation (6-7.15) and invoking part (i) of Theorem 6-7.2, we get

$$v^{[n]}(s) = (-1)^n p_0^{-1}(s) f(s) + \int_a^b \frac{\partial^n}{\partial s^n} G(t, s) f(t)\, dt \ .$$

Since the coefficient of $v^{[n]}$ in the differential form L^*v is $(-1)^n p_0$,

$$L^*v(s) = f(s) + \int_a^b L^*G(t, s) f(t)\, dt \ .$$

Since $G(t, s)$, regarded as a function of s, satisfies $L^*v = 0$, the second term on the right-hand side of the last relation is zero. Hence, $v(s)$ satisfies equation (6-7.13).

In view of formula (6-7.16), we may write

$$\tilde{\mathbf{k}}(v(s)) = \int_a^b f(t)\tilde{\mathbf{k}}_2(G(t,s))\,dt \ .$$

Therefore, using the fact that G satisfies the adjoint boundary conditions with $\tilde{\mathbf{u}}(t)\mathbf{D}^{-1}$ as the parametric vector, we may write

$$\begin{aligned}
\tilde{\mathbf{k}}(v(a))\mathbf{P}(a) &= \int_a^b f(t)\tilde{\mathbf{k}}_2(G(t,a))\mathbf{P}(a)\,dt \\
&= \int_a^b f(t)\tilde{\mathbf{u}}(t)\mathbf{D}^{-1}\,dt\,\mathbf{W}^{[a]} \ , \\
\tilde{\mathbf{k}}(v(b))\mathbf{P}(b) &= \int_a^b f(t)\tilde{\mathbf{k}}_2(G(t,b))\mathbf{P}(b)\,dt \\
&= -\int_a^b f(t)\tilde{\mathbf{u}}(t)\mathbf{D}^{-1}\,dt\,\mathbf{W}^{[b]} \ .
\end{aligned}$$

Thus, $v(s)$ satisfies the boundary condition (6-7.14) with

$$\int_a^b f(t)\tilde{\mathbf{u}}(t)\mathbf{D}^{-1}\,dt$$

as the parametric vector. This proves the theorem.

The remarks made in Section 6-4 relative to the integral operator associated with Green's matrix have their counterparts here. Thus, we may define the operator $\mathscr{G}$ with domain $C[a, b]$ by

$$u = \mathscr{G}f \ , \tag{6-7.17}$$

where

$$u(t) = \int_a^b G(t,s)f(s)\,ds \ .$$

The function u defined by relation (6-7.17) is a solution of the problem (6-7.1) and (6-7.2). Hence,

$$L(\mathscr{G}f) = f \ .$$

Also, if $u \in C^n[a, b]$ and if it also satisfies the boundary condition (6-7.2), we have

$$\mathscr{G}(Lu) = u \ .$$

Example 1. Find Green's function for the problem

$$u'' = 0 \ ,$$

$$u(0) = 0 \ , \quad 2u(1) - u'(1) = 0 \ .$$

The boundary conditions may be written as

$$\begin{pmatrix} 1 & 0 \\ 0 & 0 \end{pmatrix}\mathbf{k}(u(0)) + \begin{pmatrix} 0 & 0 \\ 2 & -1 \end{pmatrix}\mathbf{k}(u(1)) = \mathbf{o} \ .$$

If $\tilde{\mathbf{u}} = (1, t)$ is chosen as a fundamental vector, we have

$$\mathbf{K}(\mathbf{u}) = \begin{pmatrix} 1 & t \\ 0 & 1 \end{pmatrix}, \quad \mathbf{K}^{-1}(\mathbf{u}) = \begin{pmatrix} 1 & -t \\ 0 & 1 \end{pmatrix},$$

$$\mathbf{D} = \begin{pmatrix} 1 & 0 \\ 2 & 1 \end{pmatrix}, \quad \mathbf{D}^{-1} = \begin{pmatrix} 1 & 0 \\ -2 & 1 \end{pmatrix}.$$

Hence, using Formula (6-7.7), we get for Green's function

$$G(t, s) = \begin{cases} (1,t)\begin{pmatrix} 1 & 0 \\ -2 & 1 \end{pmatrix}\begin{pmatrix} 1 & 0 \\ 0 & 0 \end{pmatrix}\begin{pmatrix} 1 & 0 \\ 0 & 1 \end{pmatrix}\begin{pmatrix} 1 & -s \\ 0 & 1 \end{pmatrix}\begin{pmatrix} 0 \\ 1 \end{pmatrix}, & s<t, \\ -(1,t)\begin{pmatrix} 1 & 0 \\ -2 & 1 \end{pmatrix}\begin{pmatrix} 0 & 0 \\ 2 & -1 \end{pmatrix}\begin{pmatrix} 1 & 1 \\ 0 & 1 \end{pmatrix}\begin{pmatrix} 1 & -s \\ 0 & 1 \end{pmatrix}\begin{pmatrix} 0 \\ 1 \end{pmatrix}, & s>t, \end{cases}$$

$$= \begin{cases} s(2t-1), & s<t, \\ t(2s-1), & s>t. \end{cases}$$

Exercises

Find Green's function for each of the following boundary problems.

1. $u'' = 0$, (See Exercise 1 of Section 6-5.)
$u(0) = 0$, $u(1) = 0$.

2. $u'' = 0$,
$u(0) - u'(0) = 0$, $u(1) + u'(1) = 0$.

3. $u'' + u = 0$,
$u(0) = 0$, $u'(\pi) = 0$.

4. $u''' = 0$,
$u(0) = 0$, $u(1) = 0$, $u'(0) - u'(1) = 0$.

5. Derive a formula for the solution of

$$Lu = f,$$
$$\mathbf{W}^{[a]}\mathbf{k}(u(a)) + \mathbf{W}^{[b]}\mathbf{k}(u(b)) = \mathbf{b},$$

where the corresponding homogeneous problem is incompatible.

6. Derive the formula for Green's function from properties (i) and (ii) of Theorem 6-7.1.

7. Let $g(t, s)$ be

$$g(t,s) = \begin{cases} \tfrac{1}{2}\tilde{\mathbf{u}}(t)\mathbf{K}^{-1}(\mathbf{u}(s))\mathbf{d}_n, & s<t, \\ -\tfrac{1}{2}\tilde{\mathbf{u}}(t)\mathbf{K}^{-1}(\mathbf{u}(s))\mathbf{d}_n, & s>t, \end{cases}$$

and show that

$$G(t,s) = g(t,s) - \tilde{\mathbf{u}}(t)\mathbf{D}^{-1}[\mathbf{W}^{[a]}\mathbf{k}(g(a)) + \mathbf{W}^{[b]}\mathbf{k}(g(b))].$$

8. Show that G can be represented as the quotient of two determinants.[5]

---

[5] Compare with Ince [26], page 259, but note that his definition of g is incorrect because of reversed signs.

9. Let $K(t, s)$ be defined by

$$K(t,s) = \begin{cases} \tilde{\mathbf{u}}(t)\mathbf{K}^{-1}(\mathbf{u}(s))\mathbf{d}_n p_0^{-1}(s) \;, & s<t \;, \\ 0 \;, & s>t \;, \end{cases}$$

and show that

$$G(t,s) = K(t,s) - \tilde{\mathbf{u}}(t)\mathbf{D}^{-1}\mathbf{W}^{[b]}\mathbf{K}(\mathbf{u}(b))\mathbf{K}^{-1}(\mathbf{u}(s))\mathbf{d}_n p_0^{-1}(s) \;.$$

10. Show that, when $s<t$,

$$K(t,s) = \frac{1}{p_0(s)|\mathbf{K}(\mathbf{u}(s))|}\begin{vmatrix} u_1(s) & u_2(s) & \cdots & u_n(s) \\ u_1'(s) & u_2'(s) & \cdots & u_n'(s) \\ \cdot & \cdot & \cdot & \cdot \\ \cdot & \cdot & \cdot & \cdot \\ \cdot & \cdot & \cdot & \cdot \\ u_1^{[n-2]}(s) & u_2^{[n-2]}(s) & \cdots & u_n^{[n-2]}(s) \\ u_1(t) & u_2(t) & \cdots & u_n(t) \end{vmatrix} ,$$

where $|\mathbf{K}(\mathbf{u}(s))|$ represents the determinant of $\mathbf{K}(\mathbf{u}(s))$.

11. Let[6] $h(t, s)$ be defined by

$$h(t,s) = \begin{vmatrix} K(t,s) & \tilde{\mathbf{u}}(t) \\ \mathbf{b}(s) & \mathbf{D} \end{vmatrix} ,$$

where

$$\mathbf{b}(s) = \mathbf{W}^{[a]}\mathbf{k}(K(a,s)) + \mathbf{W}^{[b]}\mathbf{k}(K(b,s)) \;.$$

Show that G is given by

$$G(t,s) = \frac{h(t,s)}{|\mathbf{D}|} \;.$$

12. The boundary problem

$$Lu = f \;,$$

$$\mathbf{W}^{[a]}\mathbf{k}(u(a)) + \mathbf{W}^{[b]}\mathbf{k}(u(b)) = \mathbf{b} \;,$$

has a solution if and only if every solution v of the homogeneous adjoint system

$$L^*v = 0 \;,$$

$$\tilde{\mathbf{k}}(v(a))\mathbf{P}(a) = \tilde{\mathbf{a}}\mathbf{W}^{[a]} \;, \quad \tilde{\mathbf{k}}(v(b))\mathbf{P}(b) = -\tilde{\mathbf{a}}\mathbf{W}^{[b]} \;,$$

satisfies

$$\int_a^b v(t)f(t)\,dt = \tilde{\mathbf{a}}\mathbf{b} \;,$$

where $\tilde{\mathbf{a}}$ is the parametric vector associated with v.[7]

6-8. SELF-ADJOINT BOUNDARY PROBLEM

Self-adjoint boundary problems play a major role in the theory of differential equations and in the application of differential equations to concrete

---

[6] *Cf.* Coddington and Levinson [11], Problem 12, Chapter 7.
[7] Ince [26], Section 9.34.

problems. In finite-dimensional vector spaces a self-adjoint operator is one whose matrix is equal to its own transpose. It is called, therefore, a *symmetric operator*. The study of such operators is facilitated by the symmetry involved. In the realm of function spaces, self-adjoint boundary problems give rise to symmetric operators. As might be expected, the theory of such operators is much more tractable than the theory of general linear operators.

Definition 6-8.1. *The boundary problem* (6-5.2) *and* (6-5.3) *is self-adjoint if* $L = L^*$ *and if the subspace of* $C^n[a, b]$ *determined by condition* (6-5.3) *is identical with the subspace determined by the adjoint conditions* (6-6.5).

In Corollary 3-7.4b we have shown that if $Lu = 0$ is self-adjoint, then the concomitant matrix $\mathbf{P}$ is skew-symmetric. The converse result can also be demonstrated (see Exercise 3). In Section 6-6, above, we were able to show that the boundary condition (6-5.3) is self-adjoint if and only if $m = n$ and

(6-8.1) $$\mathbf{W}^{[a]}\mathbf{P}^{-1}(a)\tilde{\mathbf{W}}^{[a]} = \mathbf{W}^{[b]}\mathbf{P}^{-1}(b)\tilde{\mathbf{W}}^{[b]} .$$

With reference to Figure 6-6.1, it can be seen easily that subspace X coincides with W when the problem is self-adjoint.

The following theorem states the essential feature of a self-adjoint boundary problem.

Theorem 6-8.1. *If the boundary problem* (6-5.2) *and* (6-5.3) *is self-adjoint, then*

$$(Lu, v) = (u, Lv) ,$$

where u and v are any two functions in $C^n[a, b]$ *which satisfy the boundary condition* (6-5.3).

PROOF. The result follows directly from Green's formula (6-6.1) and the fact that $L^* = L$.

The symmetry inherent in the self-adjoint problem insures symmetry in the Green's function associated with the problem.

Theorem 6-8.2. *If the boundary problem* (6-5.2) *and* (6-5.3) *is incompatible and self-adjoint, then its Green's function is symmetric.*

PROOF. In the developments of Section 6-7 Green's function for problem (6-5.2) and (6-5.3) was determined, and its properties relative to the adjoint boundary problem were derived. If we use the symbol $G^*(t, s)$ to represent the Green's function of the adjoint problem, then the content of Theorem 6-7.3 is that

$$G^*(t, s) = G(s, t) .$$

This proves the theorem. For the converse of Theorem 6-8.2, see Exercise 4.

The following example illustrates some of the above points.

Example 1. Consider the boundary problem

$$u'' = 0 \;,$$
$$u(0) = 0 \;,$$
$$u'(1) = 0 \;.$$

A fundamental vector for the equation is given by

$$\tilde{\mathbf{u}}(t) = (1, t) \;.$$

The boundary condition matrix is given by

$$(\mathbf{W}^{[a]}\mathbf{W}^{[b]}) = \begin{pmatrix} 1 & 0 & 0 & 0 \\ 0 & 0 & 0 & 1 \end{pmatrix} .$$

The characteristic matrix **D** is the identity matrix, so that the problem is incompatible. The concomitant matrix is given by

$$\mathbf{P} = \begin{pmatrix} 0 & 1 \\ -1 & 0 \end{pmatrix} .$$

Since **P** is skew-symmetric the equation is self-adjoint. It is easily verified that relation (6-8.1) is satisfied so that the boundary condition is also self-adjoint. The fundamental vector

$$\tilde{\mathbf{v}}(t) = (-t, 1)$$

is such that $\tilde{\mathbf{K}}(v)\mathbf{P}\mathbf{K}(\mathbf{u}) = \mathbf{I}$. Hence Green's function is given by

$$G(t,s) = \begin{cases} (1,t)\mathbf{I}\begin{pmatrix} 1 & 0 \\ 0 & 0 \end{pmatrix}\begin{pmatrix} 1 & 0 \\ 0 & 1 \end{pmatrix}\begin{pmatrix} -s \\ 1 \end{pmatrix}, & s<t \;, \\ -(1,t)\mathbf{I}\begin{pmatrix} 0 & 0 \\ 0 & 1 \end{pmatrix}\begin{pmatrix} 1 & 1 \\ 0 & 1 \end{pmatrix}\begin{pmatrix} -s \\ 1 \end{pmatrix}, & s>t \;, \end{cases}$$

$$= \begin{cases} -s \;, & s<t \;, \\ -t \;, & s>t \;. \end{cases}$$

Green's function is clearly symmetric.

Exercises

1. Develop self-adjointness criteria for the general second-order boundary problem.[8]

2. Show that if $L^* = L$ there exists at least one set of boundary conditions which may be adjoined to $Lu = 0$ to make a self-adjoint boundary problem.[9]

3. Let **P** be the concomitant matrix of a real linear differential form L. Show that if **P** is skew-symmetric, then L is self-adjoint.

4. If Green's function for a given incompatible boundary problem is symmetric, prove that the boundary problem is self-adjoint.

[8] Compare with Ince [26], Section 9.4.
[9] Compare with Coddington and Levinson [11], Problem 15, Chapter 7.

7

Introduction to Eigenvalue Problems and Expansion Theory

7-1. INTRODUCTION

Historically, interest in eigenvalue problems and expansion theory arose through consideration of physical problems such as the vibrating string. These problems attracted the attention of such notable mathematicians as D'Alembert, Euler, and Fourier. Langer's monograph[1] on Fourier series provides an illuminating insight into the historical background and the analytic developments of expansion theory. The algebraic aspects of this theory are no less intriguing. In fact, the natural motivation for the study of eigenvalue and expansion problems appears to lie in the developments associated with linear operators on a finite-dimensional vector space. This point of view is ably set forth in Lorch's survey article on "The Spectral Theorem."[2]

In Section 7-2, we show how consideration of the problem of the vibrating string leads directly to an eigenvalue problem and to the associated Fourier series expansion of an arbitrary continuous function. In Section 7-3, we show that the differential boundary problem of Section 7-2 can be replaced by an integral equation and that the linear operator associated with the integral equation is formally identical with a linear operator on a finite-dimensional vector space. It is appropriate, therefore, to devote this section to a review of some facts related to the eigenvalue problem for a finite-dimensional vector space, this material and its presentation are designed to provide a pattern for the developments of Chapter 8.

7-2. THE VIBRATING STRING PROBLEM

Motivation for the study of eigenvalue problems can be provided by attempting to solve a boundary problem in partial differential equations. A classical problem of this type arises from consideration of a vibrating string.

Let a string be stretched between the origin and the point $(\pi, 0)$ of a two-dimensional Cartesian coordinate system. Such a string may be made to vibrate (in the coordinate plane) by a variety of devices that include plucking and striking. A generalization of plucking is to release the string from rest having first deformed it to coincide with the graph of a function f defined by $y = f(x)$ (see Figure 7-2.1). It is assumed that f is continuous and that $f(0) = f(\pi) = 0$.

---

[1] Langer [30].
[2] Lorch [33].

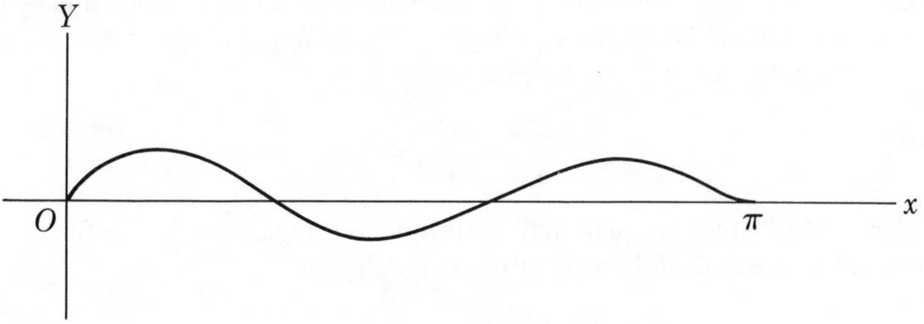

Figure 7-2.1

This merely insures that the deformation neither breaks the string nor pulls it from its fixed end points.

The displacement from the natural position of the string at the point x and at the time t is represented by $y(x, t)$, and this can be regarded as a functional value of a function y on the domain for which $0 \leqq x \leqq \pi$, $0 \leqq t < \infty$. In order to find a differential equation satisfied by y, we may proceed as follows. Let T and ρ be constants representing, respectively, the tension and the linear density of the string. Under the assumption of mild deformations, the elementary segment of the string bounded by ordinates through x and $x+\Delta x$ (see Figure 7-2.2) has a mass of $\rho\Delta x$. Under the same assumption, its motion is linear and perpendicular to the x-axis. If the inclination of the string at the point P is θ, the component of the tension perpendicular to the x-axis is $-T\sin\theta$. Similarly, if the inclination of the string at Q is $\theta+\Delta\theta$, the component of the tension perpendicular to the x-axis is $T\sin(\theta+\Delta\theta)$. The sum of these two components is the force resulting from the tension and acting on the segment in a direction perpendicular to the x-axis. It must be in equilibrium with the inertial force $-\rho\Delta x(\partial^2 y/\partial t^2)$, hence we have

$$T[\sin(\theta+\Delta\theta)-\sin\theta]-\rho\Delta x\frac{\partial^2 y}{\partial t^2}=0 .$$

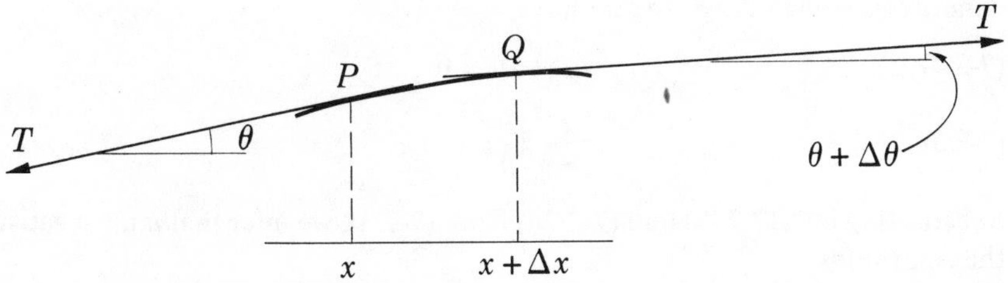

Figure 7-2.2

Since θ and $\Delta\theta$ are assumed to be small we may replace the sine function by the tangent function. Therefore, dividing by $T\Delta x$, letting Δx approach zero, and noting that $\partial \tan\theta/\partial x = \partial^2 y/\partial x^2$, we obtain

$$\frac{\partial^2 y}{\partial x^2} - \frac{\rho}{T}\frac{\partial^2 y}{\partial t^2} = 0 \ . \tag{7-2.1}$$

This is the differential equation that the function y must satisfy. The function y must also satisfy the following auxiliary conditions

$$\begin{aligned} &\left.\begin{aligned}&\text{(i)} \quad y(0,t)=0\\ &\text{(ii)} \quad y(\pi,t)=0\end{aligned}\right\} , \quad 0 \leqq t < \infty \ ,\\ &\text{(iii)} \quad \frac{\partial y(x,0)}{\partial t} = 0 \ , \quad 0 \leqq x \leqq \pi \ .\\ &\text{(iv)} \quad y(x,0) = f(x) \ , \quad 0 \leqq x \leqq \pi \ . \end{aligned} \tag{7-2.2}$$

When $f(x)$ is given, condition (iv) specifies the initial shape of the string (see Figure 7-2.1), and condition (iii) stipulates that no initial impulse is provided. Conditions (i) and (ii) require that the end points remain fixed.

We attempt to solve this problem by the method of *separation of variables*. That is, we consider the possibility that a solution y has the form

$$y(x,t) = u(x)v(t) \ . \tag{7-2.3}$$

Under this assumption, equation (7-2.1) becomes

$$u''(x)v(t) - \frac{\rho}{T}u(x)v''(t) = 0 \ .$$

If $u(x)$ and $v(t)$ are not zero, this may be rewritten as

$$\frac{u''(x)}{u(x)} = \frac{\rho}{T}\frac{v''(t)}{v(t)} \ .$$

Since the left-hand side is independent of t and the right-hand side is independent of x, we must conclude that both sides maintain a constant value. If we denote this constant by $-\lambda$, we have

$$u'' + \lambda u = 0 \ , \tag{7-2.4}$$

$$v'' + \lambda\frac{T}{\rho}v = 0 \ . \tag{7-2.5}$$

Substituting into (7-2.2i) and (7-2.2ii) from (7-2.3), we infer that u must satisfy the conditions

$$\begin{aligned} u(0) &= 0 \ ,\\ u(\pi) &= 0 \ . \end{aligned} \tag{7-2.6}$$

Equation (7-2.4) together with the conditions (7-2.6) constitute a two-point boundary problem of the type considered in Section 6-5. The fundamental vector

$$\mathbf{u}(x) = \begin{pmatrix} \sin\sqrt{\lambda}\,x \\ \cos\sqrt{\lambda}\,x \end{pmatrix}$$

for equation (7-2.4) yields the characteristic matrix

$$\mathbf{D} = \begin{pmatrix} 0 & 1 \\ \sin\sqrt{\lambda}\pi & \cos\sqrt{\lambda}\,\pi \end{pmatrix} .$$

The boundary problem is, therefore, simply compatible whenever $\sin\sqrt{\lambda}\,\pi = 0$, that is, when

$$\lambda = j^2 , \quad j = 1, 2, \ldots \quad .$$

When $\lambda = j^2$, a solution u_j of the boundary problem is

$$u_j(x) = \sin jx \ .$$

This solution is unique up to multiplication by a constant.

We may now turn our attention to equation (7-2.5) where, because of the preceding development, λ must be replaced by j^2. If (7-2.3) is substituted into (7-2.2iii), we obtain the auxiliary condition

$$(7\text{-}2.7) \qquad v'(0) = 0 \ .$$

The unique solution (up to a multiplicative constant) of equation (7-2.5), that also satisfies condition (7-2.7), is easily seen to be a function v_j given by

$$v_j(t) = \cos j\sqrt{T/\rho}\,t \ .$$

It follows, therefore, that

$$\begin{aligned} y_j(x, t) &= u_j(x)v_j(t) \\ &= \sin jx \cos j\sqrt{T/\rho}\,t \ , \quad j = 1, 2, \ldots \end{aligned}$$

is a solution of equation (7-2.1) and the conditions (7-2.2) with the exception of condition (7-2.2iv). Since equation (7-2.1) and the first three of the conditions (7-2.2) are homogeneous, any linear combination of any finite subset of the above infinite set of solutions is also a solution. Specifically, for any set of constants $c_1, c_2, \ldots, c_n$ the function y, defined by

$$y(x, t) = \sum_{j=1}^{n} c_j y_j(x, t) \ ,$$

is a solution of equation (7-2.1) and (7-2.2i, ii, iii).

We may go beyond the last conclusion and observe that, if the constants $c_1, c_2, \ldots$ are such that the series

$$\sum_{j=1}^{\infty} c_j y_j(x, t)$$

and its first and second derivatives with respect to both x and t all converge uniformly, then the function $y(x, t)$ to which the series converges must satisfy equation (7-2.1) and the conditions (7-2.2i, ii, iii). Clearly,

$$y(x,0) = \sum_{j=1}^{\infty} c_j \sin jx \ .$$

Consequently, if the constants $c_1, c_2, \ldots$ can be chosen so that

$$\sum_{j=1}^{\infty} c_j \sin jx$$

converges to $f(x)$ the corresponding function $y(x, t)$ satisfies all four conditions (7-2.2) and is a solution of the original problem.

It is a classical question to ask if constants $c_1, c_2, \ldots$ can be determined so that the series

$$\sum_{j=1}^{\infty} c_j \sin jx$$

converges to a given function $f(x)$. We see later that an affirmative answer applies for a large and important class of functions. For the present, we are content to observe that it is a problem of elementary calculus to show that

$$\int_0^{\pi} \sin jx \sin kx \, dx = \begin{cases} 0 \ , & k \neq j \ , \\ \pi/2 \ , & k = j \ . \end{cases}$$

This result makes it very easy to determine the coefficients of the expansion. For, if the series on the right-hand side of

$$f(x) = \sum_{j=1}^{\infty} c_j \sin jx \qquad \text{(7-2.8)}$$

converges uniformly on $[0, \pi]$, we may multiply both sides by $\sin kx$ and integrate. This yields the result

$$c_k = \frac{2}{\pi} \int_0^{\pi} f(x) \sin kx \, dx \ , \quad k = 1, 2, \ldots \ . \qquad \text{(7-2.9)}$$

The coefficients, therefore, are determined. This does not guarantee the validity of relation (7-2.8), but the explicit series can be examined readily for convergence. This is done later for a general case.

The above example has been used to introduce a fundamental and significant topic in the theory of ordinary differential equations. We have seen that a two-point boundary problem containing a parameter arises naturally from the attempt to solve a partial differential boundary problem. The two-point boundary problem is compatible for certain values of the parameter that form a discrete infinite set. These parameter values are called *eigenvalues*. The corresponding solutions of the two-point problem are called *eigenfunctions*. Basic to the solution of the physical problem is the question of whether or not the function f can be represented by a series of eigenfunctions. In this particular problem the eigenfunctions are trigonometric functions and the corresponding series is a *Fourier series*. The coefficients defined by formula (7-2.9) are called *Fourier coefficients* of f. The question of the representation of an "arbitrary" function by a series of eigenfunctions of an ordinary differential system is known as an *expansion problem*.

Some of the concepts introduced in Chapter 6 play an important role in the consideration of expansion problems. Notable in this connection are adjoint systems, Green's formula, and Green's function. In fact, the full significance of these concepts becomes apparent only through the consideration of expansion theory.

Exercises

1. Let the axis of a thin cylindrical metal rod coincide with a one-dimensional coordinate system and let the ends of the rod be at the points $x = 0$ and $x = 1$. If the lateral surface of the rod is insulated and if $y(x, t)$ represents the temperature of the rod at the point x and at the time t, then the temperature function must satisfy the differential equation

$$\alpha^2 \frac{\partial^2 y}{\partial x^2} - \frac{\partial y}{\partial t} = 0 .$$

The constant α depends on the material of the rod. If the ends of the rod are held at zero temperature and if the initial temperature of the rod at the point x is given by $f(x)$, $0 < x < 1$, then we have the following auxiliary conditions

$$y(0, t) = y(1, t) = 0 .$$

$$y(x, 0) = f(x) .$$

Solve the system by the method of separation of variables.

2. (a) Use formula (7-2.9) to determine the coefficients for sine series expansions of the following functions:

(i) $f(x) = x , \qquad 0 \leqq x \leqq \pi .$

(ii) $f(x) = 1 , \qquad 0 \leqq x \leqq \pi .$

(iii) $f(x) = \begin{cases} x , & 0 \leqq x \leqq \pi/2 , \\ \pi - x , & \pi/2 \leqq x \leqq \pi . \end{cases}$

(b) Draw a graph of the sum of the first three or four terms of each series in Exercise 2(a) and compare each graph with the graph of the corresponding function f.

3. Under the assumption that λ is not an eigenvalue, find Green's function for the boundary problem (7-2.4) and (7-2.6).

7-3. EIGENVALUE PROBLEM IN AN n-DIMENSIONAL VECTOR SPACE

It is shown in Chapter 8 that a general two-point boundary problem (involving a parameter) is equivalent to an integral equation with a Green's function as a kernel. By applying this result, we may conclude that the boundary problem (7-2.4) and (7-2.6) is equivalent to the integral equation

$$u(t) = -\lambda \int_a^b G(t, s)u(s)\, ds \ , \tag{7-3.1}$$

where $G(t, s)$ is Green's function for the boundary problem

$$u'' = 0 \ ,$$
$$u(0) = u(\pi) = 0 \ .$$

If the operator $\mathscr{G}$ is defined as in formula (6-7.17), then equation (7-3.1) may be rewritten as

$$\mathscr{G}u = \rho u \ ,$$

where $\rho = -\lambda^{-1}$. $\mathscr{G}$ is a linear operator, and its domain may be designated as the vector space $C[0, \pi]$. Hence, the only thing that distinguishes the eigenvalue problem of a differential boundary system from the eigenvalue problem of a linear operator A on an n-dimensional vector space is the dimension of the space. Nevertheless, it should be realized that the passage from the finite to the infinite is not usually obvious and that it frequently opens up broad new areas of investigation. The present case is no exception, since it leads to general linear operator theory and spectral analysis.

In order to provide a pattern for the developments of the next chapter, we briefly review some facts associated with the finite-dimensional case. The treatment of these facts is specifically designed to illuminate the developments of the infinite-dimensional case. The review is confined to the complex vector space $V_n(C)$, and the discussion is largely restricted to the real subspace $V_n(R)$.

Relative to the natural basis $\{\mathbf{d}_1, \mathbf{d}_2, \ldots, \mathbf{d}_n\}$, every linear transformation A of $V_n(C)$ into itself is associated with a unique matrix $\mathbf{A}$. The eigenvalue problem, therefore, is the problem of finding a scalar λ and a nontrivial vector $\mathbf{x}$ such that

$$\mathbf{A}\mathbf{x} = \lambda \mathbf{x} \ .$$

These exist if and only if the matrix $\mathbf{A} - \lambda \mathbf{I}$ is singular. Hence, the eigenvalues are the roots of the algebraic equation

$$|\mathbf{A} - \lambda \mathbf{I}| = 0 \ .$$

This equation is of degree n and must have n roots, but in Chapter 4 it is noted that $\mathbf{A}$ may have fewer than n eigenvectors. The most tractable situation is that in which $\mathbf{A}$ is a real symmetric matrix, that is $\tilde{\mathbf{A}} = \mathbf{A}$. In this case, it is easily shown[3] that the eigenvalues are all real and that an orthonormal set of n eigenvectors can be found.

Let the eigenvalues, arranged in order of decreasing magnitude, be

$$\lambda_1, \lambda_2, \ldots, \lambda_n \ ,$$

[3] Halmos [21], Section 78.

and let $\mathbf{x}_i$ be the eigenvector associated with λ_i, $i = 1, 2, \ldots, n$. Since

$$\mathbf{A}\mathbf{x}_j = \lambda_j \mathbf{x}_j \ ,$$

the square matrix $\mathbf{X}$, whose jth column is the vector $\mathbf{x}_j$, is such that

$$\mathbf{A}\mathbf{X} = \mathbf{X}(\delta_{ij}\lambda_j) \ ,$$

where δ_{ij} is Kronecker's delta. Since $\{\mathbf{x}_j\}$ is an orthonormal set, the matrix $\mathbf{X}$ is orthogonal and $\mathbf{X}^{-1} = \tilde{\mathbf{X}}$. It follows that

$$\tilde{\mathbf{X}}\mathbf{A}\mathbf{X} = (\delta_{ij}\lambda_j) \ . \tag{7-3.2}$$

The set of eigenvalues of a matrix $\mathbf{A}$ *(or a transformation* A*) is called its spectrum.* The tractability of the symmetric case arises from the fact that its matrix is reducible to the diagonal form shown in relation (7-3.2) with the spectrum forming the diagonal.

Since any orthogonal set of vectors is automatically a linearly independent set, the eigenvectors of the symmetric transformation A can be used as a basis for $V_n(R)$. That is, any vector $\mathbf{x}$ in $V_n(R)$ can be written as

$$\mathbf{x} = \sum_{j=1}^{n} \alpha_j \mathbf{x}_j \ . \tag{7-3.3}$$

If both sides of this relation are multiplied on the left by $\tilde{\mathbf{x}}_i$, we find that

$$\alpha_i = \tilde{\mathbf{x}}_i \mathbf{x} = (\mathbf{x}, \mathbf{x}_i) \ , \quad i = 1, 2, \ldots, n \ .$$

This is the *expansion theorem* associated with the symmetric transformation A. For, we have shown that an arbitrary vector in $V_n(R)$ can be represented uniquely as a linear combination of eigenvectors of A.

If the transformation A is applied to the vector $\mathbf{x}$ in formula (7-3.3), we have, since A is linear,

$$A\mathbf{x} = \sum_{j=1}^{n} \alpha_j A\mathbf{x}_j = \sum_{j=1}^{n} \alpha_j \lambda_j \mathbf{x}_j \ .$$

In any discussion involving the transformation A, the set $\{\mathbf{x}_j\}$ is clearly a natural basis to use for $V_n(R)$. Relative to this basis, the transformation A can be precisely described by saying that its effect is to magnify the jth component of any vector by a factor λ_j. The matrix of A, relative to this basis, is indeed simple. It is the diagonal matrix $(\delta_{ij}\lambda_j)$. This conclusion is easily seen to be consistent with relation (7-3.2).

When we deal with infinite-dimensional spaces, we can no longer find the eigenvalues of a transformation as the zeros of a determinant. Their determination, therefore, must be based on some other property of the transformation. A property that is useful in this connection is that the maximal magnification provided by the transformation A is the magnitude of the maximal eigenvalue and occurs in the direction of the eigenvector associated with it. This result can be inferred for the n-dimensional case from the discussion in the preceding paragraph.

Since the quadratic form

$$q(\mathbf{x}) = (A\mathbf{x}, \mathbf{x}) \ , \tag{7-3.4}$$

has values which depend, in part, on the norm of $A\mathbf{x}$, it is not unreasonable to suspect that its (constrained) extremal values may be associated with eigenvectors. We derive this result presently but, before doing so, we establish the connection between the maximum magnification factor of A and the extreme value of q. It is convenient to call the maximum magnification factor the norm of A and to represent it by the symbol $\| A \|$. The concept is made precise in the following definition.

Definition 7-3.1. *The norm of A is defined by*

$$\| A \| = \sup_{\| \mathbf{x} \| = 1} \| A\mathbf{x} \| \ .$$

Since A is linear, we also have

$$\| A \| = \sup_{\mathbf{x} \in V_n(R)} \frac{\| A\mathbf{x} \|}{\| \mathbf{x} \|} \ .$$

The following theorem establishes the desired result. It is seen that the proof is independent of the dimension of the space. It is therefore valid for operators on both finite and infinite-dimensional spaces.

Theorem 7-3.1. *If A is a symmetric bounded linear operator on a real inner-product vector space, then*

$$\| A \| = \sup_{\| x \| = 1} |(Ax, x)| \ .$$

PROOF. Let η be defined by

$$\eta = \sup_{\| x \| = 1} |(Ax, x)| \ .$$

It should be noted, that in view of this definition $|(Ax, x)| \leqq \eta \| x \|^2$ for any x in the space. By the Schwarz inequality, we have

$$|(Ax, x)| \leqq \| Ax \| \ \| x \| \ .$$

It is easily inferred from this that

$$\eta \leqq \| A \| \ . \tag{7-3.5}$$

In order to obtain the reverse inequality we have, for any x and y in the space

$$(A(x+y), x+y) = (Ax, x)+(Ay, y)+2(Ax, y) \ ,$$

$$(A(x-y), x-y) = (Ax, x)+(Ay, y)-2(Ax, y) \ .$$

Subtraction of these two relations yields the identity

$$4(Ax, y) = (A(x+y), x+y)-(A(x-y), x-y) \ .$$

From this, we can infer that

$$|(Ax, y)| \leqq \tfrac{1}{4}(\eta\| x+y \|^2+\eta\| x-y \|^2)$$
$$\leqq \frac{\eta}{2}(\| x \|^2+\| y \|^2) \ .$$

Since this inequality is valid for any x and y in the space, we may let x be any vector with a unit norm and if $Ax \neq 0$ let

$$y = \frac{Ax}{\| Ax \|} \ . \tag{7-3.6}$$

In view of relation (7-3.6), y has a unit norm. Hence the above inequality may be reduced to

$$\frac{1}{\| Ax \|}|(Ax, Ax)| \leqq \eta \ .$$

That is, $\| Ax \| \leqq \eta$ when $Ax \neq 0$. However, the inequality is obviously true when $Ax = 0$. This implies that

$$\| A \| \leqq \eta \ ,$$

and with relation (7-3.5) leads to the conclusion that

$$\| A \| = \eta \ .$$

This proves the theorem.

The following result is pertinent to the conjecture that extreme values of the quadratic form are associated with eigenvectors. Let q be the quadratic form defined by formula (7-3.4), and let the discussion be restricted to the space $V_n(R)$. If $\mathbf{A}$ is the matrix of A relative to the natural basis for $V_n(R)$, $q(\mathbf{x})$ may be rewritten as

$$q(\mathbf{x}) = \tilde{\mathbf{x}}\mathbf{A}\mathbf{x} \ .$$

We consider the possibility of extreme values of q subject to the auxiliary condition $\| \mathbf{x} \| = 1$ or $\| \mathbf{x} \|^2 = 1$.

According to the method of Lagrange,[4] the critical points of q, under the specified restraint, are among the critical points of the function

$$Q(\mathbf{x}) = q(\mathbf{x})+\lambda(1-\| \mathbf{x} \|^2)$$
$$= \tilde{\mathbf{x}}\mathbf{A}\mathbf{x}+\lambda(1-\tilde{\mathbf{x}}\mathbf{x}) \ .$$

The critical points of Q are those for which

$$\nabla Q = \mathbf{o} \ ,$$

where ∇Q (commonly called grad Q) is the n-tuple of partial derivatives of Q with respect to the components of $\mathbf{x}$. Since $\mathbf{A}$ is symmetric, we have

$$\nabla Q = 2\mathbf{A}\mathbf{x}+\lambda(-2\mathbf{x}) = 2(\mathbf{A}-\lambda\mathbf{I})\mathbf{x} \ .$$

[4] Buck [9], page 362.

It follows that ∇Q is zero if and only if λ is an eigenvalue and $\mathbf{x}$ is an eigenvector of $\mathbf{A}$. This implies that an extreme value of q can occur only when $\mathbf{x}$ is an eigenvector.

Since the region determined by $\| \mathbf{x} \| = 1$ is closed, we may argue that $| q(\mathbf{x}) |$ must have a maximum value that is achieved when $\mathbf{x}$ is an eigenvector. Also, from Theorem 7-3.1, we know that the maximum of $| q(\mathbf{x}) |$ is equal to the maximum magnification of A. It is not hard to infer that $\max | q(\mathbf{x}) |$ and $\max \| A\mathbf{x} \|$ both occur when $\mathbf{x}$ is an eigenvector associated with the eigenvalue of maximum magnitude.

In Chapter 8, where we deal with an infinite-dimensional space, we establish the existence of a vector which maximizes $|(Ax, x)|$ and $\| Ax \|$, with $\| x \| = 1$. This vector is shown to be an eigenvector associated with an eigenvalue whose magnitude is $\| A \|$. Having established the existence of one eigenvector, we see that the existence of others readily follows. A useful introduction to the technique of successive determination of eigenvalues is contained in the following discussion of the decomposition of a transformation on a finite-dimensional space.

Let A be a real symmetric transformation on $V_n(R)$ with eigenvalues $\{\lambda_1, \lambda_2, \ldots, \lambda_n\}$, not necessarily all distinct, arranged in order of decreasing magnitude. Let $\{\mathbf{x}_1, \mathbf{x}_2, \ldots, \mathbf{x}_n\}$ be a corresponding set of orthonormal eigenvectors, and let the matrix of A relative to the natural basis for $V_n(R)$ be $\mathbf{A}$. The matrix $\mathbf{P}_j$, given by

$$\mathbf{P}_j = \mathbf{x}_j \tilde{\mathbf{x}}_j ,$$

determines a transformation P_j. It may be recalled that a matrix of the form of $\mathbf{P}_j$ was introduced in Chapter 3 following Theorem 3-4.2. It is easily verified that

$$\mathbf{P}_j \mathbf{x}_i = \begin{cases} \mathbf{o} , & i \neq j , \\ \mathbf{x}_j , & i = j . \end{cases}$$

Consequently, $\mathbf{P}_j$ has rank 1, and

$$\tilde{\mathbf{X}} \mathbf{P}_j \mathbf{X} = \mathbf{d}_j \tilde{\mathbf{d}}_j .$$

Thus, the canonical form of $\mathbf{P}_j$ is a diagonal matrix with 1 in the jth diagonal position and zeros elsewhere. It is easily seen that

$$\mathbf{P}_j^2 = \mathbf{P}_j ,$$

so that $\mathbf{P}_j$ is idempotent. The effect of this transformation on any vector $\mathbf{x}$ is easily appreciated if $\mathbf{x}$ is expressed as a linear combination of eigenvectors. That is, let

$$\mathbf{x} = \alpha_1 \mathbf{x}_1 + \alpha_2 \mathbf{x}_2 + \cdots + \alpha_n \mathbf{x}_n .$$

In view of the above observations, we see that

$$\begin{aligned}\mathbf{P}_j\mathbf{x} &= \alpha_1\mathbf{P}_j\mathbf{x}_1+\alpha_2\mathbf{P}_j\mathbf{x}_2+\cdots+\alpha_j\mathbf{P}_j\mathbf{x}_j+\cdots+\alpha_n\mathbf{P}_j\mathbf{x}_n\\ &= \alpha_j\mathbf{x}_j\ .\end{aligned}$$

Hence, it is appropriate to call $\mathbf{P}_j$ a *projection* on the one-dimensional subspace generated by the eigenvector $\mathbf{x}_j$.

If we consider the transformation A_1 whose matrix $\mathbf{A}_1$ is given by

$$\mathbf{A}_1 = \mathbf{A}-\lambda_1\mathbf{P}_1\ ,$$

it is easily verified that

$$\tilde{\mathbf{X}}\mathbf{A}_1\mathbf{X} = \begin{bmatrix} 0 & 0 & 0 & \cdots & 0 \\ 0 & \lambda_2 & 0 & \cdots & 0 \\ 0 & 0 & \lambda_3 & \cdots & 0 \\ \cdot & \cdot & \cdot & \cdot & \cdot \\ \cdot & \cdot & \cdot & \cdot & \cdot \\ \cdot & \cdot & \cdot & \cdot & \cdot \\ 0 & 0 & 0 & \cdots & \lambda_n \end{bmatrix} .$$

The eigenvalues of $\mathbf{A}_1$ are, therefore, $0, \lambda_2, \lambda_3, \ldots, \lambda_n$ and its eigenvectors are identical with those of $\mathbf{A}$. The significant point here is that the eigenvalue of $\mathbf{A}_1$ with maximum magnitude is λ_2.

In general, we may define a transformation A_k with matrix $\mathbf{A}_k$, given by

$$\mathbf{A}_k = \mathbf{A}-\sum_{j=1}^{k}\lambda_j\mathbf{P}_j\ , \tag{7-3.7}$$

and note that λ_{k+1} is its eigenvalue of maximum magnitude. Recalling that $|\lambda_{k+1}| = \|A_k\|$, we see that a technique is available for specifying the eigenvalues of A one at a time and in order of decreasing magnitude. This is the technique that is adopted in Chapter 8.

If $k = n$ in formula (7-3.7), it is easy to see that $\mathbf{A}_n$ maps every eigenvector of $\mathbf{A}$ into the zero vector. It follows that $\mathbf{A}_n = \mathbf{0}$ and that

$$\mathbf{A} = \sum_{j=1}^{n}\lambda_j\mathbf{P}_j\ .$$

Since this is equivalent to

$$A = \sum_{j=1}^{n}\lambda_j P_j\ ,$$

we have succeeded in decomposing the transformation A into a linear combination of projections. It is useful to note that A_k maps the subspace spanned by $\{\mathbf{x}_1, \mathbf{x}_2, \ldots, \mathbf{x}_k\}$ into the zero vector and that it maps the orthogonal complement of this subspace into itself. Also, it can be inferred that

$$\sum_{j=1}^{n} P_j = I\ ,$$

where I is the identity transformation.

Example 1. A simple example illustrates some of these facts. The matrix

$$\mathbf{A} = \begin{pmatrix} 2 & 1 & 0 \\ 1 & 2 & 0 \\ 0 & 0 & -2 \end{pmatrix},$$

has eigenvalues 3, -2, 1. The normal eigenvector associated with 3 is $\mathbf{x}_1$, given by

$$\mathbf{x}_1 = \frac{1}{\sqrt{2}} \begin{pmatrix} 1 \\ 1 \\ 0 \end{pmatrix}.$$

The matrix

$$\mathbf{P}_1 = \mathbf{x}_1 \tilde{\mathbf{x}}_1 = \frac{1}{2} \begin{pmatrix} 1 & 1 & 0 \\ 1 & 1 & 0 \\ 0 & 0 & 0 \end{pmatrix},$$

determines a projection P_1. The matrix $\mathbf{A}_1$, where

$$\mathbf{A}_1 = \mathbf{A} - 3\mathbf{P}_1 = \frac{1}{2} \begin{pmatrix} 1 & -1 & 0 \\ -1 & 1 & 0 \\ 0 & 0 & -4 \end{pmatrix},$$

has eigenvalues 0, -2, 1, and the eigenvalue -2 is associated with the eigenvector

$$\mathbf{x}_2 = \begin{pmatrix} 0 \\ 0 \\ 1 \end{pmatrix}.$$

If P_2 is defined by

$$\mathbf{P}_2 = \mathbf{x}_2 \tilde{\mathbf{x}}_2 = \begin{pmatrix} 0 & 0 & 0 \\ 0 & 0 & 0 \\ 0 & 0 & 1 \end{pmatrix},$$

$$\mathbf{A}_2 = \mathbf{A} - 3\mathbf{P}_1 + 2\mathbf{P}_2 = \frac{1}{2} \begin{pmatrix} 1 & -1 & 0 \\ -1 & 1 & 0 \\ 0 & 0 & 0 \end{pmatrix}.$$

The eigenvalues of $\mathbf{A}_2$ are 0, 0, 1, and the eigenvalue 1 is associated with the eigenvector

$$\mathbf{x}_3 = \frac{1}{\sqrt{2}} \begin{pmatrix} 1 \\ -1 \\ 0 \end{pmatrix}.$$

Finally, with $\mathbf{P}_3$ defined by

$$\mathbf{P}_3 = \mathbf{x}_3 \tilde{\mathbf{x}}_3 = \frac{1}{2} \begin{pmatrix} 1 & -1 & 0 \\ -1 & 1 & 0 \\ 0 & 0 & 0 \end{pmatrix},$$

we have

$$\mathbf{A} = 3\mathbf{P}_1 - 2\mathbf{P}_2 + \mathbf{P}_3 .$$

The decomposition of a symmetric linear operator into a linear combination of projections is accomplished in a similar fashion when the domain of the operator is an infinite-dimensional space. In fact, the discussion given here bears a close resemblance to that of Chapter 8.[5,6]

Exercises

1. Prove that the eigenvalues of a real symmetric linear operator on the space $V_n(C)$ are all real.

2. Prove that an orthogonal set of vectors in $V_n(R)$ is linearly independent.

3. A projection on an n-dimensional vector space V may be defined as any linear operator P which is idempotent, that is, such that $P^2 = P$.

(a) If P is a projection and if R is its range and N is its null space, then prove that V is the direct sum of R and N. That is, prove that every v in V can be uniquely represented as

$$v = r + n \ ,$$

where $r \in R$ and $n \in N$. It is customary to call P the *projection on R along N.*

(b) Prove that the operator

$$Q = I - P$$

is the projection on N along R. Show also that PQ is the zero operator.

4. Relative to the natural basis of $V_3(R)$, a transformation A has the matrix **A** given by

$$\mathbf{A} = \begin{pmatrix} -1 & 0 & 0 \\ 0 & 3 & 1 \\ 0 & 1 & 3 \end{pmatrix} .$$

Find the spectrum and reduce the transformation to a linear combination of projections.

---

[5] A good treatment of finite-dimensional spectral analysis may be found in Hoffman and Kunze [25].

[6] For a discussion of the general spectral theorem, the reader is again referred to Lorch [33].

8

Self-Adjoint Eigenvalue Problems

8-1. INTRODUCTION

In this chapter we treat the eigenvalue problem associated with an nth-order linear differential boundary system. This problem has played a major role in the development of mathematics. Its relation to concrete problems was mentioned in Chapter 7, and an algebraic background was provided for the discussion to follow. This discussion is designed to emphasize the relation between eigenfunction expansion theory and the spectral decomposition of a linear operator. In this way a motivation and a foundation are provided for further work in functional analysis and operator theory.[1]

In preceding chapters, we have emphasized the correspondence between scalar systems and matrix systems. In general, a matrix system is easier to deal with than a scalar system. This is in part due to the notational advantage of matrices and, in part to the fact that a matrix system is a system of the first order. We have taken advantage of this previously and have, in many cases, inferred results for a scalar system from results developed for a matrix system. This device is of limited value here because the matrix system associated with a self-adjoint scalar system is not in general self-adjoint.

8-2. THE nth-ORDER BOUNDARY SYSTEM

The differential operator L is defined here, as in Chapter 6, by

$$Lu = p_0 u^{[n]} + p_1 u^{[n-1]} + \cdots + p_n u \ , \tag{8-2.1}$$

where $p_0 \neq 0$ on $[a, b]$ and $p_j \in C^{n-j}[a, b]$. A solution of

$$Lu = 0 \tag{8-2.2}$$

is required to satisfy the auxiliary relation

$$\mathbf{W}^{[a]}\mathbf{k}(u(a)) + \mathbf{W}^{[b]}\mathbf{k}(u(b)) = \mathbf{o} \ , \tag{8-2.3}$$

where $\mathbf{W}^{[a]}$ and $\mathbf{W}^{[b]}$ are square matrices. This boundary problem was discussed in Chapter 6, and all the results deduced there are available for use here. We assume that the problem is incompatible so that Green's function exists. We also assume that the problem is self-adjoint. Hence $L^* = L$, and from Corollary 6-6.1 we get

$$\mathbf{W}^{[a]}\mathbf{P}^{-1}(a)\tilde{\mathbf{W}}^{[a]} = \mathbf{W}^{[b]}\mathbf{P}^{-1}(b)\tilde{\mathbf{W}}^{[b]} \ .$$

[1] Birkhoff and Rota [4], Ficken [17], and Olmsted [38], in addition to articles previously mentioned, are recommended for additional reading.

Self-adjointness also implies that the concomitant matrix **P** is skew-symmetric and that Green's function is symmetric (i.e., $G(t,s) = G(s,t)$).

A boundary problem containing a parameter may be introduced by considering

$$Lu = \lambda u \tag{8-2.4}$$

together with the boundary relation (8-2.3). It is reasonable to suspect that the problem is compatible for some values of λ and incompatible for others. Certainly, according to our previous assumption, it is incompatible if $\lambda = 0$.

Definition 8-2.1. *A value of λ for which the boundary problem* (8-2.4) *and* (8-2.3) *is compatible is an* ***eigenvalue*** *for the problem, and a corresponding nontrivial solution of the problem is an* ***eigenfunction.*** *The set of all eigenvalues is the* ***spectrum*** *of the boundary problem.*

It should be noted that the boundary problem is homogeneous and, hence, that all the eigenfunctions associated with any specific eigenvalue (augmented by the zero function) form a vector subspace of $C^n[a, b]$.

If λ_0 is any eigenvalue and u_0 is a corresponding eigenfunction, then the nonhomogeneous equation

$$Lu = \lambda_0 u_0 ,$$

with the boundary condition (8-2.3), has u_0 as a unique solution. Since the solution of this boundary problem can be expressed in terms of Green's function, it must be inferred that

$$u_0(t) = \lambda_0 \int_a^b G(t,s) u_0(s)\, ds .$$

It follows that every solution of (8-2.4) and (8-2.3) is a solution of the integral equation

$$\lambda \int_a^b G(t,s) u(s)\, ds = u(t) . \tag{8-2.5}$$

The converse statement is also valid, so that the integral equation (8-2.5) is equivalent to the differential boundary problem (8-2.4) and (8-2.3). The integral operator $\mathscr{G}$ may be defined by (see Section 6-7)

$$v = \mathscr{G} u ,$$

where

$$v(t) = \int_a^b G(t,s) u(s)\, ds . \tag{8-2.6}$$

Hence, equation (8-2.5) may be written as

$$\mathscr{G} u = \rho u , \tag{8-2.7}$$

where $\rho = \lambda^{-1}$. Because of the formal equivalence of equation (8-2.7) and the corresponding relation in finite-dimensional linear algebra, we speak of *eigenvalues and eigenfunctions* of the linear operator $\mathscr{G}$. It should be noted that the eigenvalues of $\mathscr{G}$ are the reciprocals of the eigenvalues of the given differential boundary system and that the eigenfunctions of $\mathscr{G}$ are identical with those of the differential system.

Exercises

1. For each of the following boundary problems find an equivalent integral equation.

(a) $-u'' = \lambda u$,
$u(0) = 0 \ , \quad u(\pi) = 0$;

(b) $u'' + u = \lambda u$,
$u(0) = 0 \ , \quad u'(\pi) = 0$;

(c) $u^{[4]} = \lambda u$,
$u(0) = u'(0) = 0 \ , \quad u''(1) = u'''(1) = 0$.

2. Show that the boundary problem

$$(pu')' + qu = 0 \ ,$$
$$\alpha_1 u(a) + \alpha_2 u'(a) = 0 \ , \quad \beta_1 u(b) + \beta_2 u'(b) = 0 \ ,$$

is self-adjoint if $q \in C[a, b]$, $p \in C^1[a, b]$, $p(t) \neq 0$ on $[a, b]$, and α_1, α_2, β_1, and β_2 are arbitrary real numbers.

8-3. SOME PROPERTIES OF THE OPERATOR $\mathscr{G}$

Since $\mathscr{G}$ is an integral operator, it is obviously linear. At this point, it is convenient to restrict its domain to the space $C[a, b]$ of all real-valued continuous functions on the closed interval $[a, b]$. We shall observe later that this domain admits of a substantial extension. At the same time, it will be seen that the character of $\mathscr{G}$ is completely determined by its properties on this domain.

If u and v are any two functions in $C[a, b]$, their *inner product* (u, v) is

$$(u, v) = \int_a^b u(t) v(t) \, dt \ .$$

A topology for the space is provided by the metric associated with the inner product norm

$$\| u \| = (u, u)^{1/2} \ .$$

Also, two functions u and v are *orthogonal* if their inner product is zero, that is, if

$$(u, v) = 0 \ .$$

Some of the properties of inner product spaces developed in Sections 1-8 and 1-9 are used in this chapter. In particular, the Schwarz inequality

$$| (u, v) | \leqq \| u \| \, \| v \|$$

is repeatedly used. For the inner product as defined here, this inequality may be written in the explicit form

$$\left| \int_a^b u(t)v(t)\,dt \right| \leqq \left(\int_a^b u^2(t)\,dt \right)^{1/2} \left(\int_a^b v^2(t)\,dt \right)^{1/2} .$$

It is pertinent to note that this integral inequality remains valid if the interval of integration is reduced to any subinterval of $[a, b]$. The inequality in this form is used in Theorem 8-3.2.

Since the domain of $\mathcal{G}$ is a vector space, every element in it can be expressed in the form αu, where u has unit norm. Since $\mathcal{G}$ is a linear operator, we have

$$\mathcal{G}(\alpha u) = \alpha \mathcal{G} u \ .$$

This implies that the essential properties of $\mathcal{G}$ can be determined by considering its properties relative to elements with a unit norm. The following two theorems reveal significant properties of the operator.

Definition 8-3.1. *A set of functions $\{f\}$, each function being defined on an interval $[a, b]$, is* ***equibounded*** *on that interval if for some positive real number M,*

$$|f(t)| \leqq M \ , \quad a \leqq t \leqq b,$$

for every f in the set.

Theorem 8-3.1. *The set of functions $\{\mathcal{G}u : \|u\| = 1\}$ is equibounded on $[a, b]$.*

PROOF. From Theorem 6-7.1, there must exist a positive real number M such that

$$|G(t, s)| \leqq M \ ,$$

for all values of t and s on the interval $[a, b]$ except when $t = s$. Hence,

$$|\mathcal{G}u(t)| \leqq \int_a^b M|u(s)|\,ds \ ,$$

for every t in $[a, b]$. The right-hand side of this relation may be regarded as the inner product of $|u|$ with the function that has a constant value of M on $[a, b]$. Using the Schwarz inequality, therefore, and recalling that $\|u\| = 1$, we have, with $a \leqq t \leqq b$,

$$|\mathcal{G}u(t)| \leqq M(b-a)^{1/2} \ .$$

This proves the theorem.

The second theorem involves the concept of *equicontinuity* which is defined as follows.

Definition 8-3.2. *A set of functions* $\{f\}$, *each function being defined on an interval* $[a, b]$, *is* ***equicontinuous*** *on* $[a, b]$ *if, for each positive real number* ε, *there is a corresponding real number* δ *such that, for every* f *in the set,*

$$|f(t_1)-f(t_2)| < \varepsilon \ ,$$

where t_1 *and* t_2 *are any two points in* $[a, b]$ *for which* $|t_1-t_2| < \delta$.

Theorem 8-3.2. *The set of functions* $\{\mathscr{G}u : \|u\| = 1\}$ *is equicontinuous on* $[a, b]$.

PROOF. It may be recalled from Theorem 6-7.2 that Green's function is continuous in both variables on the interval $[a, b]$ except at the points where $s = t$. If the order n of the differential equation is 2 or greater, the discontinuity at these points is removable. However, if $n = 1$, the discontinuity is a finite jump at $s = t$. In either case, if the square $a \leqq t \leqq b$, $a \leqq s \leqq b$ is separated into two halves by the diagonal line $s = t$, the function G is uniformly continuous on each half. That is, if ε is any positive real number, we can find a positive number δ_1 such that

$$|G(t_2, s)-G(t_1, s)| < \frac{\varepsilon}{2(b-a)^{1/2}}$$

if $|t_2-t_1| < \delta_1$ and if the points (t_1, s) and (t_2, s) are in the square and on the same side of the diagonal $s = t$. Also, even if the points are on opposite sides of the diagonal and if $n = 1$, using $|G(t, s)| \leqq M$, as we did in the proof of Theorem 8-3.1, we have

$$|G(t_2, s)-G(t_1, s)| \leqq 2M \ .$$

Let δ_2 be a positive real number such that

$$\delta_2 < \frac{\varepsilon^2}{16M^2} \ ,$$

and let δ be the smaller of δ_1 and δ_2. Hence, assuming for definiteness that $t_1 < t_2$, we have

$$\begin{aligned}
&|\mathscr{G}u(t_2)-\mathscr{G}u(t_1)| \\
&\quad = \left| \int_a^b [G(t_2, s)-G(t_1, s)]u(s)\, ds \right| \\
&\quad \leqq \int_a^{t_1} |G(t_2, s)-G(t_1, s)|\,|u(s)|\, ds + \int_{t_2}^{b} |G(t_2, s)-G(t_1, s)|\,|u(s)|\, ds \\
&\qquad\qquad + \int_{t_1}^{t_2} |G(t_2, s)-G(t_1, s)|\,|u(s)|\, ds \\
&\quad < \int_a^b \frac{\varepsilon}{2(b-a)^{\frac{1}{2}}} |u(s)|\, ds + \int_{t_1}^{t_2} 2M|u(s)|\, ds \ ,
\end{aligned}$$

if $t_2 - t_1 < \delta$. Using the Schwarz inequality on each term of the right-hand side, we get

$$|\mathscr{G}u(t_2) - \mathscr{G}u(t_1)| \leqq \tfrac{1}{2}\varepsilon \| u \| + 2M(t_2 - t_1)^{\frac{1}{2}} \| u \| < \varepsilon ,$$

if $t_2 - t_1 < \delta$. This proves the theorem.

These theorems are concerned with individual functional values of functions in the range of $\mathscr{G}$. In this sense, they are stronger than results that involve only the norms of the functions. Indeed, we can easily derive a result of the latter kind from Theorem 8-3.1 by noting that, if the functional values of the members of $\{\mathscr{G}u\}$ are uniformly bounded, then the set of norms of the members is bounded. That is, there must exist a positive real number K such that

$$\| \mathscr{G}u \| \leqq K$$

for all u with unit norm. Alternatively, we may state that

$$\| \mathscr{G}u \| \leqq K \| u \|$$

for all u in $C[a, b]$. The operator $\mathscr{G}$ is, therefore, bounded in the norm of the space.

A bounded linear operator is automatically continuous relative to the norm. This follows from the fact that

$$\begin{aligned} \| \mathscr{G}u - \mathscr{G}v \| &= \| \mathscr{G}(u - v) \| \\ &\leqq K \| u - v \| . \end{aligned}$$

Thus, if ε is any positive real number, it is clear that

$$\| \mathscr{G}u - \mathscr{G}v \| < \varepsilon ,$$

if

$$\| u - v \| < \frac{\varepsilon}{K} .$$

We have established that the set $\{\| \mathscr{G}u \| : \| u \| = 1\}$ is a bounded set of real numbers. It must therefore have a least upper bound. This least upper bound is the *norm of the operator* and is represented by the symbol $\| \mathscr{G} \|$. We formalize this statement in the following extension of Definition 7-3.1.

Definition 8-3.3. *The norm $\| \mathscr{G} \|$ of the operator $\mathscr{G}$ is defined by*

$$\| \mathscr{G} \| = \sup_{\substack{u \in C[a, b] \\ \| u \| = 1}} \| \mathscr{G}u \| .$$

In view of the above discussion, we can infer that an equivalent definition is provided by

$$\| \mathscr{G} \| = \sup_{u \in C[a, b]} \frac{1}{\| u \|} \| \mathscr{G}u \| .$$

The significance of Theorems 8-3.1 and 8-3.2 becomes evident when we state the following theorem.

Theorem 8-3.3. The Ascoli Theorem. *If $\{f\}$ is an infinite, equibounded, equicontinuous set of functions on an interval I, then it contains a sequence $\{f_n : n = 1, 2, 3, \ldots\}$, which is uniformly convergent on I.*

PROOF. The proof of this theorem is not given here; it can be found in Coddington and Levinson[2] or Yosida.[3]

It follows from this theorem that any infinite subset of $\{\mathcal{G}u\colon \| u \| = 1\}$ contains at least one uniformly convergent sequence. This fact serves later to establish the existence of an eigenfunction of $\mathcal{G}$.

Following the lead of the algebraic developments of the previous chapter, we observe now the relation between the operator $\mathcal{G}$ and the inner product $(\mathcal{G}u, u)$. It may be noted initially that, since the boundary problem is self-adjoint, $G(t, s) = G(s, t)$. From this, it is easily inferred that

$$(\mathcal{G}u, v) = (u, \mathcal{G}v) \ , \tag{8-3.1}$$

for every u and v in $C[a, b]$. That is, the operator $\mathcal{G}$ is a *symmetric operator*. Theorem 7-3.1 is valid for the operator $\mathcal{G}$, hence we may write

$$\| \mathcal{G} \| = \sup_{\substack{u \in C[a,b] \\ \| u \| = 1}} |(\mathcal{G}u, u)| \ .$$

It should be noted that $\| \mathcal{G} \| > 0$. To prove this, we observe that the definition of $\| \mathcal{G} \|$ implies that $\| \mathcal{G}u \| \leqq \| \mathcal{G} \| \, \| u \|$ for all u in $C[a, b]$. Recalling from Section 6-7 that $L\mathcal{G}u = u$, we can infer that $\mathcal{G}u \neq 0$ unless $u = 0$. It follows that $\| \mathcal{G} \| \neq 0$.

8-4. AN ALGEBRA OF OPERATORS

The concept of the norm of an operator was introduced in Section 8-3. The use of the term "norm" is appropriate only if the postulates given in Section 1-7 are satisfied. These, in turn, have meaning only if the operators have an algebraic structure. This structure is implied by the algebra that we normally associate with functions. However, it is desirable to make some specific definitions here, since we make some use of the algebra in the rest of this chapter.

Let H and K be operators on some vector space D and let α be any real (or complex) number. The sum $H+K$ of the operators is defined by

$$(H+K)u = Hu + Ku \ ,$$

$u \in D$. The scalar product αH is

$$(\alpha H)u = \alpha(Hu) \ .$$

It follows that sets of operators can form vector spaces.

---

[2] Coddington and Levinson [11], page 5.
[3] Yosida [51], page 78.

Using the definition of a norm given in Section 8-3, it is easily verified that (see Section 1-7)

$$\text{(i)} \quad \| H \| \geqq 0 \ ,$$
$$\text{(ii)} \quad \| \alpha H \| = | \alpha | \ \| H \| \ ,$$
$$\text{(iii)} \quad \| H+K \| \leqq \| H \| + \| K \| \ .$$

We may also observe that, if H and K are symmetric operators, then

$$\begin{aligned}((H+K)u, v) &= (Hu, v)+(Ku, v) \\ &= (u, Hv)+(u, Kv) \\ &= (u, (H+K)v) \ .\end{aligned}$$

Hence, the sum of two symmetric operators is symmetric. Obviously, also, if H is symmetric, then αH is symmetric.

8-5. EXISTENCE OF EIGENVALUES AND EIGENFUNCTIONS

At this point, we are ready to establish the existence of an eigenvalue, and this is done in the following theorem. As indicated earlier, the domain of the operator $\mathscr{G}$ is restricted to the space $C[a, b]$.

Theorem 8-5.1. *Either* $\| \mathscr{G} \|$ *or* $- \| \mathscr{G} \|$ *is an eigenvalue for the operator* $\mathscr{G}$.

PROOF. For convenience let the symbol η be used to represent $\| \mathscr{G} \|$. If we assume initially that

$$\sup_{\| u \| = 1} (\mathscr{G}u, u)$$

is not less than

$$-\inf_{\| u \| = 1} (\mathscr{G}u, u) \ ,$$

we have

$$\eta = \| \mathscr{G} \| = \sup_{\| u \| = 1} (\mathscr{G}u, u) \ .$$

By virtue of the definition of a supremum, there must exist a sequence $\{u_n\}$, $\| u_n \| = 1$, such that the corresponding sequence $\{(\mathscr{G}u_n, u_n)\}$ converges to η. Since the terms of the sequence $\{\mathscr{G}u_n\}$ form a subset of $\{\mathscr{G}u : \| u \| = 1\}$, the terms are a set of equibounded and equicontinuous functions. By Theorem 8-3.3, the sequence $\{\mathscr{G}u_n\}$ must have a subsequence which converges uniformly on $[a, b]$. This subsequence may be designated by $\{\mathscr{G}v_n : n = 1, 2, 3, \ldots\}$, and we can infer that it converges to some continuous function w. Since $\{\mathscr{G}v_n\}$ converges uniformly to w, it must also converge in the norm of the space $C[a, b]$. That is,

$$\text{(8-5.1)} \qquad \lim_{n \to \infty} \| \mathscr{G}v_n - w \| = 0 \ ,$$

and

$$\lim_{n \to \infty} \| \mathscr{G}v_n \| = \| w \| \ .$$

The left-hand side of the preceding relation cannot be larger than the norm of $\mathscr{G}$; hence

$$\| w \| \leqq \eta \ . \tag{8-5.2}$$

From the identity

$$\| \mathscr{G}v_n - \eta v_n \|^2 = \| \mathscr{G}v_n \|^2 - 2\eta(\mathscr{G}v_n, v_n) + \eta^2 \| v_n \|^2 \ ,$$

we infer that

$$\lim_{n\to\infty} \| \mathscr{G}v_n - \eta v_n \|^2 = \| w \|^2 - \eta^2 \ . \tag{8-5.3}$$

Since the left-hand side is nonnegative,

$$\eta \leqq \| w \| \ . \tag{8-5.4}$$

Relations (8-5.2) and (8-5.4) imply that

$$\| w \| = \eta \ .$$

Using this result in (8-5.3), we get

$$\lim_{n\to\infty} \| \mathscr{G}v_n - \eta v_n \| = 0 \ .$$

Since we know that the sequence $\{\mathscr{G}v_n\}$ converges, the last relation shows that $\{\eta v_n\}$ also converges and that both sequences converge to the same function. Clearly, the sequence $\{v_n\}$ converges to $(1/\eta)w$ and, since $\mathscr{G}$ is continuous, Theorem 1-12.1 insures that $\{\mathscr{G}v_n\}$ converges to $\mathscr{G}((1/\eta)w)$. This implies that $w = \mathscr{G}((1/\eta)w)$ and, hence, that

$$\mathscr{G}w = \eta w \ .$$

We have therefore shown that w is an eigenfunction of $\mathscr{G}$ and that η is an eigenvalue.

The above conclusion was based on the assumption that

$$\sup_{\|u\|=1} (\mathscr{G}u, u) \geqq -\inf_{\|u\|=1} (\mathscr{G}u, u) \ .$$

If the reverse inequality holds, namely, if

$$\sup_{\|u\|=1} (\mathscr{G}u, u) < -\inf_{\|u\|=1} (\mathscr{G}u, u) \ ,$$

we may consider the operator $-\mathscr{G}$, the negative of $\mathscr{G}$. That is, $-\mathscr{G}$ is defined by formula (8-2.6) with $G(t, s)$ replaced by $-G(t, s)$. It is easily inferred that

$$\sup_{\|u\|=1} (-\mathscr{G}u, u) = -\inf_{\|u\|=1} (\mathscr{G}u, u) \ ,$$

hence

$$\eta = \| \mathscr{G} \| = \| -\mathscr{G} \| = \sup_{\|u\|=1} (-\mathscr{G}u, u) \ .$$

The earlier results can therefore be applied to $-\mathscr{G}$ to guarantee the existence of a function w such that

$$-\mathscr{G}w = \eta w \ .$$

Since this relation can be written as

$$\mathscr{G}w = -\eta w \ ,$$

we can conclude that w is an eigenfunction of $\mathscr{G}$, and $-\eta$ is an eigenvalue of $\mathscr{G}$.

Thus we have shown that $\| \mathscr{G} \|$ or $-\| \mathscr{G} \|$ is an eigenvalue of the operator $\mathscr{G}$ according as

$$\| \mathscr{G} \| = \sup_{\| u \| = 1} (\mathscr{G}u, u)$$

or

$$\| \mathscr{G} \| = -\inf_{\| u \| = 1} (\mathscr{G}u, u) \ .$$

This proves the theorem.

We shall now show that $\mathscr{G}$ has an infinite set of eigenvalues and that the associated eigenfunctions form an orthogonal set. Let the eigenvalue, whose existence was established above, be represented by ρ_0, and let u_0 be the corresponding normalized eigenfunction (that is, $u_0 = \| w \|^{-1} w$).

An elementary integral operator P_0 may be defined by

$$y = P_0 f \ , \quad f \in C[a, b],$$

where

$$y(t) = \int_a^b u_0(t) u_0(s) f(s) \, ds \ .$$

In view of the definition,

$$P_0 f = \alpha_0 u_0 \ ,$$

where $\alpha_0 = (f, u_0)$. Hence the range of P_0, represented by the symbol U_0, is the one-dimensional subspace consisting of all multiples of u_0. In particular,

$$P_0 u_0 = u_0 \ . \qquad (8\text{-}5.5)$$

Since

$$P_0^2 f = P_0(P_0 f) = P_0 \alpha_0 u_0 = \alpha_0 u_0 = P_0 f \ ,$$

we infer that $P_0^2 = P_0$. Hence P_0 is an idempotent transformation and may be called a *projection*.

Relation (8-5.5) implies that u_0 is an eigenfunction of P_0 associated with the eigenvalue 1. Hence the operator $\rho_0 P_0$ has u_0 as an eigenfunction and ρ_0 as its associated eigenvalue. There is some suggestion here that $\rho_0 P_0$ can be regarded as a "component" of the operator $\mathscr{G}$ and that the latter operator can, in fact, be decomposed into a sum of operators of this type. With this in mind, let the operator $\mathscr{G}_1$ be

$$\mathscr{G}_1 = \mathscr{G} - \rho_0 P_0 \ .$$

Let the ranges of $\mathcal{G}$ and $\mathcal{G}_1$ be designated, respectively, by R_0 and R_1. For any f in $C[a, b]$, we have

$$\mathcal{G}_1 f = \mathcal{G} f - \rho_0 \alpha_0 u_0 , \tag{8-5.6}$$

$\alpha_0 = (f, u_0)$. Since $\rho_0 \alpha_0 u_0 \in U_0$ and since $U_0 \subset R_0$, we see that $R_1 \subset R_0$. If $f = u_0$, it is clear that $\mathcal{G}_1 f = 0$. On the other hand, if we apply the operator L to both sides of the relation (8-5.6), we get

$$L\mathcal{G}_1 f = f - \alpha_0 u_0 .$$

This implies that $\mathcal{G}_1 f = 0$, only if f is a scalar multiple of u_0. It follows that the one-dimensional subspace U_0 is the kernel or null space of the operator $\mathcal{G}_1$. Moreover, $\mathcal{G}_1$ is the sum of two symmetric operators and is therefore symmetric. Hence,

$$(\mathcal{G}_1 f, u_0) = (f, \mathcal{G}_1 u_0) = 0 ,$$

and, therefore, U_0 is orthogonal to R_1. Finally, if relation (8-5.6) is rewritten as

$$\mathcal{G} f = \mathcal{G}_1 f + \rho_0 \alpha_0 u_0 ,$$

we see that every element in R_0 is the sum of an element in R_1 and an element in U_0. That is, R_0 is the direct sum of R_1 and U_0, and U_0 is the orthogonal complement of R_1 relative to the subspace R_0. The relationship of these spaces to each other is shown in Figure 8-5.1. The one-dimensional subspace U_0 is represented by a straight line through 0 and u_0.

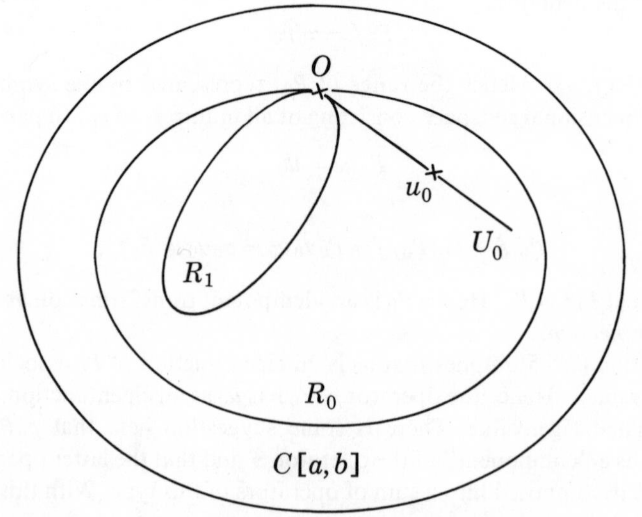

Figure 8-5.1

We have already noted that $\mathscr{G}_1 f = 0$, only if $f \in U_0$. This implies that $\| \mathscr{G}_1 \| \neq 0$. Hence, in view of Theorem 8-5.1, we may state that $\mathscr{G}_1$ has a non-zero eigenvalue ρ_1 and a corresponding normal eigenfunction u_1. Since u_1 belongs to the range R_1 of $\mathscr{G}_1$ and, since R_1 is orthogonal to U_0, it is clear that $P_0 u_1 = 0$. It follows that

$$\begin{aligned} \mathscr{G} u_1 &= \mathscr{G}_1 u_1 + \rho_0 P_0 u_1 \\ &= \rho_1 u_1 \ . \end{aligned}$$

That is, ρ_1 and u_1 are, respectively, an eigenvalue and an associated eigenfunction of $\mathscr{G}$.

It is clear that the above procedure may be repeated and that we may, in general, define an operator

$$\mathscr{G}_{i+1} = \mathscr{G}_i - \rho_i P_i \ , \quad i = 0, 1, 2, \ldots \ , \tag{8-5.7}$$

where $\mathscr{G}_0 = \mathscr{G}$, and ρ_i and u_i are, respectively, an eigenvalue and an associated normal eigenfunction of $\mathscr{G}_i$. The projection P_i is, with $f \in C[a, b]$,

$$y = P_i f \ ,$$

$$y(t) = \int_a^b u_i(t) u_i(s) f(s)\, ds \ .$$

The range U_i of P_i is the one-dimensional space spanned by the eigenfunction u_i. The range of $\mathscr{G}_i$ is designated by R_i, and it is clear that

$$U_i \subset R_i \ .$$

Hence, in view of the definition given in relation (8-5.7),

$$R_{i+1} \subset R_i \ . \tag{8-5.8}$$

Again, using the definition of $\mathscr{G}_{i+1}$, we have

$$\begin{aligned} \mathscr{G}_{i+1} u_i &= \mathscr{G}_i u_i - \rho_i P_i u_i \\ &= \rho_i u_i - \rho_i u_i \\ &= 0 \ . \end{aligned}$$

Therefore, for any f in $C[a, b]$,

$$\begin{aligned} (\mathscr{G}_{i+1} f, u_i) &= (f, \mathscr{G}_{i+1} u_i) \\ &= 0 \ . \end{aligned}$$

That is, u_i is orthogonal to every element in R_{i+1}, so that U_i is orthogonal to R_{i+1}. It may be argued, as before, that R_i is the direct sum of R_{i+1} and U_i. Figure 8-5.2 shows the relation of these subspaces to each other.

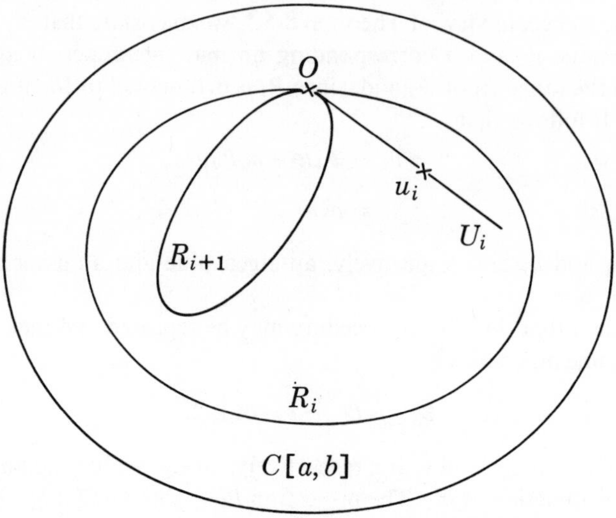

Figure 8-5.2

The successive definition of operators terminates only if $\| \mathscr{G}_j \| = 0$ for some j. That this does not happen can be seen by summing relation (8-5.7) on the index i to get

$$\mathscr{G}_j = \mathscr{G} - \sum_{i=0}^{j-1} \rho_i P_i \ . \tag{8-5.9}$$

From this, for any f in $C[a, b]$, we have

$$\mathscr{G}_j f = \mathscr{G} f - \sum_{i=0}^{j-1} \rho_i \alpha_i u_i \ ,$$

$\alpha_i = (f, u_i)$. Operating on both sides of the last relation with the differential operator L, we see that

$$L(\mathscr{G}_j f) = f - \sum_{i=0}^{i=1} \alpha_i u_i \ .$$

It follows that $\mathscr{G}_j f = 0$ only if f is a linear combination of the functions $u_0, u_1, \ldots, u_{j-1}$. This implies that $\mathscr{G}_j f \neq 0$ for some f in $C[a, b]$ and, hence, that $\| \mathscr{G}_j \| \neq 0$. There exists, therefore, an infinite sequence of operators with nonzero norms.

In view of (8-5.8), the sequence $\{R_i\}$ is a sequence of nested vector spaces. We have shown that u_i is orthogonal to R_{i+1}, and it follows that u_i is orthogonal to R_j if $j > i$. Since $u_j \in R_j$, u_i is orthogonal to u_j if $j > i$. This implies that the sequence $\{u_i\}$ is an orthonormal set of functions. Recalling the definition of P_i, therefore, we conclude that

(8-5.10) $$P_i u_j = 0 \ ,$$

if $j \neq i$.

Formula (8-5.9) may be rewritten as

$$\mathscr{G} = \mathscr{G}_j + \sum_{i=0}^{j-1} \rho_i P_i \ .$$

Hence, using (8-5.10), we have

$$\begin{aligned} \mathscr{G} u_j &= \mathscr{G}_j u_j \\ &= \rho_j u_j \ . \end{aligned}$$

This shows that ρ_j is an eigenvalue of $\mathscr{G}$ with u_j as the associated eigenfunction. Thus $\{\rho_i\}$ is an infinite sequence of eigenvalues of $\mathscr{G}$, and $\{u_i\}$ is a corresponding sequence of eigenfunctions. Since the terms of the latter sequence form an orthonormal set, they must be distinct. The eigenvalues, on the other hand, need not all be distinct. From (8-5.7), using (8-5.10), we get

$$\| \mathscr{G}_{i+1} u_{i+1} \| = \| \mathscr{G}_i u_{i+1} \| \ .$$

Since the left-hand side of this relation is equal to $|\rho_{i+1}|$ and since

$$|\rho_i| = \sup_{\|u\| = 1} \| \mathscr{G}_i u \| \ ,$$

we may write

$$|\rho_{i+1}| \leqq |\rho_i| \ .$$

This proves that the absolute values of the eigenvalues form a monotonic non-increasing sequence.

At this point it is appropriate to recall that our interest in the integral operator stems from its relation to the differential boundary problem (8-2.4) and (8-2.3). As noted in Section 8-2, the eigenfunctions of $\mathscr{G}$ are also the eigenfunctions of the boundary problem, and the eigenvalues of $\mathscr{G}$ are the reciprocals of the eigenvalues of the boundary problem. For the differential boundary problem, therefore, the set $\{\lambda_i, \ i = 0, 1, 2, \ldots\}$, where $\lambda_i = \rho_i^{-1}$ is a set of eigenvalues and

$$|\lambda_0| \leqq |\lambda_1| \leqq |\lambda_2| \leqq \cdots \ .$$

The question of whether or not our procedure has yielded all the eigenvalues and eigenfunctions of $\mathscr{G}$ should be raised here. In particular, we must consider the possibility that $\mathscr{G}$ has complex eigenvalues and eigenfunctions. In order to pursue this question, we must enlarge our basic function space to include continuous complex-valued functions defined on the real interval $[a, b]$. For two such functions u and v the inner product is

$$(u, v) = \int_a^b u(t) \bar{v}(t) \, dt \ .$$

The properties of this complex inner product were discussed in Chapter 1. The Green's function may be complex-valued in this case, and it is not hard to show that under the hypothesis of self-adjointness

$$G(t, s) = \bar{G}(s, t) \ .$$

In view of this, the relation (8-3.1)

$$(\mathscr{G}u, v) = (u, \mathscr{G}v)$$

remains valid for the enlarged domain. Hence, the functional

$$q(u) = (\mathscr{G}u, u)$$

has only real values. We can see this by observing that

$$\begin{aligned} q(u) &= (\mathscr{G}u, u) \\ &= (u, \mathscr{G}u) \\ &= \overline{(\mathscr{G}u, u)} \\ &= \bar{q}(u) . \end{aligned}$$

Let ρ be any eigenvalue of $\mathscr{G}$, and let u be a corresponding eigenfunction. The value of q associated with this u is

$$\begin{aligned} q(u) &= (\mathscr{G}u, u) \\ &= (\rho u, u) \\ &= \rho(u, u) \\ &= \rho \| u \|^2 . \end{aligned}$$

Since $q(u)$ is real, the eigenvalue ρ must also be real. The eigenfunction u may, nevertheless, be complex-valued. However, if $\mathscr{G}$ is real and if $u = x+iy$, where both x and y are real, it is easily seen that both x and y are eigenfunctions. Thus, we may always select real eigenfunctions for a real symmetric operator.

Although the above discussion reveals that no complex eigenvalues exist, it is still possible that some real eigenvalues have not been discovered. Subsequent developments suggest that this is not the case.

The method by which we have established the existence of eigenvalues does not provide a technique for their evaluation. However, if a representation of the general solution of $Lu = \lambda u$ is available, it can be substituted into the boundary conditions to yield a characteristic matrix $\mathbf{D}$ which depends on λ. The zeros of the determinant of this matrix are then the eigenvalues of the boundary problem. We give a simple example below, but it should be recognized that the general problem involves the determination of asymptotic solutions for the equation and an investigation of the zeros of an exponential sum.

Example 1. Consider the boundary problem

$$-u'' = \lambda u ,$$

$$u(0) = 0 , \quad u(\pi) = 0 .$$

A fundamental vector for the equation is

$$\tilde{\mathbf{u}}(t) = (\sin\sqrt{\lambda}\, t, \cos\sqrt{\lambda}\, t) .$$

Hence,

$$\mathbf{D} = \begin{pmatrix} 1 & 0 \\ 0 & 0 \end{pmatrix} \begin{pmatrix} 0 & 1 \\ \sqrt{\lambda} & 0 \end{pmatrix} + \begin{pmatrix} 0 & 0 \\ 1 & 0 \end{pmatrix} \begin{pmatrix} \sin\sqrt{\lambda}\pi & \cos\sqrt{\lambda}\pi \\ \sqrt{\lambda}\cos\sqrt{\lambda}\pi & -\sqrt{\lambda}\sin\sqrt{\lambda}\pi \end{pmatrix}$$

$$= \begin{pmatrix} 0 & 1 \\ \sin\sqrt{\lambda}\pi & \cos\sqrt{\lambda}\pi \end{pmatrix} .$$

The determinant of **D** is $|D(\lambda)| = -\sin\sqrt{\lambda}\pi$, and the eigenvalues are the roots (excluding $\lambda = 0$) of

$$\sin\sqrt{\lambda}\pi = 0 .$$

They are given by

$$\lambda_j = j^2 , \quad j = 1, 2, \ldots ,$$

and the corresponding normal eigenfunctions are given by

$$u_j = \sqrt{\frac{2}{\pi}} \sin jt .$$

Exercises

In Exercises 1–4 find eigenvalues and eigenfunctions for the given boundary problems.

1. $-u'' = \lambda u$,
$u(-a) = u(a) = 0$.

2. $-u'' = \lambda u$,
$u(0) = u'(1) = 0$.

3. $-u'' = \lambda u$,
$u'(0) = u(\pi) = 0$.

4. $-u'' = \lambda u$,
$u(0) + u'(0) = 0 , \quad u(1) = 0$.

5. If $L = L^*$, show that square matrices $\mathbf{W}^{[a]}$ and $\mathbf{W}^{[b]}$ can be found so that the boundary problem

$$Lu = \lambda u ,$$

$$\mathbf{W}^{[a]}\mathbf{k}(u(a)) + \mathbf{W}^{[b]}\mathbf{k}(u(b)) = \mathbf{o}$$

is self-adjoint.

6. Prove that any orthonormal set of functions in $C[a, b]$ is linearly independent.

7. Let λ_1 and λ_2 be two distinct eigenvalues of a self-adjoint boundary problem and let u_1 and u_2, respectively, be a corresponding pair of eigenfunctions. Use Green's formula to prove that u_1 and u_2 are orthogonal.

8-6. EXPANSION THEORY AND SPECTRAL DECOMPOSITION OF $\mathcal{G}$

The finite-dimensional case, treated in Chapter 7, indicates the possibility of representing any function in $C[a, b]$ by a series of eigenfunctions. We shall point out later that a much broader class of functions can be represented thus.

Our restriction of the domain of $\mathcal{G}$ to the space $C[a, b]$ has been made in order to simplify the exposition as much as possible. In Theorem 8-6.2, below, we discuss the expansion of a function that may have a discontinuity at one point. Consequently, in Theorem 8-6.1 we develop Bessel's inequality for a function in the space of integrable functions.

If x is a function in $C[a, b]$ which has the representation

$$x = \sum_{j=0}^{\infty} \alpha_j u_j \,, \tag{8-6.1}$$

where the series on the right-hand side converges uniformly on $[a, b]$, then we may multiply both sides of relation (8-6.1) by u_k and integrate from a to b. Since $\{u_j\}$ is a normal orthogonal set,

$$\alpha_k = (x, u_k) \ . \tag{8-6.2}$$

The coefficients of the series, defined by formula (8-6.2), are called the *Fourier coefficients* for the function x. The series itself is called a *generalized Fourier series* for x. The coefficients are well-defined for every x in $C[a, b]$ but, at this point, the question of whether or not the series converges to x is still open.

The set of all real-valued functions which are Riemann integrable on $[a, b]$ *is a vector space. We shall use the symbol* $R[a, b]$ *to represent this space.*

Formula (8-6.2) defines Fourier coefficients for every x in $R[a, b]$. Bessel's inequality, established in Chapter 1, for a finite orthonormal set is easily extended to an infinite set. We proceed to make this extension.

Theorem 8-6.1. *If x is any element in $R[a, b]$ and if $\{u_j\}$ is the orthonormal sequence of eigenfunctions of $\mathcal{G}$, then, if $\alpha_j = (x, u_j)$,*

$$\sum_{j=0}^{\infty} \alpha_j^2 \leqq \| x \|^2 \ . \tag{8-6.3}$$

PROOF. Theorem 1-9.1 insures that

$$\sum_{j=0}^{n} \alpha_j^2 \leqq \| x \|^2 \,,$$

for any natural number n. Since α_j^2 is positive, the series

$$\sum_{j=0}^{\infty} \alpha_j^2$$

must converge, and the inequality (8-6.3) must be valid. This proves the theorem.

We are now in a position to establish an important property of the sequence of eigenvalues.

Theorem 8-6.2. *The sequence $\{\rho_j\}$ of eigenvalues of $\mathcal{G}$ converges to zero.*

PROOF. For any fixed value of t, Green's function $G(t, s)$ regarded as a function of s on $[a, b]$ is either continuous or (if the order of the differential equation is 1) has a single jump discontinuity at $s = t$. $G(t, s)$ therefore belongs to $R[a, b]$, and its Fourier coefficients are

$$\begin{aligned}\alpha_j &= \int_a^b G(t, s) u_j(s)\, ds \\ &= \rho_j u_j(t) \ .\end{aligned}$$

Bessel's inequality implies that

$$\begin{aligned}\sum_{j=0}^{\infty} \rho_j^2 u_j^2(t) &\leqq \| G(t, s) \|^2 \\ &\leqq \int_a^b G^2(t, s)\, ds \ .\end{aligned}$$

Using M as a bound for G (see Theorem 8-3.1), we have

$$\sum_{j=0}^{\infty} \rho_j^2 u_j^2(t) \leqq M^2(b-a) \ .$$

Integration with respect to t yields

$$\sum_{j=0}^{\infty} \rho_j^2 \leqq M^2(b-a)^2 \ .$$

We have therefore shown that the series on the left-hand side of the last relation converges and, hence, that

$$\lim_{j\to\infty} \rho_j = 0 \ .$$

This proves the theorem.

Corollary 8-6.2. *The sequence $\{\lambda_j\}$ of eigenvalues of the differential boundary problem is unbounded and has no finite limit point.*

Theorem 8-6.3. (i) *If x is any function in the range of $\mathscr{G}$ and if $\alpha_j = (x, u_j)$, then*

$$x = \sum_{j=0}^{\infty} \alpha_j u_j \ .$$

(ii) *The operator $\mathscr{G}$ has the spectral representation*

$$\mathscr{G} = \sum_{j=0}^{\infty} \rho_j P_j \ ,$$

where P_j is a projection on the space spanned by the eigenfunction u_j and ρ_j is the associated eigenvalue.

PROOF. In order to prove part (ii) we may observe from the discussion in Section 8-4 that the set of bounded linear operators on the space $C[a, b]$ is itself a normed linear vector space. From formula (8-5.9), we have

$$\left\| \mathscr{G} - \sum_{i=0}^{j-1} \rho_i P_i \right\| = \| \mathscr{G}_j \| .$$

Since $\| \mathscr{G}_j \| = |\rho_j|$, Theorem 8-6.2 implies that for any positive real number ε there exists a natural number N such that

$$\left\| \mathscr{G} - \sum_{i=0}^{j-1} \rho_i P_i \right\| < \varepsilon ,$$

if $j \geqq N$. In this sense, therefore, it is appropriate to say that the series

$$\sum_{i=0}^{\infty} \rho_i P_i$$

converges to the operator $\mathscr{G}$. This proves part (ii).

The proof of part (i) parallels the above proof. If x is any function in the range of $\mathscr{G}$, there must be a function f in $C[a, b]$ such that

$$x = \mathscr{G} f .$$

Relation (8-5.9) insures that

$$\left\| \mathscr{G} f - \sum_{i=0}^{j-1} \rho_i P_i f \right\| = \| \mathscr{G}_j f \| . \tag{8-6.4}$$

It should be noted that the norm used here is the norm of the function space $C[a, b]$, whereas the norm used in the proof of part (ii) is the norm of the operator space. The operator norm appears again on the right-hand side of the next relation. This relation, which follows easily from (8-6.4), is

$$\left\| \mathscr{G} f - \sum_{i=0}^{j-1} \rho_i P_i f \right\| \leqq \| \mathscr{G}_j \| \, \| f \| .$$

The right-hand side is less than any arbitrary positive real ε if $j \geqq N$, where N is chosen so that

$$|\rho_j| < \frac{\varepsilon}{\| f \|} .$$

Since $\mathscr{G} f = x$ and $P_i f = (f, u_i) u_i$, we may write

$$x = \sum_{i=0}^{\infty} \rho_i (f, u_i) u_i .$$

It is clear that

$$\begin{aligned} \rho_i (f, u_i) &= (f, \rho_i u_i) \\ &= (f, \mathscr{G} u_i) \\ &= (\mathscr{G} f, u_i) \\ &= (x, u_i) . \end{aligned}$$

Hence, if $\alpha_i = (x, u_i)$, we have

$$x = \sum_{i=0}^{\infty} \alpha_i u_i .$$

This proves the theorem.

In Theorem 8-6.3, we have shown that the inner product norm

$$\left\| x - \sum_{i=0}^{j-1} \alpha_i u_i \right\|$$

is small when j is large. In this sense, therefore, we can say that the partial sum

$$\sum_{i=0}^{j-1} \alpha_i u_i$$

is close to x when j is large or that

$$\sum_{i=0}^{\infty} \alpha_i u_i$$

converges to x in the norm of the function space. Since

$$\left\| x - \sum_{i=0}^{j-1} \alpha_i u_i \right\|^2 = \int_a^b \left(x(t) - \sum_{i=0}^{j-1} \alpha_i u_i(t) \right)^2 dt \; ,$$

convergence in the norm is frequently called *convergence in the mean square.* The type of convergence described in most calculus texts is known as *pointwise convergence*, and it should be clear that a series which converges in the mean square on an interval $[a, b]$ need not necessarily converge pointwise at every point of that interval. However in this case we do have pointwise convergence, and this fact is established in the following theorem.

Theorem 8-6.4. *If x is any function in the range of $\mathscr{G}$, its Fourier series converges uniformly to x on* $[a, b]$.

PROOF. Using the notation of the previous theorem, we may write

$$\begin{aligned} \alpha_i u_i &= \rho_i(f, u_i) u_i \\ &= (f, u_i) \mathscr{G} u_i \; . \end{aligned}$$

Hence, for any two natural numbers p and q, with $p < q$, we have

$$\sum_{i=p}^{q} \alpha_i u_i = \mathscr{G}\left(\sum_{i=p}^{q} (f, u_i) u_i \right) .$$

Using the argument of Theorem 8-3.1, we can infer that

$$\begin{aligned} \left| \sum_{i=p}^{q} \alpha_i u_i(t) \right| &\leq M(b-a)^{1/2} \left\| \sum_{i=p}^{q} (f, u_i) u_i \right\| \\ &\leq M(b-a)^{1/2} \left(\sum_{i=p}^{q} (f, u_i)^2 \right)^{1/2} , \end{aligned} \tag{8-6.5}$$

for any t in $[a, b]$. From Theorem 8-6.1, we know that

$$\sum_{i=0}^{\infty} (f, u_i)^2$$

is a convergent series. Hence, if ε is any positive real number, there exists a natural number N such that

$$\sum_{i=p}^{q} (f, u_i)^2 < \frac{\varepsilon^2}{M^2(b-a)} ,$$

if $p, q \geqq N$. Substituting into relation (8-6.5), we get

$$\left| \sum_{i=p}^{q} \alpha_i u_i(t) \right| < \varepsilon ,$$

if $p, q \geqq N$, for every t in $[a, b]$. This implies that

$$\sum_{i=0}^{\infty} \alpha_i u_i(t)$$

converges and that the convergence to x is uniform on $[a, b]$. It must therefore converge to a continuous function. Since x is continuous, we must conclude that

$$x(t) = \sum_{i=0}^{\infty} \alpha_i u_i(t)$$

and that the convergence to x is uniform on $[a, b]$. This proves the theorem.

It must be emphasized that we have established the convergence of the Fourier expansion only for functions in R_0, the range of the operator $\mathcal{G}$. We may recall from Section 6-7 that if $x = \mathcal{G}f$, for any f in $C[a, b]$, then

$$Lx = f ,$$

$$\mathbf{W}^{[a]}\mathbf{k}(x(a)) + \mathbf{W}^{[b]}\mathbf{k}(x(b)) = \mathbf{o} .$$

It is easily inferred, therefore, that the range of $\mathcal{G}$ consists of all functions in $C^n[a, b]$ that also satisfy the homogeneous boundary conditions of the differential system. It is for these functions, and only for these functions, that we have established the validity of the Fourier expansion.

We can easily extend the result obtained in Theorem 8-6.3 to the space $C[a, b]$, if we accept the fact that R_0 is dense in $C[a, b]$. The proof of this fact is not within the scope of the present work, but it can easily be made plausible.[4] The Weierstrass approximation theorem insures that any function f in $C[a, b]$ can be approximated as closely as we please by a polynomial; all polynomials belong to $C^n[a, b]$. A polynomial p for which $\|f-p\|$ is small can be altered near the end points of $[a, b]$ so that it satisfies the boundary conditions, remains in $C^n[a, b]$, and remains close to f. This is equivalent to saying that R_0 is dense in $C[a, b]$.

The following theorem can now be proved.

Theorem 8-6.5. *The Fourier expansion of any function in $C[a, b]$ converges (in the mean square) to that function.*

[4] Birkhoff and Rota [4].

PROOF. Let x be any function in $C[a, b]$, and let ε be an arbitrary positive real number. Since R_0 is dense in $C[a, b]$, we can find a function y in R_0 such that

$$\| x-y \| < \frac{\varepsilon}{3} .$$

Let $\{\alpha_i\}$ and $\{\beta_i\}$ be the sets of Fourier coefficients of x and y, respectively. That is $\alpha_i = (x, u_i)$ and $\beta_i = (y, u_i)$. We may also note that

$$\beta_i - \alpha_i = (y-x, u_i) ,$$

so that $\beta_i - \alpha_i$ is the ith Fourier coefficient for the function $y-x$. According to Theorem 8-6.3, there exists a natural number N such that

$$\left\| y - \sum_{i=0}^{n} \beta_i u_i \right\| < \frac{\varepsilon}{3}$$

if $n \geqq N$.

We can write

$$\left\| x - \sum_{i=0}^{n} \alpha_i u_i \right\| = \left\| x-y+y- \sum_{i=0}^{n} \beta_i u_i + \sum_{i=0}^{n} \beta_i u_i - \sum_{i=0}^{n} \alpha_i u_i \right\|$$
$$\leqq \| x-y \| + \left\| y - \sum_{i=0}^{n} \beta_i u_i \right\| + \left\| \sum_{i=0}^{n} (\beta_i - \alpha_i) u_i \right\| .$$

It is easily verified (see Pythagorean relation below) that

$$\left\| \sum_{i=0}^{n} (\beta_i - \alpha_i) u_i \right\| = \left(\sum_{i=0}^{n} (\beta_i - \alpha_i)^2 \right)^{1/2} .$$

Bessel's inequality insures that the right-hand side of the above relation is no larger than $\| y-x \|$ and the same may therefore be said for the left-hand side. It follows that

$$\left\| x - \sum_{i=0}^{n} \alpha_i u_i \right\| \leqq 2 \| x-y \| + \left\| y - \sum_{i=0}^{n} \beta_i u_i \right\| < \varepsilon$$

if $n \geqq N$. Thus

$$\sum_{i=0}^{\infty} \alpha_i u_i$$

converges to x, and the theorem is proved.

It should be noted that we have not established pointwise convergence. Any attempt to do so would be bound to fail, since there exist continuous functions whose Fourier series diverge at an uncountable infinity of points.[5] In spite of this, the situation relative to mean square convergence is highly satisfactory. Every function in the fundamental space $C[a, b]$ has a Fourier expansion and it converges to the function in the norm of the space.

The question of the possibility of a Fourier representation for discontinuous functions is clearly suggested. We temporarily ignore the suggestion

[5] See Rudin [43], page 158.

and consider instead some geometrical aspects of Fourier representation. The projection operator P_i (introduced in Section 8-5) is

$$P_i x = \alpha_i u_i \ ,$$

where $\alpha_i = (x, u_i)$. Thus, the term $\alpha_i u_i$ in the Fourier expansion of x is the projection of x on the subspace U_i generated by the eigenfunction u_i. The partial sum

$$s_n = \sum_{i=0}^{n} \alpha_i u_i$$

is a point in the $(n+1)$-dimensional space S generated by the set $\{u_i : i = 0, 1, 2, \ldots, n\}$, and may clearly be called a projection of x on S. Moreover, since

$$\begin{aligned}([x-s_n], u_k) &= (x, u_k) - (s_n, u_k) \\ &= \alpha_k - \alpha_k = 0 \ , \quad k = 0, 1, 2, \ldots, n \ ,\end{aligned}$$

we infer that $x - s_n$ is orthogonal to the subspace S. That is, s_n is the orthogonal projection of x on S.

Coordinates of points in the subspace S satisfy a Pythagorean relation. Thus, if z is any point in S, it can be expressed as

$$z = \sum_{i=0}^{n} \gamma_i u_i \ ,$$

and the members of the set $\{\gamma_i\}$ may be called the coordinates of z. Also,

$$\begin{aligned}\| z \|^2 &= \left\| \sum_{i=0}^{n} \gamma_i u_i \right\|^2 \\ &= \left(\sum_{i=0}^{n} \gamma_i u_i \ , \ \sum_{i=0}^{n} \gamma_i u_i \right) \\ &= \sum_{i=0}^{n} \sum_{j=0}^{n} \gamma_i \gamma_j (u_i, u_j) = \sum_{i=0}^{n} \gamma_i^2 \ .\end{aligned}$$

Hence, the square of the norm of z is equal to the sum of the squares of its coordinates.

It is clear that any partial sum of the Fourier series of x may be regarded as an approximation to x. It is appropriate, therefore, to raise the question of which linear combination of the first $n+1$ eigenfunctions provides the best approximation to x. To obtain an answer, let

$$z = \sum_{i=0}^{n} \gamma_i u_i$$

be any point in S. We have

$$\| x - z \|^2 = \| (x - s_n) + (s_n - z) \|^2 \ ,$$

where s_n is a partial sum of the Fourier series. By expressing the right-hand side of this relation as an inner product and noting that the point $s_n - z$ is in S and hence is orthogonal to $x - s_n$, we may write (see Figure 8-6.1)

(8-6.6) $$\| x - z \|^2 = \| x - s_n \|^2 + \| s_n - z \|^2 \ .$$

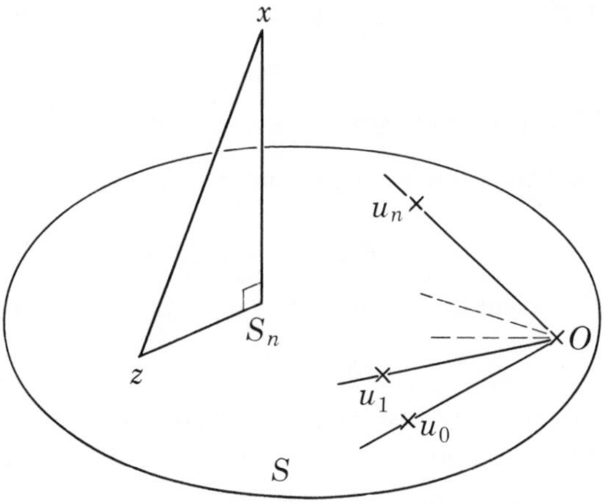

Figure 8-6.1

The right-hand side of relation (8-6.6) is obviously minimized if $z = s_n$. Hence, s_n is seen to be the best approximation to x. Since we have minimized the squared norm, it is called the *least square approximation* to x.

It was shown above that the squared norm of any point in the subspace S is equal to the sum of the squares of its coordinates. Since we have also shown that the complete set of eigenfunctions spans the space $C[a, b]$, it may be conjectured that the squared norm of any function in $C[a, b]$ is equal to the sum of the squares of all its Fourier coefficients. This result is known as the *Parseval equality*; it is presented as a theorem.

Theorem 8-6.6. *If x is any function in $C[a, b]$ and if $\alpha_i = (x, u_i)$, then*

$$\| x \|^2 = \sum_{i=0}^{\infty} \alpha_i^2 .$$

PROOF. Let s_n be the nth partial sum of the Fourier series of x. If z is replaced by 0 in relation (8-6.6), we can write

$$\| x \|^2 - \| s_n \|^2 = \| x - s_n \|^2 .$$

Since

$$\| s_n \|^2 = \sum_{i=0}^{n} \alpha_i^2$$

and since

$$\lim_{n \to \infty} \| x - s_n \|^2 = 0 ,$$

the required result follows and the theorem is proved.

Recalling the definition of a *complete orthonormal set* (see Section 1-9) we prove the following theorem.

Theorem 8-6.7. *The set of eigenfunctions $\{u_i\}$ is a complete orthonormal set.*

PROOF. Let v be a function in $C[a, b]$ that is orthogonal to every function in $\{u_i\}$. Since

$$(v, u_i) = 0 \ , \quad i = 0, 1, 2, \ldots \ ,$$

every Fourier coefficient of v is zero. The Parseval equality, then, implies that

$$\| v \| = 0 \ .$$

Since v is continuous, it must be the zero function. It follows that $\{u_i\}$ cannot be a proper subset of any orthonormal set in $C[a, b]$. This proves the theorem.

Corollary 8-6.7. *The set $\{\rho_i\}$ is a complete set of eigenvalues of $\mathcal{G}$.*

PROOF. It can be shown that eigenfunctions associated with distinct eigenvalues are of necessity orthogonal (see Exercise 7 of Section 8-5). Hence, if ρ is an eigenvalue not in the set $\{\rho_i\}$, its associated eigenfunction u must be orthogonal to every element in u_i. We have just shown that no such u exists. Consequently, no such ρ exists and the proof is complete.

This brings to a satisfactory conclusion the discussion of the operator $\mathcal{G}$ relative to the domain $C[a, b]$. We have found a complete set of eigenfunctions and have shown that they form a basis for the space $C[a, b]$ in the sense that any element in the space can be approximated by a partial sum of its Fourier series. The questions that have been answered, however, suggest others and these are discussed briefly in the following sections.

Example 1. The Green's function for the boundary problem

$$-u'' = 0 \ ,$$

$$u(0) = u(1) = 0 \ ,$$

is given by

$$G(t, s) = \begin{cases} s(1-t) \ , & s < t \ , \\ t(1-s) \ , & s > t \ . \end{cases}$$

Let the operator $\mathcal{G}$ be defined by

$$\mathcal{G}u(t) = \int_0^1 G(t, s)u(s)\, ds \ .$$

If $\lambda = (1/\rho)$ the eigenvalue problem associated with this operator is

$$\mathcal{G}u = \rho u \ ,$$

and it is equivalent to the differential boundary problem

$$-u'' = \lambda u \ ,$$
$$u(0) = u(1) = 0 \ .$$

It is easily verified that the eigenvalues and eigenfunctions for this problem are

$$\left.\begin{aligned} \lambda_j &= (j\pi)^2 \\ u_j(t) &= \sqrt{2}\sin j\pi t \end{aligned}\right\} j = 1, 2, 3, \ldots .$$

The function f, where

$$f(t) = t \ ,$$

$0 \leqq t \leqq 1$, belongs to $C[0, 1)$. Its Fourier coefficients are

$$\begin{aligned} \alpha_j &= (f, u_j) \\ &= \int_0^1 \sqrt{2}\, t \sin j\pi t \, dt \\ &= (-1)^{j-1} \frac{\sqrt{2}}{j\pi} \ . \end{aligned}$$

Hence we can write

$$t = \frac{2}{\pi}\left(\sin\pi t - \frac{1}{2}\sin 2\pi t + \frac{1}{3}\sin 3\pi t - \cdots\right) .$$

The series converges to $f(t)$ in the mean square, but since f does not belong to the range of $\mathscr{G}$, we cannot assert that the series converges uniformly to f on [0, 1]. In fact, since $f(1) = 1$ and the series obviously converges to zero when $t = 1$, the convergence is not uniform on any subinterval which includes the point $t = 1$.

The function x defined by $x = \mathscr{G}f$ is in the range of $\mathscr{G}$ and

$$\begin{aligned} x(t) &= \int_0^1 G(t, s) f(s) \, ds \\ &= \frac{t}{6}(1 - t^2) \ . \end{aligned}$$

If its jth Fourier coefficient is β_j, we have (see the proof of Thereom 8-6.4)

$$\begin{aligned} \beta_j &= \frac{1}{\lambda_j}\alpha_j \\ &= (-1)^{j-1}\frac{\sqrt{2}}{(j\pi)^3} \ . \end{aligned}$$

It follows that

$$\begin{aligned} x(t) &= \frac{t}{6}(1 - t^2) \\ &= \frac{2}{\pi^3}\left(\sin\pi t - \frac{1}{2^3}\sin 2\pi t + \frac{1}{3^3}\sin 3\pi t - \cdots\right) . \end{aligned}$$

Theorem 8-6.4 implies that the convergence is uniform in this case.

Parseval's equality may be applied to the expansion of the function f. Thus, since

$$\|f\|^2 = \int_0^1 t^2\,dt = \frac{1}{3}\,,$$

we have

$$\frac{1}{3} = \sum_{j=1}^{\infty} \frac{2}{(j\pi)^2}\,.$$

It follows that

$$\frac{\pi^2}{6} = 1 + \frac{1}{4} + \frac{1}{9} + \cdots + \frac{1}{j^2} + \cdots\,.$$

Exercises

1. Find an expansion for each of the following functions in terms of the eigenfunctions of the boundary problem in Example 1 of Section 8-6. Each function is defined on the unit interval [0, 1].

(a) $f(t) = 1$;

(b) $f(t) = 1 - t$;

(c) $f(t) = \sin^2 \pi t$;

(d) $f(t) = \cos \pi t$;

(e) $f(t) = \begin{cases} 0\,, & 0 \leqq t \leqq \frac{1}{2}\,, \\ 1\,, & \frac{1}{2} < t \leqq 1\,; \end{cases}$

(f) $f(t) = \begin{cases} \frac{1}{2}t\,, & 0 \leqq t \leqq \frac{1}{2}\,, \\ \frac{1}{2}(1-t)\,, & \frac{1}{2} < t \leqq 1\,. \end{cases}$

2. Show that the expansion for f in Exercise 1(b) can be obtained from the results of Example 1 of Section 8-6 and Exercise 1(a).

3. If G represents the Green's function in Example 1 of Section 8-6, use the result developed in the proof of Theorem 8-6.2 to obtain an eigenfunction expansion of g, where

$$g(s) = G(\tfrac{1}{2}, s) = \begin{cases} \frac{1}{2}s\,, & s < \frac{1}{2}\,, \\ \frac{1}{2}(1-s)\,, & s > \frac{1}{2}\,, \end{cases}$$

[compare with Exercise 1(f)].

4. (a) Find eigenvalues and eigenfunctions for the boundary problem

$$-u'' = \lambda u\,,$$

$$u'(0) = 0\,, \quad u'(\pi) = 0\,.$$

(b) The developments of Section 8-6 are based on the assumption that $\lambda = 0$ is not an eigenvalue. They do not therefore apply to the above problem. If we replace λ by $\eta + \frac{1}{4}$, the problem can be written as

$$-u'' - \tfrac{1}{4}u = \eta u\,,$$

$$u'(0) = 0\,, \quad u'(\pi) = 0\,.$$

Find Green's function for this problem when $\eta = 0$. Discuss the expansion theory associated with the problem in part (a).

5. Consider the boundary problem

$$-u'' = \lambda u \ ,$$

$$u(-\pi) - u(\pi) = 0 \ , \quad u'(-\pi) - u'(\pi) = 0 \ .$$

(a) Show that the problem is self-adjoint and that the eigenvalues are given by

$$\lambda_j = j^2 \ , \quad j = 0, 1, 2, \ldots$$

(b) Show that each nonzero eigenvalue λ_j is associated with two eigenfunctions u_j and v_j given by

$$\left.\begin{aligned} u_j(t) &= \frac{1}{\sqrt{\pi}} \sin jt \\ v_j(t) &= \frac{1}{\sqrt{\pi}} \cos jt \end{aligned}\right\} j = 1, 2, \ldots \ .$$

Show also that the zero eigenvalue is associated with the eigenfunction

$$v_0(t) = \frac{1}{\sqrt{2\pi}} \ .$$

(c) Use the substitution given in Exercise 4(b) to establish that any function in $C[-\pi, \pi]$ can be expanded in a series of eigenfunctions of the above problem.

6. Show that the following boundary problem is self-adjoint

$$(u^{[n]})^{[n]} + (p_1 u^{[n-1]})^{[n-1]} + \cdots + (p_{n-1} u')' + p_n u = 0$$

$$\left.\begin{aligned} u^{[j]}(a) &= 0 \\ u^{[j]}(b) &= 0 \end{aligned}\right\} j = 0, 1, \ldots, n-1 \ .$$

7. Let $\mathscr{G}$ be the symmetric integral operator of Theorem 8-5.1. Let ρ_0 be the eigenvalue of maximum magnitude, and let u_0 be the corresponding normal eigenfunction. If w is any function with a unit norm in $C[a, b]$, prove that

$$|(w, u_0)| \leqq \left| \left(\frac{\mathscr{G}w}{\|\mathscr{G}w\|}, u_0 \right) \right| \ .$$

8-7. EXTENSION TO THE SPACE $R[a, b]$

Restricting the domain of $\mathscr{G}$ to the space of continuous functions has been convenient and has simplified the exposition while permitting the determination of a complete set of eigenfunctions. We have already seen that no new eigenvalues are obtained by extending the space to include complex-valued functions. Nevertheless, $\mathscr{G}$ is an integral operator and, in a sense, its natural domain is the space $R[a, b]$ of Riemann integrable functions.

Motivation for wanting to extend the domain is found from examining physical problems. One such is the classical problem of heat conduction in a thin metal rod; this leads to a boundary problem in differential equations that is similar to the problem associated with the vibrating string and that can be solved by the method of separation of variables. The initial temperature distribution in the rod is specified by a function f that is analogous to the initial displacement function for the vibrating string. For the string problem, f must be continuous, but for the heat conduction problem it is physically reasonable to have a discontinuous initial temperature distribution. Hence, there is physical motivation for considering Fourier expansions of discontinuous functions.

It is gratifying to find that the extension of the theory to include some discontinuous functions can be made with ease. In fact, all the results obtained above (except Theorem 8-6.4) remain valid if the space $C[a, b]$ is replaced by the space $R[a, b]$. In particular, we have the following equivalent for Theorem 8-6.5.

Theorem 8-7.1. *The Fourier expansion of any function in $R[a, b]$ converges (in the mean square) to that function.*

This substantial extension of the original expansion theorem is as far as we can go without reformulating the basic concept of an integral. For, if a function f has discontinuities that make it nonintegrable, then its "Fourier coefficients" $\{(f, u_i)\}$ cannot be evaluated. In fact, an inner product norm cannot be determined for such a function. Any attempt to extend the discussion, therefore, requires a generalization of the Riemann integral.

8-8. EXTENSION TO THE SPACE $L^2[a, b]$

It was observed above that any attempt to enlarge the set of functions that allow a Fourier expansion would require a generalization of the concept of an integral. The Lebesgue integral is such a generalization and the symbol $\mathscr{L}^2[a, b]$ is commonly used to designate the set of all functions whose squares are Lebesgue integrable on the interval $[a, b]$. When using this integral it is convenient to define two functions f and g to be *equivalent* if $f(t) = g(t)$ almost everywhere. The statement "$f(t) = g(t)$ almost everywhere" means that the equality holds for all t in $[a, b]$ with the possible exception of a set of points of measure zero. The equivalence relation determines a set of equivalence classes in $\mathscr{L}^2[a, b]$, and this set of classes is designated by $L^2[a, b]$. When addition and scalar multiplication are defined in a natural way, the space $L^2[a, b]$ is a vector space. Relative to the inner product norm, $L^2[a, b]$ has the advantage of being a complete metric space. This advantage is not enjoyed by either $R[a, b]$ or $C[a, b]$, although both are complete relative to the norm defined by

$$\|f\| = \sup_{t \in [a, b]} |f(t)| .$$

A comparison may be drawn between the extension of $R[a, b]$ to $L^2[a, b]$ and the extension of the rational number system to the real number system. In both cases the realization of a complete metric space can be regarded as a primary motive for the extension.

The space R_0 is dense in $L^2[a, b]$. This fact is not proved, but it appears plausible by an argument similar to the one used in Section 8-6.

Theorem 8-8.1. *The Fourier expansion of any function in $L^2[a, b]$ converges (in the mean square) to that function.*

PROOF. The proof is identical with that of Theorem 6.5 except for the replacement of $C[a, b)$ by $L^2[a, b]$.

This brings the expansion theory for a self-adjoint differential boundary problem to a satisfactory conclusion. It is pertinent, however, to make some final remarks that are related to the above discussion. The space $L^2[a, b]$ is a complete inner-product vector space; it is therefore a *Hilbert space.* Any function x in this space has a Fourier series, and the coefficients of this series, represented by $\{\alpha_i\}$, may be thought of as the infinite analogue of an n-vector. If we define addition and scalar multiplication for these vectors in the natural way, it is easily verified that the correspondence between them and the functions that generate them is preserved under the two operations. A natural definition for the inner product of two such vectors is given by

$$(\{\alpha_i\}, \{\beta_i\}) = \sum_{i=0}^{\infty} \alpha_i \beta_i \,, \tag{8-8.1}$$

providing the series on the right-hand side converges. To establish convergence, we use the Schwarz inequality to write

$$\left| \sum_{i=p}^{q} \alpha_i \beta_i \right|^2 \leq \sum_{i=p}^{q} \alpha_i^2 \sum_{i=p}^{q} \beta_i^2 \,. \tag{8-8.2}$$

Since

$$\sum_{i=0}^{\infty} \alpha_i^2 \quad \text{and} \quad \sum_{i=0}^{\infty} \beta_i^2$$

both converge, it is clear that the right-hand side of relation (8-8.2) is small if p and q are large. This proves that

$$\sum_{i=0}^{\infty} \alpha_i \beta_i$$

converges so that formula (8-8.1) can be used to define an inner product. For the inner product norm, we have

$$\begin{aligned} \| \{\alpha_i\} \|^2 &= (\{\alpha_i\}, \{\alpha_i\}) \\ &= \sum_{i=0}^{\infty} \alpha_i^2 \,. \end{aligned}$$

By virtue of the Parseval equality, therefore,

$$\| x \| = \| \{\alpha_i\} \| \,,$$

and the two spaces are *isometric.*

We denote by l^2 the space of all sequences of real numbers $\{\alpha_i\}$ with the property that

$$\sum_{i=0}^{\infty} \alpha_i^2 < \infty .$$

This space, or its counterpart over the complex scalar field, is the original Hilbert space. We have shown that every element x in $L^2[a, b]$ corresponds to a unique element $\{\alpha_i\}$ in l^2, the components of $\{\alpha_i\}$ being the Fourier coefficients of x. The converse of this statement is the *Riesz-Fischer Theorem* that is stated without proof.[6]

Theorem 8-8.2. *If $\{\gamma_i\}$ is any set of real numbers such that*

$$\sum_{i=0}^{\infty} \gamma_i^2 < \infty ,$$

then there exists a function f in $L^2[a, b]$ such that

$$f = \sum_{i=0}^{\infty} \gamma_i u_i ,$$

where $\gamma_i = (f, u_i)$.

The correspondence between $L^2[a, b]$ and l^2 is, therefore, an isomorphism and an isometry. The geometrical properties, discovered earlier for the space $C[a, b]$ are also properties of $L^2[a, b]$. These are illuminated by the recognition that $L^2[a, b]$ and l^2 have the same structure. For, the definition of the latter space endows it with obvious geometric properties.

Exercises

1. If $\{u_i\}$ is a complete set of eigenfunctions for a given self-adjoint boundary problem and if x and y are any two functions in $C[a, b]$, show that

$$(x, y) = \sum_{i=0}^{\infty} (x, u_i)(y, u_i) .$$

2. Let $\mathscr{G}$ be the integral operator defined in Example 1 of Section 8-6, and let $f(t) = 1, 0 \leqq t \leqq 1$. Find $\mathscr{G}f$, $\mathscr{G}^2 f$, and $\mathscr{G}^3 f$. Compare $\| \mathscr{G}^2 f \| / \| \mathscr{G}^3 f \|$ with π^2, the smallest eigenvalue of the associated differential boundary problem.

3. If f is any function in $C[0, 1]$ that is not orthogonal to $\sin \pi t$, and if $\mathscr{G}$ is the operator defined in Exercise 2, prove that

$$\lim_{k \to \infty} \frac{\| \mathscr{G}^k f \|}{\| \mathscr{G}^{k+1} f \|} = \pi^2 .$$

---

[6] Rudin [43], page 217.

9

Sturmian Theory

9-1. INTRODUCTION

Second-order linear differential equations and the boundary problems associated with them find wide application in the physical sciences. Some of the properties of such systems are included as special cases in the general treatment of *n*th-order systems. However, certain properties are peculiar to second-order systems, and some of these are presented in this chapter.

The equation

$$u'' + fu' + gu = h$$

can be rewritten as

(9-1.1) $$(pu')' + qu = k \; .$$

This transformation is achieved by multiplying the given equation by the positive integrating factor

$$p(t) = \exp\left[\int_a^t f(s)\,ds\right] \; .$$

Clearly q and k are

$$q = pg \; ,$$
$$k = ph \; .$$

We assume that f is continuous on some interval I which, unless otherwise specified, may be open or closed, finite or infinite. This insures that p has a continuous derivative on I.

It is easily verified that the homogeneous counterpart of equation (9-1.1), namely

(9-1.2) $$(pu')' + qu = 0 \; ,$$

is self-adjoint and that the concomitant matrix is

$$\mathbf{P} = p\begin{pmatrix} 0 & 1 \\ -1 & 0 \end{pmatrix} .$$

The companion vector equation associated with (9-1.2) is

(9-1.3) $$\mathbf{y}' = \mathbf{A}\mathbf{y} \; ,$$

where

$$\mathbf{A} = \begin{pmatrix} 0 & 1 \\ -\dfrac{q}{p} & -\dfrac{p'}{p} \end{pmatrix} .$$

As noted in Chapter 3, the Wronskian matrix of any fundamental vector for equation (9-1.2) is a fundamental matrix for equation (9-1.3).

A second useful vector equation associated with (9-1.2) is given by

$$\mathbf{y}' = \mathbf{B}\mathbf{y} \ , \tag{9-1.4}$$

where

$$\mathbf{B} = \begin{pmatrix} 0 & \frac{1}{p} \\ -q & 0 \end{pmatrix} .$$

If $\mathbf{u}$ is a fundamental vector for (9-1.2), it may be verified that

$$\mathbf{Y} = \begin{pmatrix} 1 & 0 \\ 0 & p \end{pmatrix} \mathbf{K}(\mathbf{u}) = \begin{pmatrix} u_1 & u_2 \\ pu_1' & pu_2' \end{pmatrix} ,$$

is a fundamental matrix for (9-1.4). Conversely, the first row of any fundamental matrix for (9-1.4) is a fundamental vector for (9-1.2). Since the trace of the matrix $\mathbf{B}$ is zero, we may infer from Theorem 3-2.4 that the determinant of any fundamental matrix is a constant.

If I is the closed interval $[a, b]$, we may form a two-point boundary problem by adjoining the boundary condition

$$\mathbf{W}^{[a]}\mathbf{k}(u(a)) + \mathbf{W}^{[b]}\mathbf{k}(u(b)) = \mathbf{o} \tag{9-1.5}$$

to equation (9-1.2). It can be easily verified that the corresponding boundary condition for the vector equation (9-1.4) is

$$\mathbf{W}^{[a]}\begin{pmatrix} 1 & 0 \\ 0 & p^{-1}(a) \end{pmatrix}\mathbf{y}(a) + \mathbf{W}^{[b]}\begin{pmatrix} 1 & 0 \\ 0 & p^{-1}(b) \end{pmatrix}\mathbf{y}(b) = \mathbf{o} \ . \tag{9-1.6}$$

If q is a constant and $p(t) \equiv 1$, equation (9-1.2) reduces to

$$u'' + qu = 0 \ . \tag{9-1.7}$$

If $q = 0$, the solutions of equation (9-1.7) are first-degree polynomials. If q is negative, then the solutions are exponential functions and, therefore, any solution has at most a single zero. Finally, if q is positive, then a fundamental vector is

$$\tilde{\mathbf{u}} = (\cos\sqrt{q}\,t \ \ \sin\sqrt{q}\,t) \ .$$

Any solution of the equation can be expressed as

$$u = k \sin(\sqrt{q}\,t + \alpha) \ .$$

The number of zeros of this solution can be determined by comparing the half wave-length $\pi/\sqrt{q}$ with the length of the interval I.

It is natural to investigate the extent to which solutions of equation (9-1.2) resemble those of the special equation (9-1.7). In this connection, we recall the resemblance that was noted in Chapter 5 between the Bessel's functions J_0

and J_1 and the cosine and sine functions (see Figure 5-7.2). We see below that if equation (9-1.2) is such that $[q(t)/p(t)] > c$ for all values of t and some positive constant c, then the solutions are oscillatory and their rate of oscillation exceeds that of $\sin\sqrt{c}\,t$.

9-2. COMPARISON THEOREMS

We have observed in Section 2-5 that the solutions of a differential equation depend continuously on a parameter. In this section we discuss general conditions under which the solutions of one equation can be compared with those of another. The theorems describing these relationships are *comparison theorems* and can be used to obtain useful information about a solution without deriving an explicit representation for the solution. The first comparison theorem presented below applies to equations of the form $u' = F(t, u)$. Later theorems provide results for second-order, self-adjoint equations and are called Sturm comparison theorems.

The following lemma is used in the proof of the first comparison theorem.

Lemma 9-2.1. *If f is a differentiable function on $[a, b]$ and if, for some constant K,*

(9-2.1) $$f'(t) \leqq Kf(t) ,$$

for all t in $[a, b]$, then

$$f(t) \leqq f(a)e^{K(t-a)} ,$$

for all t in $[a, b]$.

PROOF. From (9-2.1), after multiplying both members by the positive quantity e^{-Kt} and combining terms, we have

$$e^{-Kt}(f'(t)-Kf(t)) = \frac{d}{dt}(e^{-Kt}f(t)) \leqq 0 .$$

Integrating from a to t, we obtain

$$e^{-Kt}f(t)-e^{-Ka}f(a) \leqq 0 .$$

This yields the inequality of the lemma and completes the proof.

The differential equations appearing in the following theorem are assumed to satisfy the basic hypotheses of the existence Theorem 2-2.1. Specifically, for an equation $u' = F(t, u)$, when we say that F is continuous and that F satisfies a Lipschitz condition in some region D, we expect the reader to understand that D is some open, connected, two-dimensional region and that for some Lipschitz constant K

$$| F(t, u_1)-F(t, u_2)| \leqq K| u_1-u_2| ,$$

for all points (t, u_1) and (t, u_2) in D. For simplicity, the hypotheses are somewhat more restrictive than necessary. In the first place the results of the theorem apply to solutions determined by a given initial point (τ, b) in D but are restricted to a domain for which $t \geqq \tau$. Thus the hypotheses need only be required to apply on that portion of D for which $t \geqq \tau$. Secondly, the theorem can be proved if only one of the two given equations is required to satisfy a Lipschitz condition (see Exercise 1 of Section 9-2).

Theorem 9-2.1. *Let the equations*

$$u' = F(t, u) \ , \tag{9-2.2}$$

$$u' = G(t, u) \ , \tag{9-2.3}$$

where F and G are continuous and satisfy Lipschitz conditions on some domain D, have solutions f and g, respectively, and let these solutions satisfy the same initial condition

$$u(\tau) = b \ .$$

If $F(x, y) \leqq G(x, y)$ *on D, then*

$$f(t) \leqq g(t) \ ,$$

for $t > \tau$.

PROOF. Suppose that $f(t_1) > g(t_1)$ for some point t_1, where $t_1 > \tau$. Let $h(t) = f(t) - g(t)$, then $h(\tau) = 0$ and $h(t_1) > 0$. Let t_0 be the least upper bound of the set of points on $[\tau, t_1]$ at which $h(t) = 0$. Since h is continuous, $\tau \leqq t_0 < t_1$ and $h(t) > 0$ for $t_0 < t \leqq t_1$. Moreover,

$$\begin{aligned} h'(t) &= F(t, f(t)) - G(t, g(t)) \\ &\leqq G(t, f(t)) - G(t, g(t)) \ . \end{aligned}$$

If K is the Lipschitz constant for G, we then have

$$\begin{aligned} h'(t) &\leqq K(f(t) - g(t)) \\ &\leqq Kh(t) \ . \end{aligned}$$

It follows from Lemma 9-2.1, therefore, that

$$h(t) \leqq h(t_0) e^{K(t-t_0)} \ ,$$

$t > t_0$. Since $h(t_0) = 0$, $h(t)$ is identically zero, and we have a contradiction. This forces the rejection of the initial supposition and completes the proof of the theorem.

Corollary 9-2.1a. *If the initial condition* $f(\tau) = g(\tau) = b$ *is replaced by*

$$f(\tau) = b_1 \quad \textit{and} \quad g(\tau) = b_2 \ ,$$

where $b_1 < b_2$, *then*

$$f(t) < g(t) \ ,$$

for $t > \tau$.

PROOF. We are given that f is the solution of equation (9-2.2) that satisfies the initial condition $f(\tau) = b_1$. Let $\hat{f}$ be the solution of the same equation that satisfies the initial condition $\hat{f}(\tau) = b_2$. Since the solutions are continuous and since $b_1 < b_2$,

$$f(t) < \hat{f}(t) \tag{9-2.4}$$

for all values of t for which both solutions are defined. This conclusion follows from the fact that the equality of the two solutions at any point would violate the uniqueness property of a solution. Theorem 9-2.1 implies that $\hat{f}(t) \leqq g(t)$ for $t > \tau$ and this fact, together with relation (9-2.4) insures that $f(t) < g(t)$ for $t > \tau$.

Corollary 9-2.1b. *Under the hypotheses of Theorem* 9-2.1, *there is a point* $t_0 \geqq \tau$ *such that*

$$f(t) = g(t)\ , \quad \tau \leqq t \leqq t_0\ ,$$

$$f(t) < g(t)\ , \quad t > t_0\ .$$

PROOF. The point t_0 may be defined as the least upper bound of the set of points for which $f(t) = g(t)$ and $t \geqq \tau$. It is clearly impossible to have $f(t_0) < g(t_0)$. Moreover, if t_1 is a point on $[\tau, t_0)$ such that $f(t_1) < g(t_1)$, Corollary 9-2.1a implies that $f(t) < g(t)$ for $t > t_1$. This is inconsistent with the definition of t_0. The conclusion of Corollary 9-2.1b follows.

Corollary 9-2.1c. *Under the hypotheses of Theorem* 9-2.1 *with the additional condition that* $F(x, y) < G(x, y)$ *for all* (x, y) *in* D, *then* $t_0 = \tau$, *where* t_0 *is the point defined in Corollary* 9-2.1*b*.

At this point, we return to consider the second-order equation (9-1.2). We may observe at once that the zeros of any nontrivial solution of this equation are isolated. This result may be established by supposing that, for some solution u, t_0 is a limit point of the zeros of u. It follows from this supposition that $u(t_0) = 0$ and also that $u'(t_0) = 0$. This implies that u is the zero solution, and the desired result follows.

Theorem 9-2.2. Sturm's Fundamental Theorem. *If* u_1 *and* u_2 *are, respectively, real solutions of*

$$(pu')' + q_1 u = 0\ ,$$

$$(pu')' + q_2 u = 0\ ,$$

and if, on the fundamental interval I, $p(t) > 0$, *and* $q_2(t) \geqq q_1(t) \geqq 0$, and $q_2(t) \not\equiv q_1(t)$, *then* u_2 *has a zero between any pair of consecutive zeros of* u_1.

PROOF. Let t_1 and t_2 $(t_1 < t_2)$ be any two consecutive zeros of u_1. Since the zeros of any solution are not affected if the solution is multiplied by a nonzero constant, we may assume that

$$u_1(t) > 0 \ ,$$

$t \in (t_1, t_2)$. Consequently,

$$u_1'(t_1) > 0 \quad \text{and} \quad u_1'(t_2) < 0 \ .$$

Green's formula relative to the self-adjoint operator $Lu = (pu')'$ on the interval $[t_1, t_2]$ is

$$\int_{t_1}^{t_2} (vLu - uLv)\, dt = p(vu' - v'u) \Big|_{t_1}^{t_2} \ .$$

If, in this formula, u is replaced by u_1 and v by u_2, we have

$$\int_{t_1}^{t_2} (q_2 - q_1) u_1 u_2 \, dt = p(u_1' u_2 - u_1 u_2') \Big|_{t_1}^{t_2} \ . \tag{9-2.5}$$

In order to provide a proof by contradiction, we suppose that u_2 has no zero on (t_1, t_2). As in the case of u_1, it is not an essential restriction to assume that $u_2(t) > 0$ on (t_1, t_2). It follows that the left-hand side of relation (9-2.5) is positive. Since $u_1(t_1) = u_1(t_2) = 0$, the right-hand side of the same relation reduces to

$$p(t_2) u_1'(t_2) u_2(t_2) - p(t_1) u_1'(t_1) u_2(t_1) \ .$$

The factor $u_1'(t_2)$ is negative, and the other five factors are nonnegative. Hence the expression is nonpositive, and we have a contradiction. This forces us to reject the supposition that u_2 has no zero on (t_1, t_2) and establishes the theorem.

Corollary 9-2.2. *The zeros of two independent solutions of*

$$(pu')' + qu = 0 \ ,$$

where $p(t) > 0$ and $q(t) \geqq 0$ on I, separate each other. (That is, between two successive zeros of any solution of this equation, there is a zero of any independent solution.)

PROOF. Let $q_1 = q_2 = q$ in the above theorem, so that u_1 and u_2 are solutions of the same equation. In this case, the left-hand side of relation (9-2.5) is zero, and the same must therefore be true of the right-hand side. Since u_2 is independent of u_1, by hypothesis, $u_2(t_1) \neq 0$ and, as before, we may assume that $u_2(t_1) > 0$. This implies that $u_2(t_2) < 0$ and, hence that u_2 has a zero on (t_1, t_2). Since the two solutions play a symmetric role in this case, we must also infer that u_1 has a zero between any two consecutive zeros of u_2. This proves the corollary.

Exercises

1. Note that the proof of Theorem 9-2.1 did not require the hypothesis that F satisfy a Lipschitz condition. Prove the theorem under the hypothesis that F satisfies a Lipschitz condition but without imposing the condition on G.

2. Use Corollary 9-2.2 to prove that the zeros of

$$\alpha_1 \sin t + \beta_1 \cos t \quad \text{and} \quad \alpha_2 \sin t + \beta_2 \cos t$$

alternate if $\alpha_1\beta_2 \neq \alpha_2\beta_1$.

3. Prove Corollary 9-2.1c.

9-3. THE PRÜFER SUBSTITUTION AND COMPARISON THEORY

We can obtain a generalization of Theorem 9-2.2 by extending the method used above.[1] We however introduce a method which involves a useful substitution and which provides more insight into comparison theory than does the classical method.

In Section 9-1, we indicated our intention of investigating possible similarity between solutions of

$$(pu')' + qu = 0 \tag{9-3.1}$$

and solutions of the special case of that equation where $p(t) \equiv 1$ and q is a constant. When q is a positive constant, a solution of the equation is a sine function. The oscillations of the sine function may be simply described by identifying its functional values with the ordinates of points on a unit circle. The abscissas of the same points are functional values of the cosine function, and we may point out that the cosine function is the derivative of the sine function. In view of these remarks, we may anticipate some advantage by defining two functions t and θ by the relations

$$\begin{aligned} u &= r\sin\theta \ , \\ pu' &= r\cos\theta \ , \end{aligned} \tag{9-3.2}$$

where u is a nontrivial solution of equation (9-3.1). In the event that $p(t) \equiv q(t) \equiv 1$, we have

$$\begin{aligned} r &= c \ , \\ \theta &= t + \alpha \ . \end{aligned}$$

The constant c is uniquely determined by the choice of the solution u. On the other hand, any suitable value of α remains equally suitable if it is increased by any integral multiple of 2π. Thus the substitution relations (9-3.2) define θ uniquely only if we make a suitable specification of the value of θ at some point t_0 on I. The substitution (9-3.2) is known as the *Prüfer substitution.*

In order to find relations which r and θ must satisfy, we may differentiate the first relation with respect to t and multiply by p. Comparing this with the second relation, we get

$$r'p\sin\theta + \theta' rp\cos\theta = r\cos\theta \ . \tag{9-3.3}$$

[1] See Ince [26], page 225.

Differentiating the second relation in (9-3.2), adding the result to q times the first relation, and recognizing that u is assumed to be a solution of equation (9-3.1), we get

$$r'\cos\theta - \theta' r\sin\theta = -qr\sin\theta \tag{9-3.4}$$

Equations (9-3.3) and (9-3.4) are linear in r' and θ', and their determinant has the value $-pr$. Since by (9-3.2)

$$r^2 = (pu')^2 + u^2$$

and since u and u' are not simultaneously zero, r cannot be zero, and we assume that r is positive. Thus, the determinant of the two equations is not zero, and explicit expressions for r' and θ' are

$$\begin{aligned} r' &= \left(\frac{1}{p} - q\right) r\sin\theta\cos\theta \ , \\ \theta' &= \frac{1}{p}\cos^2\theta + q\sin^2\theta \ . \end{aligned} \tag{9-3.5}$$

This pair of equations is called the *Prüfer system* and r and θ are the *Prüfer functions* associated with equation (9-3.1). Clearly, the system is satisfied by any r and θ determined by (9-3.2) when u is a solution of equation (9-3.1). Conversely, if (r, θ) is a solution vector for the Prüfer system, the function u determined by the first relation of (9-3.2) has a derivative which satisfies the second relation. This follows by virtue of the fact that r' and θ' satisfy (9-3.3). Finally, since r' and θ' satisfy equation (9-3.4), u satisfies (9-3.1). Hence, the system (9-3.5) is equivalent to equation (9-3.1).

The Prüfer system is not a linear system, but it has the notable property that the second equation in the system does not involve the function r. Moreover, this second equation has the form $\theta' = F(t, \theta)$, where F satisfies a Lipschitz condition. Consequently, if an initial condition

$$\theta(\tau) = \alpha$$

is specified, the initial-value problem has a unique solution. The solution can be substituted in the first equation of the Prüfer system, whereupon r can be found by a quadrature. Specifically,

$$r(t) = c\exp\left[\int_a^t \left(\frac{1}{p(s)} - q(s)\right)\sin\theta\cos\theta\right] ds \ , \tag{9-3.6}$$

where, of course, θ is a function of s as found from the second equation of (9-3.5).

The function θ which satisfies the second Prüfer equation is called the *phase function*. Since r is positive and since $u = r\sin\theta$, the zeros of u correspond to values of θ which are integral multiples of π. The right-hand side of the second Prüfer equation is positive when $\theta = k\pi$, $k = 0, \pm 1, \pm 2, \ldots$ Hence the curve formed by plotting $(r(t), \theta(t))$ on a polar coordinate system can cross the critical rays ($\theta = k\pi,\ k = 0,\ \pm 1,\ \pm 2, \ldots$) only in a counter clockwise direction for increasing values of t.

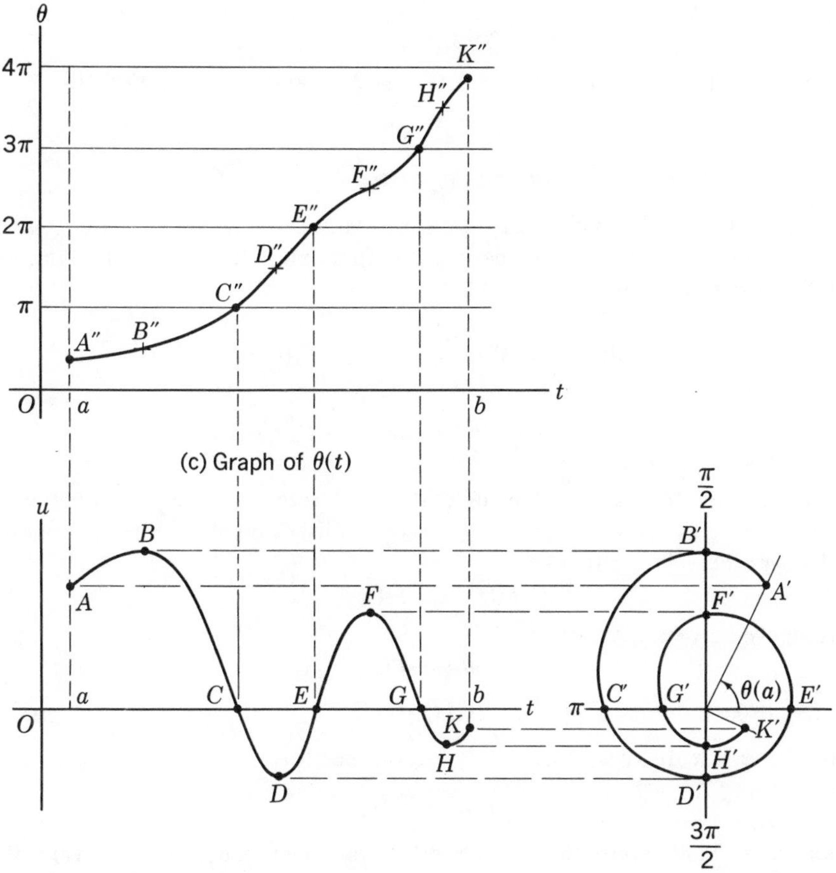

(a) Graph of $u(t)$

(b) Polar graph of $(r(t),\ \theta(t))$

Figure 9-3.1

Figure 9-3.1 shows the relationship between a solution of equation (9-3.1) and its associated Prüfer functions. The graph of a solution $u(t)$ is shown in Figure 9-3.1(a), the polar graph of the corresponding Prüfer functions r and θ is shown in Figure 9-3.1(b), and the Cartesian graph of the phase function θ is shown in Figure 9-3.1(c). Corresponding points are indicated by the same letter unprimed in Figure 9-3.1(a), primed in Figure 9-3.1(b) and double-primed in Figure 9-3.1(c).

We are now in a position to prove the extended form of Sturm's fundamental comparison theorem.

Theorem 9-3.1. *Let the operator L_i be*

$$L_i u = (p_i u')' + q_i u \ , \quad i = 1, 2 \ .$$

If $0 < p_2(t) \leqq p_1(t)$ and $q_2(t) \geqq q_1(t)$, $t \in I$, and *if u_i is a solution of*

$$L_i u = 0 \ ,$$

then u_2 has a zero between any pair of consecutive zeros of u_1.

PROOF. Let τ and σ $(\tau < \sigma)$ be two consecutive zeros of u_1. As in Theorem 9-2.2, we assume that $u_2(\tau)$ is nonnegative. The function u_i has a phase function θ_i that satisfies a Prüfer equation. That is,

$$\theta_1' = \frac{1}{p_1} \cos^2\theta_1 + q_1 \sin^2\theta_1 = F_1(t, \theta_1) \ ,$$

$$\theta_2' = \frac{1}{p_2} \cos^2\theta_2 + q_2 \sin^2\theta_2 = F_2(t, \theta_2) \ .$$

We prove the theorem by showing that $\theta_2(t) = \pi$ for some value of t between τ and σ and that, consequently, $u_2 = r \sin\theta$ vanishes there. The inequalities in the hypothesis insure that

$$F_1(t, \theta) \leqq F_2(t, \theta) \ .$$

Also, we may specify that

$$\theta_1(\tau) = 0 \ ,$$

$$\theta_2(\tau) = \alpha \ ,$$

for $0 \leqq \alpha < \pi$. In view of Corollary 9-2.1a, therefore,

$$\theta_1(t) < \theta_2(t) \ ,$$

for $t > \tau$. This implies that $\theta_2(\hat{t}) = \pi$ for some $\hat{t}$ in (τ, σ). Hence, $u_2(\hat{t}) = 0$, and the theorem is proved.

Theorem 9-3.2. Sturm's First Comparison Theorem. *Let the conditions set forth in Theorem* 9-3.1 *hold, together with the additional hypothesis that at the end point a of the interval* $[a, b]$

$$\frac{p_2(a) u_2'(a)}{u_2(a)} \leqq \frac{p_1(a) u_1'(a)}{u_1(a)} \ . \tag{9-3.7}$$

Then, if u_1 has exactly n zeros on $(a, b]$, u_2 has at least n zeros on the same interval.

PROOF. If θ_1 and θ_2 are the Prüfer phase functions corresponding to u_1 and u_2, respectively, we may interpret relation (9-3.7) as implying that

$$\cot\theta_2(a) \leqq \cot\theta_1(a) \ .$$

Hence, initial values for the phase functions can be specified so that

$$0 \leqq \theta_1(a) \leqq \theta_2(a) < \pi \ .$$

As in Theorem 9-3.1, therefore, we deduce that for $t \in [a, b]$

$$\theta_1(t) \leqq \theta_2(t) \ .$$

If the zeros of u_1 occur at the points $t_1, t_2, \ldots, t_n$, then we have $\theta_1(t_j) = j\pi$, $j = 1, 2, \ldots, n$. Since, in particular, $\theta_2(t_n) \geqq \theta_1(t_n)$, it is clear that u_2 has at least n zeros on $(a, b]$. This proves the theorem.

Implicit in the preceding theorem is the fact that, if we increase the values taken on by the coefficient q of a given equation, then we tend to increase the number of zeros of a solution of the equation. Consequently, if we define q by

$$q(t, \lambda) = \lambda\rho(t) + \sigma(t)$$

so that it depends linearly on a parameter λ, we may investigate the effect of variations in λ on the solutions of the equation. The equation resulting from this definition of q is called a *Sturm-Liouville equation*; its properties are discussed in Section 9-4.

Exercises

1. If $q(t)$ is positive and bounded from zero on $[0, \infty)$ prove that a nontrivial solution of

$$u'' + qu = 0$$

has infinitely many zeros on $[0, \infty)$.

2. Show that the distance between successive zeros of a nontrivial solution of the Airy equation

$$u'' + tu = 0$$

tends to zero as t becomes large.

3. Prove Theorem 9-3.1 by expanding

$$\frac{d}{dt}[(u_1/u_2)(p_1 u_1' u_2 - p_2 u_1 u_2')]$$

to get Picone's formula

$$\int_\tau^\sigma \left[(q_1 - q_2) u_1^2 + (p_1 - p_2) u_1'^2 + p_2 \frac{u_1' u_2 - u_1 u_2'}{u_2^2} \right] dt = \frac{u_1}{u_2} (p_1 u_1' u_2 - p_2 u_1 u_2') \Bigg|_\tau^\sigma \ .$$

The proof may be completed along the lines of Theorem 9-2.2.[2]

---

[2]See Ince [26], page 225.

4. If the equation

$$(pu')' + qu = 0$$

is such that, with $t \in [a, b]$,

$$0 < p(t) \leqq M_p \quad \text{and} \quad q(t) \geqq m_q \ ,$$

where M_p and m_q are positive numbers, show that any solution of the equation has at least n zeros on $[a, b]$ if

$$M_p / m_q \leqq (b-a)^2 / n^2 \pi^2 \ .$$

5. Prove that if $\{t_j\}$ is the sequence of successive zeros of a nontrivial solution of

$$u'' + qu = 0$$

and if q is a nonnegative increasing function of t, then

$$t_{j+1} - t_j < t_j - t_{j-1} \ .$$

6. (a) Show that Bessel's equation

$$t^2 u'' + tu' + (t^2 - n^2) u = 0$$

can be transformed into

$$v'' + \left(1 + \frac{1 - 4n^2}{4t^2}\right) v = 0$$

by the relation

$$u = \frac{1}{\sqrt{t}} v \ .$$

Note that the transformation does not disturb the location of the zeros of a solution.

(b) Show that the distance between successive zeros of Bessel's function J_n does not exceed π if $0 \leqq n < \frac{1}{2}$.

(c) If $n > \frac{1}{2}$ show that the distance between successive zeros of J_n approaches π for large values of t.

9-4. STURM-LIOUVILLE SYSTEMS

Let the operator L_λ be

(9-4.1) $$L_\lambda u = (pu')' + (\lambda \rho + \sigma) u \ ,$$

where $p \in C^1[a, b]$; $\rho, \sigma \in C[a, b]$, $p(t) > 0$, and $\rho(t) > 0$ on $[a, b]$. Let a solution of

$$L_\lambda u = 0$$

be represented by $u(t, \lambda)$, the Prüfer phase function of the solution by $\theta(t, \lambda)$, and the location of the nth zero of the solution by $t_n(\lambda)$. The following two theorems are a consequence of preceding results. Their proofs are left as exercises.[3]

[3] See Birkhoff and Rota [5], Section X.7.

Theorem 9-4.1. *The function $t_n(\lambda)$ is continuous and decreasing on $[\hat{\lambda}, \infty)$, where $\hat{\lambda}$ is defined by $t_n(\hat{\lambda}) = b$; furthermore,*

$$\lim_{\lambda \to \infty} t_n(\lambda) = a \ .$$

Theorem 9-4.2. *The phase function $\theta(t, \lambda)$ is a continuous and strictly increasing function of λ for each value of t in $(a, b]$. Moreover,*

$$\lim_{\lambda \to \infty} \theta(t, \lambda) = \infty \ ,$$

and (under the assumption that, for all values of λ, $\theta(a, \lambda) = \alpha$, where $0 \leqq \alpha < \pi$)

$$\lim_{\lambda \to -\infty} \theta(t, \lambda) = 0 \ .$$

The boundary problem

$$L_\lambda u = 0 \ , \tag{9-4.2}$$

$$\mathbf{W}^{[a]}\mathbf{k}(u(a)) + \mathbf{W}^{[b]}\mathbf{k}(u(b)) = \mathbf{o} \ , \tag{9-4.3}$$

where the 2 by 4 matrix $(\mathbf{W}^{[a]}\mathbf{W}^{[b]})$ is of rank 2 and where

$$\mathbf{W}^{[a]}\mathbf{P}^{-1}(a)\tilde{\mathbf{W}}^{[a]} = \mathbf{W}^{[b]}\mathbf{P}^{-1}(b)\tilde{\mathbf{W}}^{[b]} \ , \tag{9-4.4}$$

is self-adjoint and is known as a *Sturm–Liouville system*. Any value of λ for which the system is compatible is called an *eigenvalue* and a corresponding solution of the system is an *eigenfunction*. We confine our attention to boundary conditions for which

$$(\mathbf{W}^{[a]}\mathbf{W}^{[b]}) = \begin{pmatrix} w_1 & w_1' & 0 & 0 \\ 0 & 0 & w_2 & w_2' \end{pmatrix} .$$

Written in scalar form, such conditions are

$$\begin{aligned} w_1 u(a) + w_1' u'(a) &= 0 \ , \\ w_2 u(b) + w_2' u'(b) &= 0 \ , \end{aligned} \tag{9-4.5}$$

and it is easily verified that they satisfy the self-adjointness criterion (9-4.4). These conditions are commonly referred to as *separated* or *unmixed*, because each condition involves the solution and its derivative at only one point.

By multiplying each of the relations in equation (9-4.5) by an appropriate constant, we can find two real numbers α and β on the interval $[0, \pi)$ such that the relations can be rewritten as

$$\begin{aligned} \cos\alpha\, u(a) - \sin\alpha\, p(a) u'(a) &= 0 \ , \\ \cos\beta\, u(b) - \sin\beta\, p(b) u'(b) &= 0 \ . \end{aligned} \tag{9-4.6}$$

The motivation for selecting this form becomes obvious when we replace (9-4.6) by the equivalent equations

$$\frac{u(a)}{p(a)u'(a)} = \tan\alpha \ ,$$
(9-4.7)
$$\frac{u(b)}{p(b)u'(b)} = \tan\beta \ .$$

The relations (9-3.2) determine the Prüfer phase function θ so that

$$\tan\theta(t) = \frac{u(t)}{p(t)u'(t)} \ .$$

Consequently a set of boundary conditions for θ, corresponding to (9-4.7), is

(9-4.8) $$\tan\theta(a) = \tan\alpha \ ,$$

(9-4.9) $$\tan\theta(b) = \tan\beta \ .$$

We are now in a position to prove the following fundamental theorem.

Theorem 9-4.3. *The system consisting of* (9-4.2) *and* (9-4.5) *has an infinite set of eigenvalues and a corresponding infinite set of eigenfunctions.*

PROOF. Let equation (9-4.2) be replaced by its equivalent Prüfer system. We have just noted that the boundary conditions (9-4.8) and (9-4.9) are equivalent to the conditions (9-4.5). The Prüfer equation

(9-4.10) $$\theta' = \frac{1}{p}\cos^2\theta + (\lambda\rho + \sigma)\sin^2\theta$$

and the condition

$$\theta(a) = \alpha$$

constitute an initial-value problem with a unique solution $\theta(t, \lambda)$ for each value of the parameter λ. This solution obviously satisfies condition (9-4.8). It also satisfies condition (9-4.9) if λ can be chosen so that

(9.4-11) $$\theta(b, \lambda) = \beta + n\pi$$

for some integral value of n. Theorem 9-4.2, with $t = b$, guarantees the existence of a unique value of λ satisfying relation (9-4.11), providing n is nonnegative. This value of λ may be designated by λ_n, and we may infer from the same theorem that

$$\lambda_0 < \lambda_1 < \lambda_2 < \cdots \ .$$

The phase function $\theta(t, \lambda_n)$ is clearly a solution of equation (9-4.10) (with $\lambda = \lambda_n$) and the conditions (9-4.8) and (9-4.9). If this function is substituted into formula (9-3.6), we obtain a function r which may be designated by $r_n(t)$. Hence,

$$u_n(t) = r_n(t)\sin\theta(t, \lambda_n) \ ,$$

defines a solution of the Sturm–Liouville system when $\lambda = \lambda_n$. It is unique up to a constant multiplier and is the eigenfunction corresponding to λ_n. That is to say, $\{\lambda_n\}$ is an infinite set of distinct eigenvalues and $\{u_n(t)\}$ is the corresponding set of eigenfunctions. This completes the proof of the theorem.

Corollary 9-4.3. *The eigenfunction u_n has exactly n zeros on the interval (a, b).*

PROOF. Since

$$\theta(a, \lambda_n) = \alpha \quad \text{and} \quad \theta(b, \lambda_n) = \beta + n\pi$$

and since $\theta(t, \lambda_n)$ is a continuous function of t, it must take on each of the values

$$\pi, 2\pi, 3\pi, \cdots, n\pi ,$$

at least once on the interval (a, b). Since it was noted in Section 9-3 that none of these values can be taken on more than once and since each corresponds to a zero of $u_n(t)$, we must conclude that the eigenfunction has exactly n zeros on (a, b).

We now show that the eigenfunctions satisfy a generalized orthogonality relation.

Definition 9-4.1. *Two functions u and v in $C[a, b]$ are* ***orthogonal relative to a weight function*** *ω if*

$$\int_a^b u(t)v(t)\omega(t)\,dt = 0 .$$

Theorem 9-4.4. *The eigenfunctions of the Sturm–Liouville system* (9-4.2) *and* (9-4.5) *form an orthogonal set relative to the weight function ρ.*

PROOF. If the operator L is defined by

$$Lu = (pu')' + \sigma u ,$$

the Sturm–Liouville equation (9-4.2) may be written as

$$Lu = -\lambda \rho u .$$

Green's formula for the self-adjoint operator L may be applied to the eigenfunctions u_j and u_k to yield

$$\int_a^b (-u_k \lambda_j \rho u_j + u_j \lambda_k \rho u_k)\,dt = \tilde{\mathbf{k}}(u_k(t))\mathbf{P}(t)\mathbf{k}(u_j(t))\Big|_a^b .$$

Since u_j and u_k both satisfy the boundary conditions, the right-hand side of this relation is zero. Hence, we have

$$(\lambda_k - \lambda_j) \int_a^b u_j(t)u_k(t)\rho(t)\,dt = 0 .$$

Since the eigenvalues are distinct, this proves the theorem.

The conclusion of the above theorem sets the stage for a discussion of expansion theory. This discussion is not given here, but it may be noted that the case where $\rho(t) = 1$ for all t in $[a, b]$ is covered in the results of Chapter 8. In particular, this includes the important Fourier series expansion. When ρ is not restricted to a constant value the developments of Chapter 8 can be modified to establish the convergence of a formal expansion. However, a more direct and efficient treatment of the expansion theory can be achieved by comparing partial sums of a Fourier expansion with partial sums of a Sturm–Liouville expansion.[4]

Exercises

1. Prove Theorem 9-4.1.

2. Prove Theorem 9-4.2.

3. Find eigenvalues and eigenfunctions for each of the following Sturm–Liouville problems:

(a) $u'' + \lambda u = 0$,
$u'(0) = 0$, $u'(\pi) = 0$;

(b) $u'' + \lambda u = 0$,
$u(a) = 0$, $u(b) = 0$;

(c) $u'' + \lambda u = 0$,
$u(0) = 0$, $wu(1) + u'(1) = 0$
(w is a constant) ;

(d) $(tu')' + \lambda \frac{1}{t} u = 0$,
$u(1) = 0$, $u(e^{\pi}) = 0$.

4. Find Green's function for each problem in Exercise 3.

5. Find the expansion of

$$f(t) = t ,$$

$0 \leqq t \leqq \pi$, in a series of eigenfunctions of Exercise 3(a).

[4]See Ince [26], page 276.

10

Non-Self-Adjoint Eigenvalue Problems

10-1. INTRODUCTION

In Chapter 8 the hypothesis of self-adjointness and the resulting symmetry of Green's function played a major role in the development of the theory. Since symmetry is not assumed in this chapter, we may anticipate a treatment of the problem which is substantially different from the earlier treatment.

One consequence of symmetry is the existence of an enumerably infinite set of eigenvalues with no finite limit point. Simple examples show that this may not be true in the non-self-adjoint case. Thus, the equation

$$-u'' = \lambda u$$

and the homogeneous boundary conditions determined by

$$(W^{[a]}\,W^{[b]}) = \begin{pmatrix} 1 & 0 & 1 & 0 \\ 0 & 1 & 0 & -1 \end{pmatrix},$$

$a = 0, b = \pi$, provide a problem that is compatible for all values of λ. However, if

$$(W^{[a]}\,W^{[b]}) = \begin{pmatrix} 1 & 0 & 2 & 0 \\ 0 & 1 & 0 & -2 \end{pmatrix},$$

the problem is not compatible for any λ.[1] These examples reveal the necessity of imposing conditions that prevent the occurrence of a degenerate characteristic function. Such conditions are commonly called *regularity conditions.*

By imposing regularity conditions we can insure the existence of an enumerably infinite set $\{u_j\}$ of eigenfunctions for a non-self-adjoint problem. However, the set is not, in general, an orthogonal set. This apparent defect is not serious, for the adjoint boundary problem has a corresponding set $\{v_j\}$ of eigenfunctions, and it can be shown that

$$(u_i, v_j) = 0 \ , \quad i \neq j \ .$$

This relation is called a *biorthogonality relation.* By means of it, the coefficients of a formal expansion for an "arbitrary" function f are easily obtained.

The operator L is defined here, as usual, by

$$Lu = p_0 u^{[n]} + p_1 u^{[n-1]} + \cdots + p_n u \ ,$$

[1] These examples are given by Coddington and Levinson [11], page 300.

$p_0(t) \neq 0$ on $[a, b]$. The boundary problem to be considered is

$$Lu = \lambda u \ , \tag{10-1.1}$$

$$\mathbf{W}^{[a]}\mathbf{k}(u(a)) + \mathbf{W}^{[b]}\mathbf{k}(u(b)) = \mathbf{o} \ , \tag{10-1.2}$$

where $(\mathbf{W}^{[a]}\mathbf{W}^{[b]})$ is an n by $2n$ matrix of rank n. If $\mathbf{u}$ is some specific fundamental vector for equation (10-1.1), the corresponding characteristic matrix for the problem is

$$\mathbf{D} = \mathbf{W}^{[a]}\mathbf{K}(\mathbf{u}(a)) + \mathbf{W}^{[b]}\mathbf{K}(\mathbf{u}(b)) \ ,$$

and the determinant D of this matrix is a characteristic function for the problem. Since the components of $\mathbf{u}$ must involve the parameter λ, the same may be said for the components of $\mathbf{D}$. We use the symbol $\mathbf{D}(\lambda)$ to represent the characteristic matrix and the symbol $D(\lambda)$ to represent the characteristic function whenever we want to emphasize their dependence on the parameter. The set of zeros of $D(\lambda)$ are the eigenvalues of the problem. This set may be represented by $\{\lambda_j, j = 1, 2, \ldots\}$ in anticipation of the imposition of suitable regularity conditions.

The adjoint of problem (10-1.1) and (10-1.2) is given by

$$L^*v = \lambda v \ , \tag{10-1.3}$$

$$\begin{cases} \tilde{\mathbf{k}}(v(a))\mathbf{P}(a) = \tilde{\mathbf{a}}\mathbf{W}^{[a]} \ , \\ \tilde{\mathbf{k}}(v(b))\mathbf{P}(b) = -\tilde{\mathbf{a}}\mathbf{W}^{[b]} \ , \end{cases} \tag{10-1.4}$$

where the operator L^* and the matrix $\mathbf{P}$ are defined in Chapter 3. The two problems have the same set of eigenvalues. The Green's function for the boundary problem (10-1.1) and (10-1.2) is given by [see formula (6-7.7)]

$$G(t, s, \lambda) = \begin{cases} \tilde{\mathbf{u}}(t)\mathbf{D}^{-1}(\lambda)\mathbf{W}^{[a]}\mathbf{K}(\mathbf{u}(a))\mathbf{K}^{-1}(\mathbf{u}(s))\mathbf{d}_n p_0^{-1}(s) \ , \ s < t \ , \\ -\tilde{\mathbf{u}}(t)\mathbf{D}^{-1}(\lambda)\mathbf{W}^{[b]}\mathbf{K}(\mathbf{u}(b))\mathbf{K}^{-1}(\mathbf{u}(s))\mathbf{d}_n p_0^{-1}(s) \ , \ s > t \ . \end{cases} \tag{10-1.5}$$

This function is defined for any λ which is not an eigenvalue. It is pertinent to observe that the Green's function used in Chapter 8 was defined for a problem that contained no parameter. In terms of the notation used in formula (10-1.5), it can be represented by $G(t, s, 0)$. It will be seen that the structure of Green's function relative to the parameter plays a significant role in the present development of an expansion theory.

In order to appreciate the nature of the role played by Green's function, we may proceed as follows. Let λ_i be an eigenvalue of the boundary problem (10-1.1) and (10-1.2) and let u_i be a corresponding eigenfunction. If λ is not an eigenvalue, the boundary problem consisting of the nonhomogeneous equation

$$Lu - \lambda u = -(\lambda - \lambda_i)u_i$$

together with the boundary condition (10-1.2) has a unique solution u_i. It follows that u_i must satisfy the integral relation

$$u_i(t) = -(\lambda - \lambda_i) \int_a^b G(t, s, \lambda) u_i(s) \, ds \quad (10\text{-}1.6)$$

If the operator $\mathscr{G}$ is defined by

$$v = \mathscr{G}u ,$$

where

$$v(t) = \int_a^b G(t, s, \lambda) u(s) \, ds ,$$

we may rewrite (10-1.6) as

$$-\mathscr{G}u_i = \frac{1}{\lambda - \lambda_i} u_i .$$

Since the operator is linear we have, for any finite set of scalars $\{\alpha_i : i = 1, 2, \ldots, n\}$,

$$-\mathscr{G}\left(\sum_{i=1}^{n} \alpha_i u_i \right) = \sum_{i=1}^{n} \frac{1}{\lambda - \lambda_i} \alpha_i u_i .$$

If $\{u_i\}$ is an infinite set of eigenfunctions and if a set of scalars $\{\alpha_i\}$ exists such that the series

$$\sum_{i=1}^{\infty} \alpha_i u_i$$

converges uniformly to a function f on $[a, b]$, then we may clearly write

$$-\mathscr{G}f = \sum_{i=1}^{\infty} \frac{1}{\lambda - \lambda_i} \alpha_i u_i . \quad (10\text{-}1.7)$$

The right-hand side of relation (10-1.7) is a meromorphic function of λ with a simple pole at each eigenvalue. If the eigenvalues are all distinct the residue of the right-hand side at $\lambda = \lambda_i$ is clearly $\alpha_i u_i$. If Γ_m is a simple closed curve in the λ-plane which encloses the first m eigenvalues and no others, then

$$-\frac{1}{2\pi i} \int_{\Gamma_m} \int_a^b G(t, s, \lambda) f(s) \, ds \, d\lambda = \sum_{i=1}^{m} \alpha_i u_i . \quad (10\text{-}1.8)$$

The relation (10-1.8) provides a clue to a possible treatment of the expansion problem. Let f be a function in $R[a, b]$, and let h be defined by

$$h = -\mathscr{G}f .$$

It is clear that h depends on the parameter λ and that we may write

$$h(t, \lambda) = -\int_a^b G(t, s, \lambda) f(s) \, ds . \quad (10\text{-}1.9)$$

An eigenfunction expansion of f will be established if we can show that the residue of $h(t, \lambda)$ at λ_i is a scalar multiple of u_i and that

$$\lim_{m\to\infty} \frac{1}{2\pi i} \int_{\Gamma_m} h(t, \lambda)\, d\lambda = f(t) \ .$$

We shall see that this can be done if suitable restrictions are placed on the function f.

The intent of the discussion that follows is to indicate the method by which the expansion theory associated with non-self-adjoint problems can be attacked. We have no interest in obtaining maximum relaxation of the conditions under which the expansion of a function f can be established. For this reason, we impose conditions which are more stringent than necessary, both on f and on the boundary problem, whenever such restrictions serve to facilitate the exposition.

10-2. A BIORTHOGONALITY RELATION AND THE FORMAL EXPANSION

We assume here, in the interest of simplicity, that each eigenvalue is a simple zero of the characteristic function D. It is seen later that this insures the existence of a corresponding unique eigenfunction. Let λ_i and λ_j be two distinct eigenvalues. Let u_i be a solution of the boundary problem (10-1.1) and (10-1.2) when $\lambda = \lambda_i$, and let v_j be a solution of the boundary problem (10-1.3) and (10-1.4) when $\lambda = \lambda_j$. The Green's formula relative to the operators L and L^* yields

$$\int_a^b v_j(t) L u_i(t)\, dt - \int_a^b u_i(t) L^* v_j(t)\, dt = \tilde{\mathbf{k}}(v_j(t))\mathbf{P}(t)\mathbf{k}(u_i(t))\Big|_a^b \ .$$

This can be reduced to

$$(\lambda_i - \lambda_j) \int_a^b v_j(t) u_i(t)\, dt = \tilde{\mathbf{k}}(v_j(b))\mathbf{P}(b)\mathbf{k}(u_i(b)) - \tilde{\mathbf{k}}(v_j(a)\mathbf{P}(a)\mathbf{k}(u_i(a)) \ .$$

Since v_j satisfies conditions (10-1.4), the relation can be written as

$$\begin{aligned}(\lambda_i - \lambda_j)(u_i, v_j) &= -\tilde{\mathbf{a}}\mathbf{W}^{[a]}\mathbf{k}(u_i(a)) - \tilde{\mathbf{a}}\mathbf{W}^{[b]}\mathbf{k}(u_i(b)) \\ &= -\tilde{\mathbf{a}}[\mathbf{W}^{[a]}\mathbf{k}(u_i(a)) + \mathbf{W}^{[b]}\mathbf{k}(u_i(b))] \ .\end{aligned}$$

Since u_i satisfies condition (10-1.2), the right-hand side of the last relation is zero. Hence

$$(u_i, v_j) = 0 \qquad (10\text{-}2.1)$$

if $i \neq j$. This relation is called a *biorthogonality relation*, and we say that the sets $\{u_i\}$ and $\{v_i\}$ form a biorthogonal pair. We may assume, further, that the eigenfunctions have been chosen so that

$$(u_i, v_i) = 1 \ , \quad i = 1, 2, \ldots \ . \qquad (10\text{-}2.2)$$

Let f be a function in $R[a, b]$ and assume, tentatively, that f has the representation

(10-2.3)
$$f = \sum_{i=1}^{\infty} \alpha_i u_i \ ,$$

where the series on the right-hand side converges uniformly to f on $[a, b]$. Multiplying both sides by v_j and integrating we infer, in view of (10-2.1) and (10-2.2), that

(10-2.4)
$$\alpha_j = (f, v_j) \ .$$

The series on the right-hand side of (10-2.3), where α_j is defined by (10-2.4), is called the *formal expansion of the function f*. Here, as in Chapter 8, the question of whether or not the formal expansion converges to f is entirely open. It is significant that this formal expansion is identical with the corresponding formal expansion in Chapter 8 when we restrict L to be a self-adjoint operator.

We have indicated in Section 10-1 that we expect to identify the terms of the formal expansion of f with the residues of the function h defined by formula (10-1.9). The following identity is therefore useful in subsequent developments. In order to establish it, we must assume that f belongs to the space $C^n[a, b]$. For such an f, and for $G(t, s, \lambda)$ regarded as a function of s with t and λ fixed, we have (using the Lagrange identity)

$$G(t, s, \lambda)Lf(s) - f(s)L^*G(t, s, \lambda) = (\tilde{\mathbf{k}}(G)\mathbf{P}\mathbf{k}(f))' \ .$$

This identity is valid for every s in $[a, b]$, except for $s = t$ where the $(n-1)$st derivative of G has a discontinuity. Integrating, therefore, from a to t and from t to b, we get

(10-2.5)
$$\int_a^b (G(t, s, \lambda)Lf(s) - f(s)L^*G(t, s, \lambda))\, ds$$
$$= \tilde{\mathbf{k}}_2(G(t, s, \lambda))\mathbf{P}(s)\mathbf{k}(f(s))\Big|_a^{t^-} + \tilde{\mathbf{k}}_2(G(t, s, \lambda))\mathbf{P}(s)\mathbf{k}(f(s))\Big|_{t^+}^{b} \ .$$

Since G is a formal solution of the adjoint boundary problem, we have (Theorem 6-7.2)

(10-2.6)
$$L^*G = \lambda G \ ,$$

(10-2.7)
$$\tilde{\mathbf{k}}_2(G(t, a, \lambda))\mathbf{P}(a) = \tilde{\mathbf{a}}\mathbf{W}^{[a]} \ ,$$
$$\tilde{\mathbf{k}}_2(G(t, b, \lambda))\mathbf{P}(b) = -\tilde{\mathbf{a}}\mathbf{W}^{[b]} \ ,$$

where

(10-2.8)
$$\tilde{\mathbf{a}} = \tilde{\mathbf{a}}(t, \lambda) = \tilde{\mathbf{u}}(t, \lambda)\mathbf{D}^{-1}(\lambda) \ .$$

In view of (10-2.7), the right-hand side of relation (10-2.5) may be written as

(10-2.9)
$$-[\mathbf{k}_2(G(t, t^+, \lambda)) - \mathbf{k}_2(G(t, t^-, \lambda))]\mathbf{P}(t)\mathbf{k}(f(t)) - \tilde{\mathbf{a}}[\mathbf{W}^{[a]}\mathbf{k}(f(a)) + \mathbf{W}^{[b]}\mathbf{k}(f(b))] \ .$$

In the proof of Theorem 6-7.2, it was determined that

$$\tilde{\mathbf{k}}_2(G(t, t^+, \lambda)) - \tilde{\mathbf{k}}_2(G(t, t^-, \lambda)) = -\tilde{\mathbf{d}}_1\mathbf{P}^{-1}(t) \ .$$

Consequently, the first term in (10-2.9) reduces to $\tilde{\mathbf{d}}_1\mathbf{k}(f(t))$ which is equal to $f(t)$. In view of this result and relation (10-2.6), we may replace (10-2.5) by

$$\int_a^b G(t, s, \lambda)Lf(s)\,ds - \lambda \int_a^b G(t, s, \lambda)f(s)\,ds$$
$$= f(t) - \tilde{\mathbf{a}}[\mathbf{W}^{[a]}\mathbf{k}(f(a)) + \mathbf{W}^{[b]}\mathbf{k}(f(b))] \ .$$

Multiplying this relation by $1/\lambda$ and rearranging the terms, we get

$$-\int_a^b G(t, s, \lambda)f(s)\,ds$$
$$= \frac{1}{\lambda}f(t) - \frac{1}{\lambda}\tilde{\mathbf{a}}[\mathbf{W}^{[a]}\mathbf{k}(f(a)) + \mathbf{W}^{[b]}\mathbf{k}(f(b))] - \frac{1}{\lambda}\int_a^b G(t, s, \lambda)Lf(s)\,ds \ .$$

If the last relation is multiplied by $1/2\pi i$ and integrated around the contour Γ_m, we have

$$\text{(10-2.10)} \qquad -\frac{1}{2\pi i}\int_{\Gamma_m}\int_a^b G(t, s, \lambda)f(s)\,ds\,d\lambda = f(t) + B_m(t) + A_m(t) \ ,$$

where

$$\text{(10-2.11)} \qquad A_m(t) = -\frac{1}{2\pi i}\int_{\Gamma_m}\frac{1}{\lambda}\int_a^b G(t, s, \lambda)Lf(s)\,ds\,d\lambda \ ,$$

$$B_m(t) = -\frac{1}{2\pi i}\int_{\Gamma_m}\frac{1}{\lambda}\tilde{\mathbf{a}}(t, \lambda)[\mathbf{W}^{[a]}\mathbf{k}(f(a)) + \mathbf{W}^{[b]}\mathbf{k}(f(b))]\,d\lambda \ .$$

Relation (10-2.10) may be regarded as a fundamental identity for the development of the expansion theory. We show below that the left-hand side is equal to the mth partial sum of the formal expansion of f. This result follows directly from an evaluation of the residues of Green's function. To complete the demonstration that the mth partial sum converges to $f(t)$, we need only show that $A_m(t)$ and $B_m(t)$ converge to zero. In the limited discussion given here, we require f to satisfy the boundary conditions. This insures that $B_m(t)$ is identically zero. Thus, the expansion theorem consists essentially of the demonstration that $A_m(t)$ converges to zero as m becomes large.

Before attacking the general problem, it is instructive to apply the technique outlined above to the Fourier sine expansion. The eigenfunctions of the problem which generates this expansion are trigonometric functions, and Green's function can be determined explicitly. The example serves to illustrate the points we have made above and provides a useful introduction to the continuing discussion of the general problem.

10-3. FOURIER SINE SERIES EXPANSION

The boundary problem to be considered is

$$u'' + \lambda u = 0 \ ,$$
$$u(0) = u(\pi) = 0 \ .$$

In order to exhibit this problem as a special case of the general problem defined in Section 10-1, we define L, $W^{[a]}$, and $W^{[b]}$ by

$$Lu = -u'' ,$$

$$(W^{[a]}\, W^{[b]}) = \begin{pmatrix} 1 & 0 & 0 & 0 \\ 0 & 0 & 1 & 0 \end{pmatrix},$$

where $a = 0$ and $b = \pi$. A fundamental vector for

$$Lu = \lambda u$$

is

$$\tilde{\mathbf{u}}(t) = (\sin\sqrt{\lambda}\, t\ ,\quad \cos\sqrt{\lambda}\, t)\ .$$

The corresponding Wronskian matrix and its inverse are

$$\mathbf{K}(\mathbf{u}(t)) = \begin{pmatrix} \sin\sqrt{\lambda}\, t & \cos\sqrt{\lambda}\, t \\ \sqrt{\lambda}\cos\sqrt{\lambda}\, t & -\sqrt{\lambda}\sin\sqrt{\lambda}\, t \end{pmatrix},$$

$$\mathbf{K}^{-1}(\mathbf{u}(t)) = \frac{-1}{\sqrt{\lambda}} \begin{pmatrix} -\sqrt{\lambda}\sin\sqrt{\lambda}\, t & -\cos\sqrt{\lambda}\, t \\ -\sqrt{\lambda}\cos\sqrt{\lambda}\, t & \sin\sqrt{\lambda}\, t \end{pmatrix}.$$

It may be verified easily that the corresponding characteristic matrix and its inverse are

$$\mathbf{D}(\lambda) = \begin{pmatrix} 0 & 1 \\ \sin\sqrt{\lambda}\,\pi & \cos\sqrt{\lambda}\,\pi \end{pmatrix}, \mathbf{D}^{-1}(\lambda) = \frac{-1}{\sin\sqrt{\lambda}\,\pi} \begin{pmatrix} \cos\sqrt{\lambda}\,\pi & -1 \\ -\sin\sqrt{\lambda}\,\pi & 0 \end{pmatrix}.$$

Using these determinations in formula 6-7.7, we get Green's function

$$\text{(10-3.1)}\quad G(t, s, \lambda) = \frac{-1}{\sqrt{\lambda}\sin\sqrt{\lambda}\,\pi} \begin{cases} \sin\sqrt{\lambda}(t-\pi)\sin\sqrt{\lambda}\, s\ , & s < t\ , \\ \sin\sqrt{\lambda}\, t \sin\sqrt{\lambda}(s-\pi)\ , & s > t\ . \end{cases}$$

The eigenvalues of the problem are the zeros of the characteristic function $D(\lambda)$, given by

$$\begin{aligned} D(\lambda) &= |\,\mathbf{D}(\lambda)\,| \\ &= -\sin\sqrt{\lambda}\,\pi\ . \end{aligned}$$

The eigenvalues are therefore

$$\lambda_j = j^2\ ,\quad j = 1, 2, \ldots\ .$$

The corresponding eigenfunctions are

$$\begin{aligned} u_j(t) &= \sqrt{2/\pi}\sin\sqrt{\lambda_j}\, t \\ &= \sqrt{2/\pi}\sin jt\ . \end{aligned}$$

The scalar factor $\sqrt{2/\pi}$ is suggested by experience with this problem as a self-adjoint problem; it may be replaced by any nonzero factor that we care to select. Since the problem is self-adjoint the eigenfunction u_j may also be represented by the symbol v_j. Clearly, the scalar factor chosen has the advantage that

$$(u_j, v_j) = 1 \ .$$

The contour Γ_m for this problem may be chosen as the circle defined by

$$|\lambda| = (m+\tfrac{1}{2})^2 \ .$$

It is convenient later to have some information on the behavior of the function $D(\lambda)e^{\sqrt{\lambda}\pi i}$ when λ is on any contour in the set $\{\Gamma_j\}$. Consider, therefore, the mapping defined by

$$z = e^{\varrho 2\pi i} - 1 \ .$$

The zeros of this function are the members of the set $\{\rho_j : \rho_j = j, j = 0, \pm 1, \pm 2, \ldots\}$. Let S_j represent the square neighborhood of ρ_j defined by

$$S_j = \{\rho : |\text{Re}(\rho - \rho_j)| < \tfrac{1}{4} \ , \quad |\text{Im}(\rho - \rho_j)| < \tfrac{1}{4}\} \ .$$

Since the function is periodic, it is not difficult to show that z is bounded from zero if ρ is excluded from any of the square neighborhoods. It is clear that no circle in the set $\{C_j\}$, where

$$C_j = \{\rho : |\rho| = j + \tfrac{1}{2}\} \ ,$$

has a point in common with any neighborhood in the set $\{S_j\}$. Hence, z is bounded from zero if ρ is restricted to be a point on any circle in the set $\{C_j\}$.

Let ρ and λ be related by

$$\rho = \sqrt{\lambda} \ ,$$

where the ambiguity inherent in the symbol $\sqrt{\lambda}$ is removed by specifying that

$$0 \leqq \arg\sqrt{\lambda} < \pi \ .$$

The contour Γ_m on the λ-plane maps into that half of the circle C_m that lies in the upper half of the ρ-plane. Since

$$D(\lambda)e^{\sqrt{\lambda}\pi i} = -\frac{1}{2i}(e^{\sqrt{\lambda}2\pi i} - 1) \ ,$$

we may conclude that a positive real number δ exists such that

$$|D(\lambda)e^{\sqrt{\lambda}\pi i}| > \delta \qquad (10\text{-}3.2)$$

if $\lambda \in \Gamma_m$, $m = 1, 2, \ldots$.

The formal expansion of a function f is given by

$$\sum_{j=1}^{\infty} \alpha_j u_j \ ,$$

where

$$\alpha_j = (f, v_j) = (f, u_j) \ .$$

This is the familiar sine series expansion of f, and the conditions for its convergence are discussed in Chapter 8. We assume here that $f \in C^2[0, \pi]$ and that

$$f(0) = f(\pi) = 0 \ . \tag{10-3.3}$$

The latter restriction is the requirement that f satisfy the boundary conditions of the differential boundary problem.

In order to analyze the expansion by the method outlined above, we must determine the residues of Green's function at the eigenvalues. To do this we recall the familiar fact that a function g with a simple pole at z_0 may be written as

$$g(z) = \frac{n(z)}{m(z)} \ ,$$

where n and m are analytic at z_0, where m has a simple zero at that point, and where $n(z_0) \neq 0$. Moreover, the residue at z_0 is

$$\mathrm{Res}_{z=z_0} g(z) = \frac{n(z_0)}{m'(z_0)} \ .$$

Using this formula on the expression for G in formula (10-3.1), we get

$$\begin{aligned}\mathrm{Res}_{\lambda=\lambda_j} G(t, s, \lambda) &= -\frac{2}{\pi} \sin jt \sin js \\ &= -u_j(t)\, v_j(s) \ .\end{aligned}$$

It should be noted that the result is independent of the location of s relative to t. We may now write

$$\begin{aligned}-\frac{1}{2\pi i}\int_{\Gamma_m}\int_a^b G(t, s, \lambda) f(s)\, ds\, d\lambda &= -\int_a^b \frac{1}{2\pi i}\int_{\Gamma_m} G(t, s, \lambda)\, d\lambda f(s)\, ds \\ &= -\int_a^b \sum_{j=1}^m \mathrm{Res}_{\lambda=\lambda_j} G(t, s, \lambda) f(s)\, ds \\ &= \int_a^b \sum_{j=1}^m u_j(t)\, v_j(s) f(s)\, ds \\ &= \sum_{j=1}^m (f, v_j) u_j(t) \ .\end{aligned}$$

Thus, for this problem, the left-hand side of the identity (10-2.10) has been reduced to the mth partial sum of the formal expansion of f.

To complete the demonstration we must examine the right-hand side of the same identity. We see at once, in view of hypothesis (10-3.3), that

$$B_m(t) = 0 \ .$$

We may, therefore, direct our attention to $A_m(t)$. It is clear that formula (10-3.1) may be rewritten as

$$G(t, s, \lambda) = \frac{N(t, s, \lambda)}{D(\lambda)} \ ,$$

where $D(\lambda)$ is the characteristic function and

$$N(t, s, \lambda) = \frac{1}{\sqrt{\lambda}} \begin{cases} \frac{1}{4}\{\exp[\sqrt{\lambda}\, i(t+s-\pi)] + \exp[-\sqrt{\lambda}\, i(t+s-\pi)] \\ \quad -\exp[\sqrt{\lambda}\, i(t-s-\pi)] - \exp[-\sqrt{\lambda}\, i(t-s-\pi)]\}\,, & s < t, \\ \frac{1}{4}\{\exp[\sqrt{\lambda}\, i(t+s-\pi)] + \exp[-\sqrt{\lambda}\, i(t+s-\pi)] \\ \quad -\exp[\sqrt{\lambda}\, i(s-t-\pi)] - \exp[-\sqrt{\lambda}\, i(s-t-\pi)]\}, & s > t. \end{cases}$$

Because of the definition of $N(t, s, \lambda)$, the integration with respect to s in formula (10-2.11) appears as the sum of two integrals, one over the interval $[a, t)$ and the other over $(t, b]$. Each of these in turn may be expressed as the sum of four integrals corresponding to the four terms in the expression for N. In order to simplify the discussion of these eight integrals we may express N as

$$N(t, s, \lambda) = \frac{1}{\sqrt{\lambda}} \begin{cases} \sum_{j=1}^{4} \gamma_j^- \exp[\sqrt{\lambda}\, \phi_j^-(t, s)]\,, & s < t\,, \\ \sum_{j=1}^{4} \gamma_j^+ \exp[\sqrt{\lambda}\, \phi_j^+(t, s)]\,, & s > t\,, \end{cases}$$

where γ_j^- and γ_j^+ is either $\frac{1}{4}$ or $-\frac{1}{4}$, and

$$\begin{aligned} \phi_1^-(t, s) &= \phi_1^+(t, s) = i(t+s-\pi)\,, \\ \phi_2^-(t, s) &= \phi_2^+(t, s) = -i(t+s-\pi)\,, \\ \phi_3^-(t, s) &= i(t-s-\pi)\,, \qquad \phi_3^+(t, s) = i(s-t-\pi)\,, \\ \phi_4^-(t, s) &= -i(t-s-\pi)\,, \quad \phi_4^+(t, s) = -i(s-t-\pi)\,. \end{aligned} \tag{10-3.4}$$

With reference to formula (10-2.11), therefore, we may infer that $A_m(t)$ is the sum of eight integrals of the form

$$\frac{1}{2\pi i}\int_{\Gamma_m} \lambda^{-3/2} J(t, \lambda)\, d\lambda\,, \tag{10-3.5}$$

where

$$J(t, \lambda) = \gamma \int_c^d \frac{1}{D} \exp[\sqrt{\lambda}\, \phi(t, s)] f''(s)\, ds\,. \tag{10-3.6}$$

In this relation, the interval (c, d) is either (a, t) or (t, b); $\phi(t, s)$ is one of the ϕ-functions defined in (10-3.4); and γ is a constant.

Throughout the discussion, t is to be regarded as an arbitrary but fixed point on the interval $[a, b]$. The relation

$$z = \phi(t, s)$$

may be looked upon as a transformation mapping the s interval (c, d) into a complex z-plane. Each of the various ϕ functions, defined in (10-3.4), which may be used in this relation has the property that the image of (c, d) is a straight-line segment whose end points are on the line joining $-\pi i$ and πi. Consequently,

$$z = \phi(t, s) + i\pi$$

maps (c, d) into a line segment between 0 and $2\pi i$. The definition of $\sqrt{\lambda}$ given above was such that $0 \leqq \arg\sqrt{\lambda} < \pi$. Hence, for any value of the parameter λ, the relation

$$z = \sqrt{\lambda}(\phi(t, s) + i\pi)$$

maps (c, d) into a ray whose inclination angle is between $\frac{1}{2}\pi$ and $\frac{3}{2}\pi$.

The significant conclusion that may be drawn from the above discussion is that

$$\text{(10-3.7)} \qquad \mathrm{Re}[\sqrt{\lambda}(\phi(t, s) + i\pi)] \leqq 0$$

for any s in (c, d). Let relation (10-3.6) be rewritten as

$$J(t, \lambda) = \gamma \int_c^b \frac{\exp\{\sqrt{\lambda}[\phi(t, s) + i\pi]\}}{D(\lambda)\exp[\sqrt{\lambda}\, i\pi]} f''(s)\, ds\ .$$

In view of (10-3.2) and (10-3.7) and the fact that $f''(s)$ is continuous on $[a, b]$, we see that the integrand is bounded and hence that, for some positive real number M, with $t \in [a, b]$, $\lambda \in \Gamma_m$, $m = 1, 2, \ldots,$

$$|J(t, \lambda)| \leqq M\ .$$

It follows that

$$\left| \frac{1}{2\pi i} \int_{\Gamma_m} \lambda^{-3/2} J(t, \lambda)\, d\lambda \right| \leqq \frac{1}{2\pi}(m+\tfrac{1}{2})^{-3} M 2\pi (m+\tfrac{1}{2})^2$$

$$\leqq \frac{M}{m+\frac{1}{2}}\ .$$

Recalling that $A_m(t)$ was expressed as the sum of eight integrals of the type exhibited in (10-3.5), we may write

$$|A_m(t)| \leqq \frac{8M}{m+\frac{1}{2}}\ .$$

It follows at once that

$$\lim_{m\to\infty} A_m(t) = 0\ .$$

Hence, the formal expansion converges uniformly to $f(t)$ on $[a, b]$.

As indicated earlier, the convergence of the expansion can be established under conditions on f that are less stringent than those applied above. Thus, if f is assumed to have a continuous first derivative, the expression

$$-\frac{1}{2\pi i} \int_{\Gamma_m} \int_a^b G(t, s, \lambda) f(s)\, ds\, d\lambda$$

can be integrated with respect to s by parts. Its convergence to $f(t)$ can then be established. It is interesting to note that a second integration by parts yields the identity (10-2.10). Convergence may also be established without imposing the condition that f should satisfy the boundary conditions. Obviously, when this restriction is not imposed, we cannot expect the series to converge to f at the boundary points. The interesting fact is that these are the only points at which the series does not converge to f. That is to say, the series converges (but not uniformly) to f on the open interval (a, b).

Exercises

1. Develop the expansion theory for the boundary problem

$$-u'' = \lambda u \ ,$$

$$u'(0) = u'(\pi) = 0 \ .$$

2. Give a detailed proof of the fact that $e^{\rho 2\pi i} - 1$ is bounded from zero if ρ is excluded from the square neighborhoods which belong to the set $\{S_j\}$.

3. Derive formula (10-2.10) for the second-order boundary problem of Section 10-3 by performing two integrations by parts on the expression

$$\int_a^b G(t, s, \lambda) f(s)\, ds \ .$$

Note that $G(t, s, \lambda)$, regarded as a function of s, satisfies $-u'' = \lambda u$. Hence, $G(t, s, \lambda)$ may be replaced by $-(1/\lambda) G_{ss}(t, s, \lambda)$.

10-4. RESIDUES OF GREEN'S FUNCTION

The fundamental relation (10-2.10) was developed above in Section 10-2, and it was indicated there, as well as in Section 10-3, that the left-hand side of the relation is reducible to the partial sum of a formal expansion of f. In order to achieve the reduction, we need only interpret the contour integral as a sum of residues of the integrand and then proceed to evaluate the residues. The residues are contributed by Green's function which [see formula (6-7.9)] has the representation

$$G(t, s, \lambda) = \begin{cases} \tilde{\mathbf{u}}(t)\mathbf{D}^{-1}(\lambda)\mathbf{W}^{[a]}\mathbf{K}(\mathbf{u}(a))\mathbf{v}(s) \ , & s < t \ , \\ -\tilde{\mathbf{u}}(t)\mathbf{D}^{-1}(\lambda)\mathbf{W}^{[b]}\mathbf{K}(\mathbf{u}(b))\mathbf{v}(s) \ , & s > t \ , \end{cases}$$

if the fundamental vectors $\mathbf{u}$ and $\mathbf{v}$ are chosen so that $\tilde{\mathbf{K}}(\mathbf{v})\mathbf{P}\mathbf{K}(\mathbf{u}) = \mathbf{I}$. Here, the symbol $\mathbf{D}^{-1}(\lambda)$ has been used instead of $\mathbf{D}^{-1}$ to point up the fact that the matrix depends on the parameter λ. It should be noted, however, that the factors $\mathbf{u}$, $\mathbf{K}(\mathbf{u})$, and $\mathbf{v}$ also depend on the parameter. In this connection, we may observe (see the remark at the end of Chapter 2 and the references cited there) that the components of $\mathbf{u}$ and $\mathbf{v}$ are analytic functions of λ. It follows, therefore, that the components of $\mathbf{K}(\mathbf{u})$ and $\mathbf{D}$ are analytic functions of λ. This implies that the components of $\mathbf{D}^{-1}(\lambda)$ are meromorphic functions with possible poles at the eigenvalues. It is also clear that the residues of G are contributed by $\mathbf{D}^{-1}$.

We noted in Chapter 6 that Green's function is uniquely determined by the boundary problem. That is to say, it is independent of the choice of the fundamental vectors **u** and **v** and is not affected if, for any nonsingular matrix **C**, the boundary condition matrix $(\mathbf{W}^{[a]}\mathbf{W}^{[b]})$ is replaced by $\mathbf{C}(\mathbf{W}^{[a]}\mathbf{W}^{[b]})$. This statement does not apply to the characteristic matrix, and we presently take advantage of this to alter **D** in such a way as to facilitate the ensuing analysis.

Let λ_β be an eigenvalue of multiplicity s. Since $\mathbf{D}(\lambda)$ is analytic at λ_β, its components may be expressed as power series in $(\lambda-\lambda_\beta)$. Hence, it may be written as

$$\mathbf{D}(\lambda)=\mathbf{P}(\lambda)+(\lambda-\lambda_\beta)^{s+1}\mathbf{Q}(\lambda) ,$$

where the components of $\mathbf{P}(\lambda)$ are polynomials of degree s in $(\lambda-\lambda_\beta)$, and the components of $\mathbf{Q}(\lambda)$ are convergent power series in $(\lambda-\lambda_\beta)$. Let the fundamental vector $\tilde{\mathbf{u}}$ be replaced by $\tilde{\mathbf{u}}\mathbf{C}_1$, and let the boundary condition matrix $(\mathbf{W}^{[a]}\mathbf{W}^{[b]})$ be replaced by $\mathbf{C}_2(\mathbf{W}^{[a]}\mathbf{W}^{[b]})$. This has the effect of replacing **D**, **P**, and **Q** by $\mathbf{C}_2\mathbf{D}\mathbf{C}_1$, $\mathbf{C}_2\mathbf{P}\mathbf{C}_1$, and $\mathbf{C}_2\mathbf{Q}\mathbf{C}_1$, respectively. It is a familiar fact[2] that nonsingular matrices $\mathbf{C}_1$ and $\mathbf{C}_2$, whose components are polynomials in $(\lambda-\lambda_\beta)$, can be found so that

$$\mathbf{C}_2\mathbf{P}\mathbf{C}_1=(\delta_{ij}p_j) ,$$

where

(10-4.1)
(i) p_j is a polynomial in $(\lambda-\lambda_\beta)$,
(ii) p_j divides p_{j+1},
(iii) the coefficient of the lowest power of $(\lambda-\lambda_\beta)$ in p_j. is 1.

To avoid additional symbols, we assume that the boundary conditions were initially modified as suggested and that the appropriate fundamental vector **u** was originally selected. With this assumption, we have

$$\mathbf{D}(\lambda)=\mathbf{P}(\lambda)+(\lambda-\lambda_\beta)^{s+1}\mathbf{Q}(\lambda) ,$$

where

$$\mathbf{P}(\lambda)=(\delta_{ij}p_j) ,$$

and each p_j, for $j=1,2,\ldots,n$, has the properties listed in (10-4.1).

The following incidental result is significant and is stated in the form of a theorem.

Theorem 10-4.1. *The multiplicity of an eigenvalue is at least as great as its index of compatibility.*

PROOF. If the index of compatibility of λ_β is k, then precisely k of the diagonal components of **P** must have $(\lambda-\lambda_\beta)$ as a factor. Since each of these components divides its successor, the last k components must have $(\lambda-\lambda_\beta)$ as a factor. This implies that $(\lambda-\lambda_\beta)$ is a common factor of the components of each of the last k rows of the matrix **D**. The determinant $|\mathbf{D}|$, therefore, has $(\lambda-\lambda_\beta)^k$ as a factor and, hence, the multiplicity of λ_β is at least k. This proves the theorem.

[2] See Bôcher [7], page 267.

Corollary 10-4.1a. *If $s > k$, then some of the p's, including p_n, have $(\lambda - \lambda_\beta)$ as a multiple factor.*

Corollary 10-4.1b. *If $s = k$, then $(\lambda - \lambda_\beta)$ is a simple factor of p_j, $j = n-k+1$, $n-k+2, \ldots, n$.*

Corollary 10-4.1c. *If λ_β is a simple eigenvalue (i.e., of multiplicity 1), then its index of compatibility is 1.*

In the interest of simplifying the text, we assume henceforth that *all the eigenvalues are simple.* In view of Corollary 10-4.1b, therefore, λ_β is a simple zero of p_n. Moreover, property (iii) of (10-4.1) implies that

$$p_j(\lambda_\beta) = 1 \ , \quad j = 1, 2, \ldots, n-1 \ .$$

It follows that

$$\mathbf{D}(\lambda_\beta) = \begin{pmatrix} 1 & 0 & \cdots & 0 & 0 \\ 0 & 1 & \cdots & 0 & 0 \\ \cdot & \cdot & \cdot & \cdot & \cdot \\ \cdot & \cdot & \cdot & \cdot & \cdot \\ \cdot & \cdot & \cdot & \cdot & \cdot \\ 0 & 0 & \cdots & 1 & 0 \\ 0 & 0 & \cdots & 0 & 0 \end{pmatrix}$$

Since $\mathbf{d}_n$ is orthogonal to $\mathbf{D}(\lambda_\beta)$ on the right, the function u_β, defined by (see Theorem 6-5.1)

$$u_\beta(t) = \tilde{\mathbf{u}}(t, \lambda_\beta)\mathbf{d}_n \ , \tag{10-4.2}$$

is an eigenfunction of the boundary problem associated with the eigenvalue λ_β. This eigenfunction is unique up to a constant multiplier. Further, since $-\tilde{\mathbf{d}}_n$ is orthogonal to $\mathbf{D}(\lambda_\beta)$ on the left, it is a suitable choice for the parametric vector $\tilde{\mathbf{a}}$ in the formula for a solution of the adjoint problem. Thus, by substituting $-\tilde{\mathbf{d}}_n$ for $\tilde{\mathbf{a}}$ in formulas (6-6.12) and (6-6.13), we get the following pair of equivalent expressions for an eigenfunction v_β of the adjoint problem:

$$v_\beta(t) = -\tilde{\mathbf{d}}_n \mathbf{W}^{[a]}\mathbf{K}(\mathbf{u}(a, \lambda_\beta))\mathbf{v}(t, \lambda_\beta) \ , \tag{10-4.3}$$

$$v_\beta(t) = \tilde{\mathbf{d}}_n \mathbf{W}^{[b]}\mathbf{K}(\mathbf{u}(b, \lambda_\beta))\mathbf{v}(t, \lambda_\beta) \ . \tag{10-4.4}$$

In order to reveal the structure of $\mathbf{D}^{-1}$, let the relation

$$\mathbf{D}(\lambda) = \mathbf{H}(\lambda) \begin{pmatrix} 1 & 0 & \cdots & 0 & 0 \\ 0 & 1 & \cdots & 0 & 0 \\ \cdot & \cdot & \cdot & \cdot & \cdot \\ \cdot & \cdot & \cdot & \cdot & \cdot \\ \cdot & \cdot & \cdot & \cdot & \cdot \\ 0 & 0 & \cdots & 1 & 0 \\ 0 & 0 & \cdots & 0 & \lambda - \lambda_\beta \end{pmatrix}$$

define the matrix **H**. It is clear that **H** is analytic at λ_β and that $\mathbf{H}(\lambda_\beta) = \mathbf{I}$. Hence, $\mathbf{H}^{-1}(\lambda)$ exists and is analytic in some neighborhood of λ_β and

$$\mathbf{H}^{-1}(\lambda_\beta) = \mathbf{I} \ .$$

If $\lambda \neq \lambda_\beta$,

$$\mathbf{D}^{-1}(\lambda) = \begin{bmatrix} 1 & 0 & \cdots & 0 & 0 \\ 0 & 1 & \cdots & 0 & 0 \\ \cdot & \cdot & \cdot & \cdot & \cdot \\ \cdot & \cdot & \cdot & \cdot & \cdot \\ \cdot & \cdot & \cdot & \cdot & \cdot \\ 0 & 0 & \cdots & 1 & 0 \\ 0 & 0 & \cdots & 0 & \dfrac{1}{\lambda - \lambda_\beta} \end{bmatrix} \mathbf{H}^{-1}(\lambda) \ .$$

This implies that

$$\operatorname{Res}_{\lambda=\lambda_\beta} \mathbf{D}^{-1} = \begin{bmatrix} 0 & 0 & \cdots & 0 \\ 0 & 0 & \cdots & 0 \\ \cdot & \cdot & \cdot & \cdot \\ \cdot & \cdot & \cdot & \cdot \\ \cdot & \cdot & \cdot & \cdot \\ 0 & 0 & \cdots & 1 \end{bmatrix} \mathbf{I} = \mathbf{d}_n \tilde{\mathbf{d}}_n \ .$$

It follows that

$$\operatorname{Res}_{\lambda=\lambda_\beta} G(t, s, \lambda) = \begin{cases} \tilde{\mathbf{u}}(t, \lambda_\beta)\mathbf{d}_n\tilde{\mathbf{d}}_n \mathbf{W}^{[a]}\mathbf{K}(u(a))\mathbf{v}(s, \lambda_\beta) \ , & s < t \ , \\ -\tilde{\mathbf{u}}(t, \lambda_\beta)\mathbf{d}_n\tilde{\mathbf{d}}_n \mathbf{W}^{[b]}\mathbf{K}(u(b))\mathbf{v}(s, \lambda_\beta) \ , & s > t \ . \end{cases}$$

Using (10-4.2), (10-4.3), and (10-4.4), we may write this as

(10-4.5) $$\operatorname{Res}_{\lambda=\lambda_\beta} G(t, s, \lambda) = -u_\beta(t) v_\beta(s) \ .$$

If the order of integration is reversed on the left-hand side of relation (10-2.10), we get

$$\sum_{\beta=1}^{m} \alpha_\beta u_\beta(t) = f(t) + B_m(t) + A_m(t) \ ,$$

where

$$\alpha_\beta = \int_a^b f(s) v_\beta(s)\, ds = (f, v_\beta) \ .$$

The convergence of the formal expansion will be established, therefore, if we can show that $A_m(t)$ and $B_m(t)$ tend to zero for large values of m.

In order to show this, we need to obtain an explicit representation of Green's function. To this end, Section 10-5 is devoted to a description of asymptotic representations of solutions of the differential equation. These representations are used in Section 10-6 to determine the form of the characteristic function. The characteristic function and the asymptotic solutions are used in Section 10-7 to obtain a representation of Green's function and to determine some of its properties.

Exercises

1. If $\mathbf{P}$ is a square matrix of order n whose components are polynomials in $(\lambda-\lambda_\beta)$, prove that nonsingular matrices $\mathbf{C}_1$ and $\mathbf{C}_2$ exist such that

$$\mathbf{C}_2\mathbf{P}\mathbf{C}_1 = (\delta_{ij}p_j) \ ,$$

where p_j, $j = 1, 2, \ldots, n$, satisfy the conditions given in (10-4.1).

2. The matrix

$$\mathbf{P} = \begin{pmatrix} -\lambda-1 & -\lambda+1 \\ \lambda^2+1 & \lambda^2-1 \end{pmatrix}$$

is singular when $\lambda = 1$. Find $\mathbf{C}_1$ and $\mathbf{C}_2$ as described in Exercise 1 and express p_1 and p_2 as polynomials in $\lambda-1$.

10-5. ASYMPTOTIC SOLUTIONS

Let the operator L be defined by

$$Lu = u^{[n]} + p_1 u^{[n-1]} + \cdots + p_n u \ , \tag{10-5.1}$$

where p_i, $i = 1, 2, \ldots, n$, is indefinitely differentiable on the interval $[a, b]$. The assumption that $p_0 = 1$ is a convenience rather than an essential restriction, since we have previously required $p_0(t)$ to be nonzero on $[a, b]$. It was established in Chapter 5 that

$$Lu = \lambda u \tag{10-5.2}$$

has analytic solutions for every value of the parameter λ. For the subsequent developments, we need representations[3] of these solutions that reveal their dependence on the parameter and that are valid when $|\lambda|$ is large. The derivation of these representations is somewhat involved and is not given here. Nevertheless, the results are plausible since it is seen that the solutions approach the solutions of

$$u^{[n]} = \lambda u$$

as $|\lambda|$ approaches infinity.

We replace λ by ρ^n and write equation (10-5.2) as

$$Lu = \rho^n u \ . \tag{10-5.3}$$

This equation has a fundamental set of solutions $u_1, u_2, \ldots, u_n$, such that

$$u_i(t, \rho) = \tag{10-5.4}$$
$$= \exp[\rho\omega_i(t-a)]\left(1 + u_{i1}(t)\frac{1}{\rho} + u_{i2}(t)\frac{1}{\rho^2} + \cdots + u_{im}(t)\frac{1}{\rho^m} + E_i(t, \rho)\frac{1}{\rho^{m+1}}\right),$$

where m is an arbitrary positive integer; $\omega_1, \omega_2, \ldots, \omega_n$ are the n distinct nth roots of unity; each function $u_{ij}(t)$ is indefinitely differentiable; and each function $E_i(t, \rho)$ is indefinitely differentiable with respect to t and bounded and

[3] The representations used are those obtained by Birkhoff [1] and [2].

analytic in ρ if $|\rho|$ is large. The representation given in (10-5.4) is an *asymptotic expansion* of the solution u_i. It is convenient and suggestive to say that a function $f(t, \rho)$ is asymptotic to a polynomial in $1/\rho$ if

$$f(t, \rho) = \sum_{j=0}^{m} \alpha_j(t)\frac{1}{\rho^j} + E(t, \rho)\frac{1}{\rho^{m+1}} , \tag{10-5.5}$$

where $\alpha_j(t) \in C^\infty[a, b]$ and $E(t, \rho)$ is indefinitely differentiable with respect to t and bounded and analytic in ρ when $|\rho|$ is large. Thus, we can say that $u_i(t, \rho)$ is $\exp[\rho\omega_i(t-a)]$ multiplied by a function that is asymptotic to a polynomial in $1/\rho$. Also, the kth derivative, $(d^k/dt^k)u_i(t, \rho)$, can be described as $\rho^k \exp[\rho\omega_i(t-a)]$ multiplied by a function which is asymptotic to a polynomial in $1/\rho$.

If $\mathbf{u}$ is a fundamental vector for equation (10-5.3) and if its components are given by (10-5.4), then

$$\mathbf{K}(\mathbf{u}) = (\delta_{ij}\rho^{i-1})\mathbf{V}(\delta_{ij}\exp[\rho\omega_j(t-a)]) , \tag{10-5.6}$$

where each component of the matrix $\mathbf{V}$ is asymptotic to a polynomial in $1/\rho$. It can be verified (see Exercise 5 of Section 10-5) that the inverse Wronskian matrix is

$$\mathbf{K}^{-1}(\mathbf{u}) = (\delta_{ij}\exp[-\rho\omega_j(t-a)])\mathbf{V}^{-1}(\delta_{ij}\rho^{-[i-1]})) , \tag{10-5.7}$$

where the components of $\mathbf{V}^{-1}$ are asymptotic to polynomials in $1/\rho$.

If $\mathbf{v}$ is the vector whose components form the last column of $\mathbf{K}^{-1}(\mathbf{u})$, it is a fundamental vector for the adjoint equation and

$$\tilde{\mathbf{K}}(\mathbf{v})\mathbf{P}\mathbf{K}(\mathbf{u}) = \mathbf{I} ,$$

where $\mathbf{P}$ is the concomitant matrix associated with Lu. It is easily seen that the ith component of $\mathbf{v}$ has the form

$$v_i(t, \rho) = \rho^{-[n-1]}\exp[-\rho\omega_i(t-a)] \times \left(v_{i0}(t) + v_{i1}(t)\frac{1}{\rho} + \cdots + v_{im}(t)\frac{1}{\rho^m} + E_i(t, \rho)\frac{1}{\rho^{m+1}}\right) . \tag{10-5.8}$$

Exercises

1. If $f(t, \rho)$ and $g(t, \rho)$ are asymptotic to polynomials in $1/\rho$, and α and β are constants, show that $\alpha f(t, \rho) + \beta g(t, \rho)$ is asymptotic to a polynomial.

2. Prove that the product of two functions that are asymptotic to polynomials is asymptotic to a polynomial.

3. If in formula (10-5.5) $\alpha_0(t) \neq 0$ on $[a, b]$, prove that $1/f(t, \rho)$ is asymptotic to a polynomial.

4. Prove that the components of $\mathbf{V}^{-1}$ in formula (10-5.7) are asymptotic to polynomials in $1/\rho$.

10-6. CHARACTERISTIC FUNCTION AND EIGENVALUES

If $\mathbf{u}$ is the fundamental vector specified in the previous section, its Wronskian matrix is given by (10-5.6), and the corresponding characteristic matrix is

$$\mathbf{D} = \mathbf{W}^{[a]}(\delta_{ij}\rho^{i-1})\mathbf{V}(a, \rho)+\mathbf{W}^{[b]}(\delta_{ij}\rho^{i-1})\mathbf{V}(b, \rho)(\delta_{ij}\exp[\rho\omega_j(b-a)]) \ . \tag{10-6.1}$$

If the first term on the right-hand side of this relation is represented by $\mathbf{U}^{[1]}$ and the second by $\mathbf{U}^{[2]}$, we have

$$\mathbf{D} = \mathbf{U}^{[1]}+\mathbf{U}^{[2]} \ . \tag{10-6.2}$$

The determinant D of the matrix $\mathbf{D}$ is the characteristic function. A representation of this function may be obtained as follows. Let R be any subset of the first n natural numbers, and let $\bar{R}$ be the complement of R. Let $\mathbf{I}_{jj}$ be a matrix of zeros except for a unit element in the jth diagonal position (see Theorem 3-2.4). Then

$$\mathbf{U}^{[1]}\sum_{j\in\bar{R}}\mathbf{I}_{jj}+\mathbf{U}^{[2]}\sum_{j\in R}\mathbf{I}_{jj}$$

is seen to represent a matrix whose jth column is the jth column of $\mathbf{U}^{[1]}$ or the jth column of $\mathbf{U}^{[2]}$ according as j belongs to $\bar{R}$ or to R. It follows from an elementary property of determinants that

$$D = |\mathbf{D}| = \sum_{R\subset N_n}\left|\mathbf{U}^{[1]}\sum_{j\in\bar{R}}\mathbf{I}_{jj}+\mathbf{U}^{[2]}\sum_{j\in R}\mathbf{I}_{jj}\right| \ , \tag{10-6.3}$$

where N_n represents the set of the first n natural numbers and where R ranges over all the subsets of N_n including the null set and the whole set.

It is easily seen that each component of $\mathbf{U}^{[1]}$ is asymptotic to a polynomial in $1/\rho$ multiplied by some nonnegative power of ρ. Also, each component in the jth column of $\mathbf{U}^{[2]}$ is asymptotic to a polynomial in $1/\rho$ multiplied by some nonnegative power of ρ and by $\exp[\rho\omega_j(b-a)]$. If we use the symbols a_1 and a_2, respectively, as alternative labels for the points a and b, we may describe $\mathbf{U}^{[1]}$ and $\mathbf{U}^{[2]}$ in a single statement. That is, any component in the jth column of $\mathbf{U}^{[\mu]}$ is asymptotic to a polynomial in $1/\rho$ multiplied by a nonnegative power of ρ and by $\exp[\rho\omega_j(a_\mu-a)]$. Clearly, the exponential factor has the value 1 when $\mu = 1$. It follows that formula (10-6.3) may be rewritten as

$$D = \sum_{R\subset N_n}\rho^{\sigma_R}p_R\exp\left[\rho\sum_{\alpha=1}^{n}\omega_\alpha(a_{k_\alpha}-a)\right] \ , \tag{10-6.4}$$

where σ_R is a nonnegative integer; p_R is asymptotic to a polynomial in $1/\rho$; and

$$k_\alpha = \begin{cases} 1 \ , & \text{if } \alpha\in\bar{R} \ , \\ 2 \ , & \text{if } \alpha\in R \ . \end{cases}$$

By combining terms with the same exponential factor, we obtain[4]

$$D = \sum_{\alpha} \rho^{\sigma_\alpha} A_\alpha e^{\varrho \Omega_\alpha} , \tag{10-6.5}$$

where σ_α is a nonnegative integer, A_α is asymptotic to a polynomial in $1/\rho$, Ω_α is a complex constant, and α ranges over some finite index set. Let the set $\{\Omega_\alpha\}$ of constants which occur in formula (10-6.5) be designated by E_D. This set is a subset of the set

$$E = \left\{ \sum_{\alpha=1}^{n} \omega_\alpha (a_{k_\alpha} - a) \right\} , \tag{10-6.6}$$

where each k_α, $\alpha = 1, 2, \ldots, n$ may be arbitrarily chosen as 1 or 2.

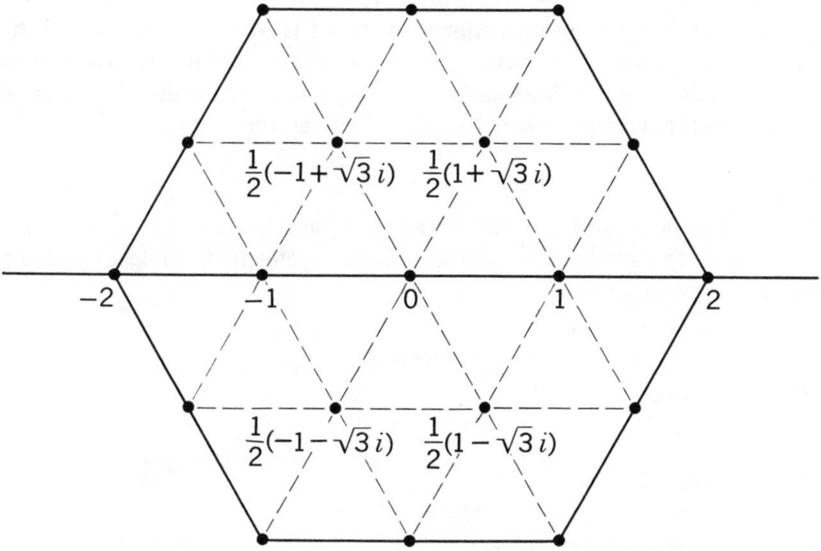

Figure 10-6.1

Let the elements of the set E be plotted on a complex plane, and let P be the closed convex polygonal region of minimum area which contains the points of E. Figure 10-6.1 shows the set E and the region P for the case $n = 6$ and $b - a = 1$. The boundary of P is a regular hexagon. The dotted lines in the interior of the region merely serve to emphasize the location of the points of E. In the general case the boundary of the region P is a regular polygon.

[4]Langer [29], page 173.

Definition 10-6.1. *The boundary problem is* ***regular*** *if the set E_D contains all the points of E that form vertices of the boundary of P.*

The characteristic function D, given by (10-6.5), is an exponential sum. We assume henceforth that we are dealing with a regular boundary problem. Consequently, the exponential sum D has at least two terms. This implies that it has an infinite set of zeros with no finite limit point.[5] The set of values of ρ which make D zero provide, through the relation $\lambda = \rho^n$, a corresponding set of values of λ. These are the eigenvalues of the boundary problem, and they are designated by $\{\lambda_j : j = 1, 2, \ldots\}$, where it is assumed that $|\lambda_1| \leqq |\lambda_2| \leqq |\lambda_3| \leqq \cdots$. In order to simplify the exposition we restrict our attention to boundary problems for which the closed contour Γ_m (see Section 10-1) can be chosen as a circle with its center at the origin of the λ-plane. Moreover, we assume that the circles have been drawn so that no one of them is closer than some specifiable distance to any eigenvalue.

Let $\{\hat{\Omega}_\beta\}$ designate those members of the set $\{\Omega_\alpha\}$ that are vertices of the boundary polygon of P. The corresponding exponents of ρ form a subset of $\{\sigma_\alpha\}$, and this subset is designated by $\{\hat{\sigma}_\beta\}$. If σ is the smallest member of $\{\hat{\sigma}_\beta\}$ and $\hat{\Omega}_\beta$ is any member of $\{\hat{\Omega}_\beta\}$, then the function

$$\rho^{-\sigma} D e^{-\varrho \hat{\Omega}_\beta} \qquad (10\text{-}6.7)$$

is bounded from zero when ρ^n is restricted to the contours of $\{\Gamma_j\}$. To prove this result or to establish the location of the eigenvalues would extend the present discussion unduly.[6]

Exercises

1. Find the roots of

$$e^{2\varrho} - 3e^{\varrho} + 2 = 0 \; .$$

2. Find the roots of

$$e^{\alpha\varrho} - \beta = 0 \; ,$$

where α and β are complex constants.

3. Find the roots of

$$\sum_{j=0}^{n} C_j (e^{\alpha\varrho})^j = 0 \; ,$$

where α and C_j are complex constants.

4. Plot the set E and the boundary of the region P for the cases $n = 5$ and $n = 8$.

5. Derive formula (10-6.3) from first principles.

[5] See Langer [28], page 213.

[6] The interested reader should consult Langer [29], pages 172–176, and the references cited therein.

10-7. GREEN'S FUNCTION

Using the fundamental vectors defined in Section 10-5, we have for Green's function

$$(10\text{-}7.1)\qquad G(t, s, \rho^n) = \begin{cases} \tilde{\mathbf{u}}(t, \rho)\mathbf{D}^{-1}\mathbf{U}^{[1]}\mathbf{v}(s, \rho)\ , & s < t\ , \\ -\tilde{\mathbf{u}}(t, \rho)\mathbf{D}^{-1}\mathbf{U}^{[2]}\mathbf{v}(s, \rho)\ , & s > t\ , \end{cases}$$

where $\mathbf{U}^{[1]}$ and $\mathbf{U}^{[2]}$ (defined in Section 10-6) are such that $\mathbf{D} = \mathbf{U}^{[1]} + \mathbf{U}^{[2]}$. In order to obtain an explicit expression for $\mathbf{D}^{-1}$, we note that the cofactor of the component in the jth row and ith column of $\mathbf{D}$ is given by $|\,\mathbf{D}\mathbf{I}^{ii} + \mathbf{I}_{ji}\,|$. Since this cofactor, divided by the determinant D, is the component in the ith row and jth column of $\mathbf{D}^{-1}$, we have

$$\mathbf{D}^{-1} = \frac{1}{D}(|\,\mathbf{D}\mathbf{I}^{ii} + \mathbf{I}_{ji}\,|)\ .$$

In anticipation of substituting this expression for $\mathbf{D}^{-1}$ into formula (10-7.1), we write

$$\mathbf{D}^{-1}\mathbf{U}^{[\mu]} = \frac{1}{D}\left(\sum_{k=1}^{n} |\,\mathbf{D}\mathbf{I}^{ii} + \mathbf{I}_{ki}\,|\, u_{kj}{}^{[\mu]}\right)$$

$$= \frac{1}{D}\left(\sum_{k=1}^{n} |\,\mathbf{D}\mathbf{I}^{ii} + u_{kj}{}^{[\mu]}\mathbf{I}_{ki}\,|\right)\ .$$

The general component of the matrix on the right-hand side of this relation is exhibited as the sum of n determinants. Since these determinants differ from each other only with respect to their ith columns, we may add the determinants by adding their ith columns. The sum of these is seen to be the jth column of $\mathbf{U}^{[\mu]}$. Hence,

$$\mathbf{D}^{-1}\mathbf{U}^{[\mu]} = \frac{1}{D}(|\,\mathbf{D}\mathbf{I}^{ii} + \mathbf{U}^{[\mu]}\mathbf{I}_{ji}\,|)\ .$$

The diagonal components of this matrix can be separated from the nondiagonal components by writing

$$(10\text{-}7.2)\quad \mathbf{D}^{-1}\mathbf{U}^{[\mu]} = \left(\frac{\delta_{ij}}{D}|\,\mathbf{D}\mathbf{I}^{ii} + \mathbf{U}^{[\mu]}\mathbf{I}_{ji}\,|\right) + \left(\frac{1-\delta_{ij}}{D}|\,\mathbf{D}\mathbf{I}^{ii} + \mathbf{U}^{[\mu]}\mathbf{I}_{ji}\,|\right)\ .$$

The first matrix on the right-hand side is represented by $\mathbf{H}^{[\mu]}$. Since it is a diagonal matrix, we may replace i by j and write

$$(10\text{-}7.3)\qquad \mathbf{H}^{[\mu]} = \left(\frac{\delta_{ij}}{D}|\,\mathbf{D}\mathbf{I}^{jj} + \mathbf{U}^{[\mu]}\mathbf{I}_{jj}\,|\right)\ .$$

The second matrix on the right-hand side of (10-7.2) is further decomposed as follows:

$$\left(\frac{1-\delta_{ij}}{D}\,|\,\mathbf{D}\mathbf{I}^{ii}+\mathbf{U}^{[\mu]}\mathbf{I}_{ji}\,|\right)=\left(\frac{1-\delta_{ij}}{D}\,|\,\mathbf{D}\mathbf{I}^{ii}\mathbf{I}^{jj}+\mathbf{D}\mathbf{I}_{jj}+\mathbf{U}^{[\mu]}\mathbf{I}_{ji}\,|\right)$$

$$=\left(\frac{1-\delta_{ij}}{D}\,|\,\mathbf{D}\mathbf{I}^{ii}\mathbf{I}^{jj}+(\mathbf{U}^{[1]}+\mathbf{U}^{[2]})\mathbf{I}_{jj}+\mathbf{U}^{[\mu]}\mathbf{I}_{ji}\,|\right)$$

$$=\mathbf{H}^{[\mu,1]}+\mathbf{H}^{[\mu,2]}\ ,$$

where

$$\text{(10-7.4)}\quad \mathbf{H}^{[\mu,\nu]}=\left(\frac{1-\delta_{ij}}{D}\,|\,\mathbf{D}\mathbf{I}^{ii}\mathbf{I}^{jj}+\mathbf{U}^{[\nu]}\mathbf{I}_{jj}+\mathbf{U}^{[\mu]}\mathbf{I}_{ji}|\right)\ ,\quad \nu=1,2\ .$$

If $\mu=\nu$, the ith column and the jth column of the determinant appearing in this formula are identical. It follows that $\mathbf{H}^{[\mu,\mu]}=\mathbf{0}$ and that

$$\mathbf{D}^{-1}\mathbf{U}^{[1]}=\mathbf{H}^{[1]}+\mathbf{H}^{[1,2]}\ ,$$

$$\mathbf{D}^{-1}\mathbf{U}^{[2]}=\mathbf{H}^{[2]}+\mathbf{H}^{[2,1]}\ .$$

Substituting into formula (10-7.1) from these relations, we have

$$G(t,s,\rho^n)=\begin{cases}\tilde{\mathbf{u}}(t,\rho)(\mathbf{H}^{[1]}+\mathbf{H}^{[1,2]})\mathbf{v}(s,\rho)\ , & s<t\ ,\\ -\tilde{\mathbf{u}}(t,\rho)(\mathbf{H}^{[2]}+\mathbf{H}^{[2,1]})\mathbf{v}(s,\rho)\ , & s>t\ .\end{cases}$$

If we define $G^{[\mu]}$ and $G^{[\mu,\nu]}$ by

$$\text{(10-7.5)}\qquad G^{[\mu]}(t,s,\rho^n)=\tilde{\mathbf{u}}(t,\rho)\mathbf{H}^{[\mu]}\mathbf{v}(s,\rho)\ ,\quad \mu=1,2,$$

$$\text{(10-7.6)}\quad G^{[\mu,\nu]}(t,s,\rho^n)=\tilde{\mathbf{u}}(t,\rho)\mathbf{H}^{[\mu,\nu]}\mathbf{v}(s,\rho)\ ,\quad \mu,\nu=1,2,\quad \mu\neq\nu\ ,$$

we may write

$$\text{(10-7.7)}\quad G(t,s,\rho^n)=\begin{cases}G^{[1]}(t,s,\rho^n)+G^{[1,2]}(t,s,\rho^n)\ , & s<t\ ,\\ -(G^{[2]}(t,s,\rho^n)+G^{[2,1]}(t,s,\rho^n))\ , & s>t\ .\end{cases}$$

At this point, it is clear that the character of Green's function is largely determined by the components of the matrices $\mathbf{H}^{[\mu]}$ and $\mathbf{H}^{[\mu,\nu]}$. These matrices are defined in formulas (10-7.3) and (10-7.4), and it only remains to interpret the definitions. The jth diagonal component of $\mathbf{H}^{[\mu]}$ is the quotient of two determinants. The denominator determinant is D, and the numerator determinant differs from D only in the composition of its jth column. Thus, recalling formula (10-6.4), where D is expressed as an exponential sum, we see that the numerator is also an exponential sum. Hence, the component, $h_{jj}^{[\mu]}$, is given by

$$h_{jj}^{[\mu]}=\frac{1}{D}\sum_{R\subset N_n-j}\rho^{\theta_{R;j}}h_{R;j}^{[\mu]}\exp\left\{\rho\left[\omega_j(a_\mu-a)+\sum_{\alpha=1,\,\alpha\neq j}^{n}\omega_\alpha(a_{k_\alpha}-a)\right]\right\}\ ,$$

where N_n-j is the set of the first n natural numbers with j deleted, and R ranges over all subsets of this set; $\theta_{R;j}$ is a nonnegative integer; $h_{R;j}^{[\mu]}$ is asymptotic to a polynomial in $1/\rho$; and

$$k_\alpha = \begin{cases} 1, & \text{if } \alpha \in \bar{R} , \\ 2, & \text{if } \alpha \in R . \end{cases}$$

Similarly, the component in the ith row and jth column of $\mathbf{H}^{[\mu,\nu]}$ is the quotient of two exponential sums. The denominator is again D, and we have

$$h_{ij}^{[\mu,\nu]} = \frac{1}{D} \sum_{R \subset N_n - i - j} \rho^{\theta_{R;ij}} h_{R;ij}^{[\mu,\nu]} \times \exp\left\{\rho\left[\omega_j(a_\mu - a) + \omega_j(a_\nu - a) + \sum_{\alpha=1,\, \alpha\neq i,j}^{n} \omega_\alpha(a_{k_\alpha} - a)\right]\right\} ,$$

where $N_n - i - j$ is the set of the first n natural numbers with i and j deleted, and R ranges over all subsets of this set; $\theta_{R;ij}$ is a nonnegative integer; $h_{R;ij}^{[\mu,\nu]}$ is asymptotic to a polynomial in $1/\rho$; and

$$k_\alpha = \begin{cases} 1, & \text{if } \alpha \in \bar{R} , \\ 2, & \text{if } \alpha \in R . \end{cases}$$

Formulas (10-7.5) and (10-7.6) show that $G^{[\mu]}$ and $G^{[\mu,\nu]}$ may be regarded as bilinear forms in the components of $\mathbf{u}$ and $\mathbf{v}$. Since $\mathbf{H}^{[\mu]}$ is a diagonal matrix, we have

$$G^{[\mu]}(t, s, \rho^n) = \sum_{j=1}^{n} h_{jj}^{[\mu]} u_j(t, \rho) v_j(s, \rho) .$$

Recalling the definition of u_i and v_i in (10-5.4) and (10-5.8), we infer that $G^{[\mu]}$ is a sum of terms of the form

$$\text{(10-7.8)} \qquad \frac{1}{D}\rho^{\theta_{R;j}-(n-1)} g_{R;j}^{[\mu]} \exp(\rho\phi_{R;j}^{[\mu]}) ,$$

where $g_{R;j}^{[\mu]}$ is asymptotic to a polynomial in $1/\rho$ and

$$\text{(10-7.9)} \qquad \phi_{R;j}^{[\mu]}(t, s) = \omega_j(t-a) - \omega_j(s-a) + \omega_j(a_\mu - a) + \sum_{\alpha=1,\, \alpha\neq j}^{n} \omega_\alpha(a_{k_\alpha} - a) .$$

Similarly, the function $G^{[\mu,\nu]}$ is given by

$$G^{[\mu,\nu]}(t, s, \rho^n) = \sum_{i,j=1,\, i\neq j}^{n} h_{ij}^{[\mu,\nu]} u_i(t, \rho) v_j(s, \rho) .$$

Therefore, $G^{[\mu,\nu]}$ is a sum of terms of the form

$$\text{(10-7.10)} \qquad \frac{1}{D}\rho^{\theta_{R;ij}-(n-1)} g_{R;ij}^{[\mu,\nu]} \exp[\rho\phi_{R;ij}^{[\mu,\nu]}] ,$$

where $g_{R;ij}^{[\mu,\nu]}$ is asymptotic to a polynomial in $1/\rho$ and

$$\text{(10-7.11)} \qquad \phi_{R;ij}^{[\mu,\nu]}(t, s) = \omega_i(t-a) - \omega_j(s-a) + \omega_j(a_\mu - a) + \omega_j(a_\nu - a) + \sum_{\alpha=1,\, \alpha\neq i,j}^{n} \omega_\alpha(a_{k_\alpha} - a).$$

In view of formula (10-7.7), we can now state that each term in the sum that constitutes Green's function has the form of either (10-7.8) or (10-7.10). Since we need to examine the value of Green's function when $|\rho|$ is large, it is useful to determine the relationship between the values of the ϕ-functions, defined by (10-7.9) and (10-7.11), and the members of the set E. To this end, we use

$$z = \phi(t, s) ,$$

where ϕ is a function defined by formula (10-7.9) or formula (10-7.11), to map the domain of Green's function into a complex z-plane. The convex polygonal region P (defined in Section 10-6) is plotted on the z-plane, and we show that the range of the mapping is contained in P. The domain of Green's function is the square region for which $a \leqq t \leqq b$, $a \leqq s \leqq b$, but the function has distinct definitions on the two halves into which the square is divided by the line $s = t$. These triangular halves form the domains for the mappings under consideration. In order to designate them it is convenient to use the symbol $[a_\mu, t]$ to represent the interval $[a, t]$ or $[t, b]$ according as $\mu = 1$ or $\mu = 2$.

Theorem 10-7.1. *The relation*

$$z = \phi_{R;j}{}^{[\mu]}(t, s) \ , \ \mu = 1, 2$$

where $t \in [a, b]$ *and* $s \in [a_\mu, t]$, *has a range which lies in* P.

PROOF. Substituting a_μ for s into formula (10-7.9), we have

$$\phi_{R;j}{}^{[\mu]}(t, a_\mu) = \omega_j(t-a) + \sum_{\alpha=1, \alpha \neq j}^{n} \omega_\alpha(a_{k_\alpha} - a) \ .$$

Recalling the definition of the set E (see formula (10-6.6)), we infer that $\phi_{R;j}{}^{[\mu]}(a, a_\mu)$ and $\phi_{R;j}{}^{[\mu]}(b, a_\mu)$ are both points of E. Since P is convex and ϕ is linear in t,

$$\phi_{R;j}{}^{[\mu]}(t, a_\mu) \in P \ ,$$

for all t in $[a, b]$. Substituting t for s into formula (10-7.9), we find that

$$\phi_{R;j}{}^{[\mu]}(t, t) \in P$$

for all t in $[a, b]$. Since P is convex and ϕ is linear in s,

$$\phi_{R;j}{}^{[\mu]}(t, s) \in P$$

if $t \in [a, b]$ and $s \in [a_\mu, t]$. This proves the theorem.

Theorem 10-7.2. *The relation*

$$z = \phi_{R;ij}{}^{[\mu,\nu]}(t, s) \ ,$$

$(\mu, \nu) = (1, 2)$ *or* $(2, 1)$, *where* $t \in [a, b]$ *and* $s \in [a_\mu, t]$, *has a range which lies in* P.

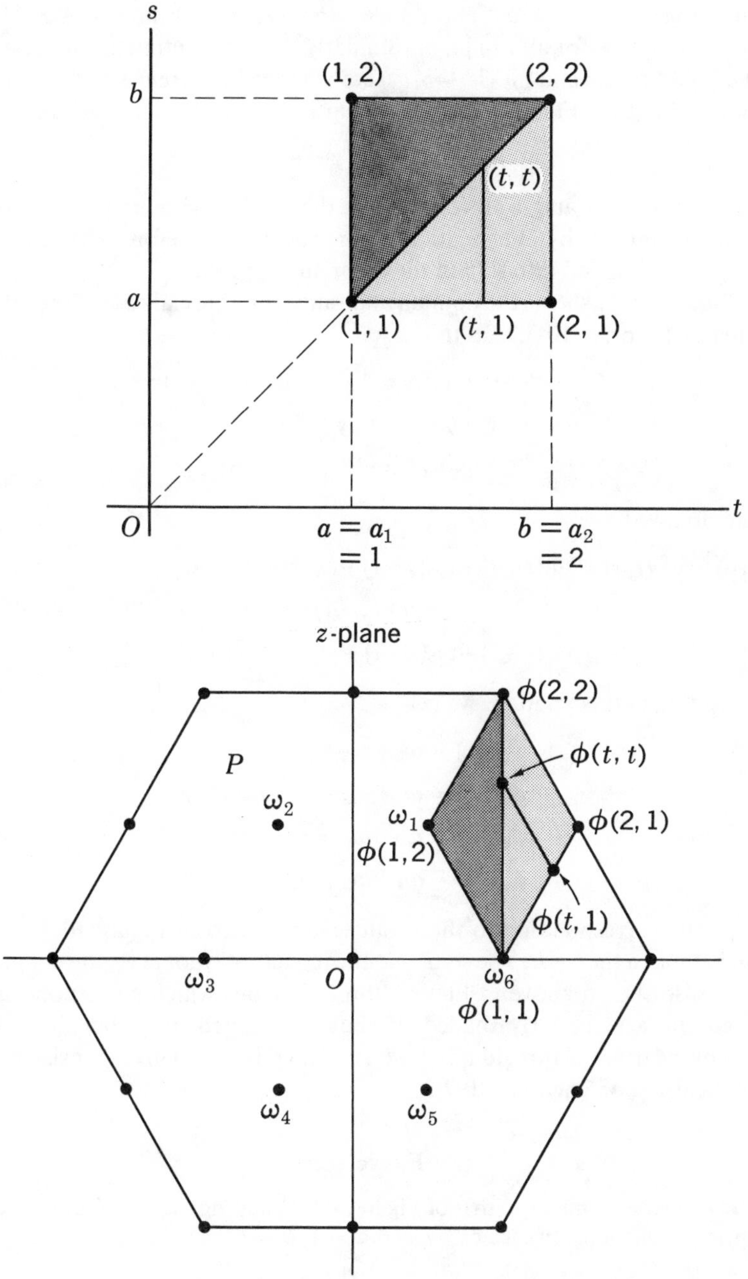
s
b
a
O
t
(1, 2)
(2, 2)
(t, t)
(1, 1)
(t, 1)
(2, 1)
a = a1
= 1
b = a2
= 2
z-plane
P
ω2
ω1
ϕ(1,2)
ϕ(2, 2)
ϕ(t, t)
ϕ(2, 1)
ϕ(t, 1)
ω3
O
ω6
ϕ(1, 1)
ω4
ω5

Figure 10-7.1

PROOF. Substituting a_μ for s, and a and b in turn for t, into formula (10-7.11), we find that $\phi_{R;ij}{}^{[\mu,\nu]}(a, a_\mu)$ and $\phi_{R;ij}{}^{[\mu,\nu]}(b, a_\mu)$ are both points of E. Hence, $\phi_{R;ij}{}^{[\mu,\nu]}(t, a_\mu) \in P$ for all t in $[a, b]$. Similarly, by substituting a_ν for s, we infer that $\phi_{R;ij}{}^{[\mu,\nu]}(a, a_\nu)$ and $\phi_{R;ij}{}^{[\mu,\nu]}(b, a_\nu)$ both belong to E. Hence, $\phi_{R;ij}{}^{[\mu,\nu]}(t, a_\nu) \in P$ for all t in $[a, b]$. Finally, since ϕ is linear in s,

$$\phi_{R;ij}{}^{[\mu,\nu]}(t, s) \in P \ ,$$

for all s between a_μ and a_ν. It follows that the whole square, $t \in [a, b]$, $s \in [a, b]$, is mapped into P by the relation. In particular, therefore, the triangular subregion is mapped into P, and the theorem is proved.

Figure 10-7.1 shows the domain and range for a special case of the relation treated in Theorem 10-7.2. In this case,

$$n = 6,\ a = 1,\ b = 2,\ \text{so that } b - a = 1;$$
$$\mu = 1,\ \nu = 2,\ i = 1,\ j = 5;$$
$$N_6 - i - j = \{2, 3, 4, 6\} \quad \text{and} \quad R = \{2, 6\} \ .$$

Therefore, we have

$$\begin{aligned}\phi_{\{2,6\};1,5}{}^{[1,2]}(t, s) &= \omega_1(t-1) - \omega_5(s-1) + \omega_1(1-1) + \omega_5(2-1) \\ &\quad + [\omega_2(2-1) + \omega_3(1-1) + \omega_4(1-1) + \omega_6(2-1)] \\ &= \omega_1(t-1) - \omega_5(s-1) + \omega_5 + \omega_2 + \omega_6 \ .\end{aligned}$$

Substituting in this relation, we get

$$\begin{aligned}\phi(1, 1) &= \omega_5 + \omega_2 + \omega_6 = \omega_6 \ , \\ \phi(2, 1) &= \omega_1 + \omega_5 + \omega_2 + \omega_6 = \omega_1 + \omega_6 \ , \\ \phi(1, 2) &= \omega_2 + \omega_6 = \omega_1 \ , \\ \phi(2, 2) &= \omega_1 + \omega_2 + \omega_6 \ .\end{aligned}$$

The points corresponding to these values are labeled in Figure 10-7.1, all of them belong to the set E. The set E and the regular polygonal region containing it were also shown above in Figure 10-6.1. Regions which correspond under the relation are similarly shaded. It should be noted in particular that the image of the triangular region, $t \in [a, b]$, $s \in [a, t]$, is in P. This is consistent with the conclusion of Theorem 10-7.2.

Exercises

1. Draw diagrams similar to that of Figure 10-7.1 showing the range for each of the following ϕ functions. In each case $n = 6$, $a = 1$, $b = 2$.

(a) $z = \phi_{\{4,5\};2,3}{}^{[1,2]}(t, s)$; (b) $z = \phi_{\{2\};1,4}{}^{[1,2]}(t, s)$;

(c) $z = \phi_{\{4,5\};2,3}{}^{[2,1]}(t, s)$; (d) $z = \phi_{\{4,5\};3}{}^{[1]}(t, s)$;

(e) $z = \phi_{\{2,6\};1}{}^{[2]}(t, s)$.

2. Plot the ranges of each of the following ϕ-functions for the case $n=4$, $a=1$, $b=2$.

(a) $z=\phi_{\{3,4\};2}{}^{[1]}(t,s)$; (b) $z=\phi_{\{1\};2}{}^{[2]}(t,s)$;

(c) $z=\phi_{\{2\};3,4}{}^{[1,2]}(t,s)$; (d) $z=\phi_{\{2\};1,3}{}^{[2,1]}(t,s)$.

3. Consider Green's function in Example 1 of Section 10-3 and use it to illustrate the developments of Section 10-7.

4. Consider the boundary problem

$$-u''=\lambda u\ ,$$

$$u(0)+u'(\pi)=0\ ,\quad u'(0)+u(\pi)=0\ .$$

(a) Find a characteristic function and determine the eigenvalues. (b) Find Green's function and analyze it in the manner indicated in Section 10-7.

10-8. CONVERGENCE OF THE FORMAL EXPANSION

In this section, we present an outline of a proof of convergence. Some of the details which have been omitted are incorporated in the Exercises at the end of the section. The omission of some of the details should make it easier to appreciate the essence of the development. We may again remind the reader that we have no interest in developing a theory that includes a major portion of the specialized results which have been obtained in this area.

A brief review of some of the above developments serves to place the final result in perspective. Relation (10-2.10) is fundamental and is repeated here for convenience. It is

$$\text{(10-8.1)}\qquad -\frac{1}{2\pi i}\int_{\Gamma_m}\int_a^b G(t,s,\lambda)f(s)\,ds\,d\lambda=f(t)+B_m(t)+A_m(t)\ ,$$

where

$$\text{(10-8.2)}\qquad A_m(t)=-\frac{1}{2\pi i}\int_{\Gamma_m}\frac{1}{\lambda}\int_a^b G(t,s,\lambda)Lf(s)\,ds\,d\lambda\ ,$$

$$B_m(t)=-\frac{1}{2\pi i}\int_{\Gamma_m}\frac{1}{\lambda}\tilde{\mathbf{a}}(t,\lambda)[\mathbf{W}^{[a]}\mathbf{k}(f(a))+\mathbf{W}^{[b]}\mathbf{k}(f(b))]\,d\lambda\ .$$

The contour integral on the left-hand side of relation (10-8.1) yields the sum of the first m residues of the integrand. These are contributed by the residues of Green's function, and it was shown in Section 10-4 that

$$\mathrm{Res}_{\lambda=\lambda_j}G(t,s,\lambda)=-u_j(t)v_j(s)\ .$$

This implies that the left-hand side of (10-8.1) is equal to

$$\sum_{j=1}^{m}\left[\int_a^b f(s)v_j(s)\,ds\right]u_j(t)$$

which is the mth partial sum of the formal expansion of f. We limit our attention to a function f which satisfies the homogeneous boundary conditions and, for such functions, we recall that $B_m(t) = 0$. Thus, if

$$\alpha_j = \int_a^b f(s) v_j(s)\, ds \ ,$$

the relation (10-8.1) becomes

$$\sum_{j=1}^{m} \alpha_j u_j(t) = f(t) + A_m(t) \ .$$

Consequently, if we can show that

$$\lim_{m\to\infty} A_m(t) = 0 \ ,$$

uniformly in t, we shall have established the uniform convergence of the formal series to $f(t)$.

If in formula (10-8.2) we let $\lambda = \rho^n$, we get

(10-8.3) $$A_m(t) = -\frac{n}{2\pi i}\int_{C_m} \frac{1}{\rho} \int_a^b G(t, s, \rho^n) Lf(s)\, ds\, d\rho \ ,$$

where C_m is the image of Γ_m under the transformation. Expressions (10-7.8) and (10-7.10) reveal that Green's function is a sum of terms of the form

(10-8.4) $$\frac{1}{D}\rho^\theta g \exp[\rho\phi] \ ,$$

where θ is an integer (positive, negative, or zero), g is asymptotic to a polynomial in $1/\rho$, and ϕ is given by (10-7.9) or (10-7.11). Since D is a sum of terms of the form [see formula (10-6.5)]

$$\rho^{\sigma_\alpha} A_\alpha \exp[\rho\Omega_\alpha] \ ,$$

we see that G is a quotient of two exponential sums. The comparison of $\rho\phi$ and $\rho\Omega_\alpha$ is therefore a matter of prime importance. The foundation for this comparison was laid in Section 10-7 where it was found that

(10-8.5) $$z = \phi(t, s)$$

maps a half domain of Green's function into the region P (see Figure 10-7.1). For any complex number ρ, the relation

(10-8.6) $$\zeta = \rho z$$

maps the image plane of relation (10-8.5) into a ζ-plane. This mapping magnifies any configuration in the z-plane by a factor $|\rho|$ and rotates it through an angle $\arg\rho$ (see Figure 10-8.1). Hence, it maps the region P into a polygonal region P' with vertices $\{\rho\hat{\Omega}_\beta\}$. Also, it maps the range Q of relation (10-8.5) into a region Q' which lies in P'. For each value of ρ, some vertex of P' has a maximum real part. That is to say, some vertex, which we designate by $\rho\hat{\Omega}_{\beta_1}$, has the property that

$$\operatorname{Re}(\rho\hat{\Omega}_{\beta_1}) \geqq \operatorname{Re}(\rho\hat{\Omega}_{\beta}) \ , \quad \beta = 1, 2, \ldots, k \ ,$$

where k is the number of vertices of P'. The vertex in question retains this distinguishing property for every value of ρ that lies in some sector S_1 of the ρ-plane (see Figure 10-8.1). The whole ρ-plane is covered by k of these sectors, and each sector is associated with a vertex of P.

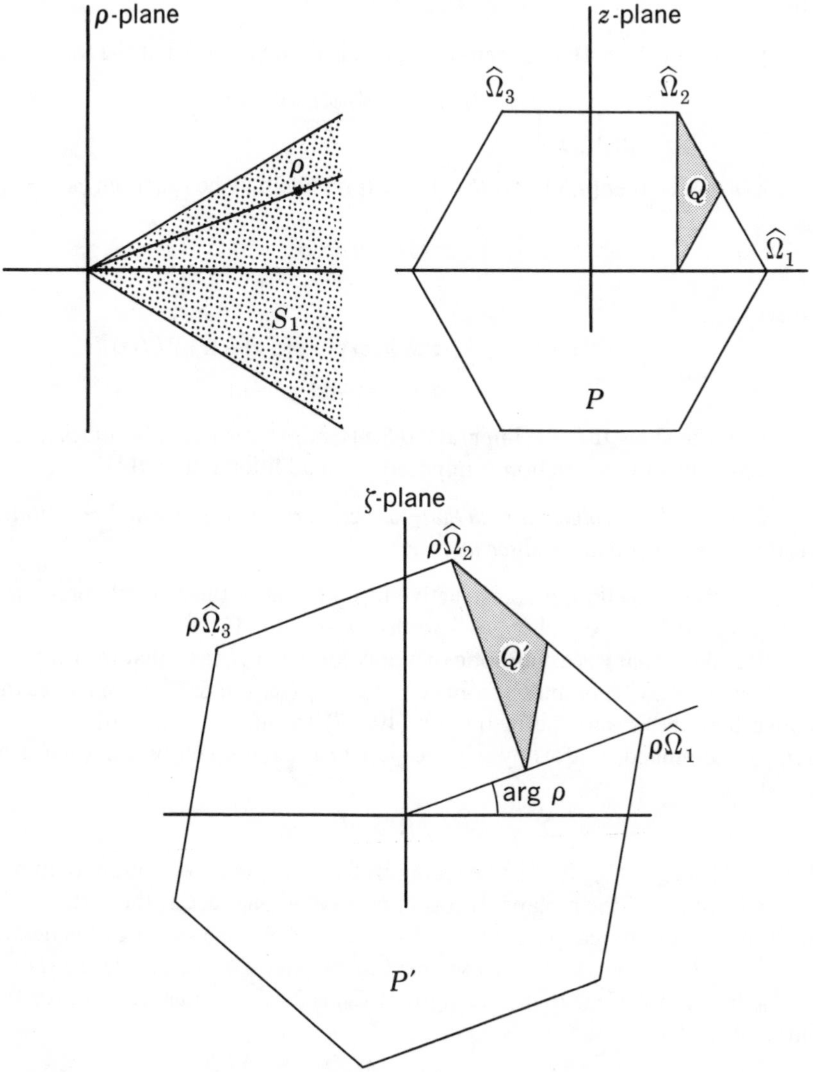

Figure 10-8.1

The composition of (10-8.5) and (10-8.6) yields

$$\zeta = \rho\phi(t, s)$$

which maps a half domain of Green's function into the region Q'. It follows that

$$\mathrm{Re}(\rho\phi(t, s)) \leqq \mathrm{Re}(\rho\hat{\Omega}_{\beta_1})$$

for any ρ in S_1 and for any (t, s) in the appropriate half domain of Green's function. This implies that

$$(10\text{-}8.7) \qquad |\exp[\rho(\phi(t, s) - \hat{\Omega}_{\beta_1})]| \leqq 1 \ .$$

In view of (10-8.4), it is seen that $A_m(t)$ is a sum of terms of the form

$$-\frac{n}{2\pi i}\int_{C_m}\frac{1}{\rho}\int_c^d \frac{\rho^\theta g(t, s, \rho)\exp[\rho\phi(t, s)]Lf(s)}{D}\,ds\,d\rho \ ,$$

where (c, d) is either (a, t) or (t, b). This expression may be rewritten as

$$(10\text{-}8.8) \qquad \int_{C_m} \rho^{-2} J(t, \rho)\,d\rho \ ,$$

where

$$J(t, \rho) = \frac{-n}{2\pi i}\int_c^d \frac{\rho^{\theta-\sigma+1} g(t, s, \rho)\exp[\rho(\phi(t, s) - \hat{\Omega}_{\beta_1})]Lf(s)\,ds}{\rho^{-\sigma} D\exp[-\rho\hat{\Omega}_{\beta_1}]} \ .$$

We intend to show that the integral (10-8.8) tends to zero as m becomes large.

The following restriction is imposed as an additional hypothesis.

The boundary problem is such that, for each term in the sum which constitutes $A_m(t)$, $\theta - \sigma + 1$ *is a nonpositive integer.*

In this connection, it is instructive to note that in the example presented in Section 10-3, $\sigma = 0$ and $\theta = -1$ so that $\theta - \sigma + 1 = 0$.

Recalling that g is asymptotic to a polynomial in $1/\rho$ and that the function $\rho^{-\sigma} D\exp[-\rho\hat{\Omega}_{\beta_1}]$ is bounded from zero if $\rho \in C_m$ (see (10-6.7)), we may use the above hypothesis and the inequality (10-8.7) to infer that the integrand of $J(t, \rho)$ is bounded, uniformly with respect to t. Consequently, for some real constant M

$$|J(t, \rho)| \leqq M \ ,$$

if $t \in [a, b]$ and $\rho \in C_m$. It must be recognized that C_m may be in more than one of the k sectors of the ρ-plane. If it is in more than one sector, the vertex of P' with the maximum real part changes as ρ passes from one sector to the next.

Since Γ_m is a circle, C_m is a segment of a circle. If we designate the radius of C_m by r_m, it is clear that the length of C_m is $2\pi r_m/n$. Thus we have for the integral (10-8.8)

$$\left|\int_{C_m} \rho^{-2} J(t, \rho)\,d\rho\right| \leqq \frac{M}{{r_m}^2}\cdot\frac{2\pi r_m}{n} = \frac{2\pi M}{n r_m} \ .$$

Since

$$\lim_{m\to\infty} r_m = \infty \ ,$$

the integral tends to zero as m becomes large. It follows immediately that

$$\lim_{m\to\infty} |A_m(t)| = 0 \ ,$$

uniformly with respect to t. Therefore, the formal expansion of f converges uniformly to $f(t)$ on $[a, b]$.

Exercises

1. Draw a graph of the polygonal region P for the cases $n = 2, 3, 4, 5$.

2. Show that P is an n-gon or a $2n$-gon according as n is even or odd.

3. If ρ is restricted to the appropriate sector of the ρ-plane, show that

$$\lim_{|\rho|\to\infty} \exp[\rho(\phi(t,s) - \hat{\Omega}_{\beta_1})] = 0$$

when s is bounded away from a, b, and t.

4. Use the result of Exercise 3 to establish convergence of the formal expansion for the case where $\theta = \sigma$.

5. Show that the formal expansion converges to $f(t)$ on the open interval (a, b) when the requirement that f should satisfy the boundary conditions is removed.

Bibliography

1. Birkhoff, G.D., "On the Asymptotic Character of the Solutions of Certain Linear Differential Equations Containing a Parameter," *Transactions of the American Mathematical Society*, Vol. 9 (1908), pp. 219–231.

2. Birkhoff, G.D., "Boundary Value and Expansion Problems of Ordinary Linear Differential Equations," *Transactions of the American Mathematical Society*, Vol. 9 (1908), pp. 373–395.

3. Birkhoff, G.D., and Langer, R.E., "The Boundary Problems and Developments Associated with a System of Ordinary Differential Equations of the First Order," *Proceedings of the American Academy of Arts and Sciences*, Vol. 58, No. 2 (1923), pp. 51–128.

4. Birkhoff, G., and Rota, G., "On the Completeness of Sturm-Liouville Expansions," *American Mathematical Monthly*, Vol. 67 (1960), pp. 835–841.

5. Birkhoff, G., and Rota, G. *Ordinary Differential Equations*, Boston, Ginn and Company, 1962.

6. Bôcher, M., *Leçons sur les Méthodes de Sturm*, Paris, Gauthier-Villars, 1917.

7. Bôcher, M., *Introduction to Higher Algebra*, New York, The MacMillan Company, 1936.

8. Brand, L., "The Companion Matrix and its Properties," *American Mathematical Monthly*, Vol. 71 (1964), pp. 629–634.

9. Buck, R.C., *Advanced Calculus*, 2nd ed., New York, McGraw-Hill Book Company, Inc., 1965.

10. Cater, S., "An Elementary Development of the Jordan Canonical Form," *American Mathematical Monthly*, Vol. 69 (1962), pp. 391–393.

11. Coddington, E.A., and Levinson, N., *Theory of Ordinary Differential Equations*, New York, McGraw-Hill Book Company, Inc., 1955.

12. Cole, R.H., "Relations between Moments of Order Statistics," *Annals of Mathematical Statistics*, Vol. 22 (1951), pp. 308–310.

13. Cole, R.H., "General Boundary Conditions for an Ordinary Linear Differential System," *Transactions of the American Mathematical Society*, Vol. 111 (1964), pp. 521–550.

14. Cole, R.H., "The Two-Point Boundary Problem," *American Mathematical Monthly*, Vol. 72 (1965), pp. 701–711.

15. Curtis, C.W., *Linear Algebra*, Boston, Allyn and Bacon, Inc., 1963.

16. Duff, G.F.D., and Naylor, D., *Differential Equations of Applied Mathematics*, New York, John Wiley & Sons, Inc., 1966.

17. Ficken, F.A., "Some Uses of Linear Spaces in Analysis," *American Mathematical Monthly*, Vol. 66 (1959), pp. 259–275.

18. Gandhi, J.M., "Advanced Problems," *American Mathematical Monthly*, Vol. 72, p. 1135 (1965).

19. Golomb, M., "An Algebraic Method in Differential Equations," *American Mathematical Monthly*, Vol. 72 (1965), pp. 1107–1110.

20. Greenspan, D., *Theory and Solution of Ordinary Differential Equations*, New York, The MacMillan Company, 1960.

21. Halmos, P.R., *Finite-Dimensional Vector Spaces*, 2nd ed., New York, D. Van Nostrand Company, Inc., 1958.

22. Halmos, P.R., "What does the Spectral Theorem Say?," *American Mathematical Monthly*, Vol. 70 (1963), pp. 241–247.

23. Hartman, P., *Ordinary Differential Equations*, New York, John Wiley & Sons, Inc., 1964.

24. Hochstadt, H., *Differential Equations*, New York, Holt, Rinehart and Winston, Inc., 1964.

25. Hoffman, K., and Kunze, R., *Linear Algebra*, Englewood Cliffs, N.J., Prentice-Hall, Inc., 1961.

26. Ince, E.L., *Ordinary Differential Equations*, London, Longmans, Green and Co., Ltd., 1927.

27. Kreider, L., Kuller, R., Osterberg, D., and Perkins, F., *An Introduction to Linear Analysis*, Reading, Mass., Addison-Wesley Publishing Company, Inc., 1966.

28. Langer, R.E., "On the Zeros of Exponential Sums and Integrals," *Bulletin of the American Mathematical Society*, Vol. 37 (1931), pp. 213–239.

29. Langer, R.E., "The Boundary Problem of an Ordinary Linear Differential System in the Complex Domain," *Transactions of the American Mathematical Society*, Vol. 46 (1939), pp. 151–190.

30. Langer, R.E., "Fourier's Series, the Genesis and Evolution of a Theory," *American Mathematical Monthly*, Vol. 54 (1947), Supplement, No. 1 Herbert Ellsworth Slaught Memorial Papers.

31. Langer, R.E., *Ordinary Differential Equations*, New York, John Wiley & Sons, Inc., 1954.

32. Lefschetz, S., *Differential Equations: Geometric Theory*, 2nd ed., New York, Interscience Publishers, Inc., 1957.

33. Lorch, E.R., "The Spectral Theorem," *Studies in Modern Analysis*, Buffalo, The Mathematical Association of America, 1962.

34. Lorch, E. R., *Spectral Theory*, New York, Oxford University Press, Inc., 1962.

35. Miller, K.S., *Linear Differential Equations in the Real Domain*, New York, W.W. Norton & Company, Inc., 1963.

36. Nering, E. D., *Linear Algebra and Matrix Theory*, New York, John Wiley & Sons, Inc., 1963.

37. Olmsted, J. M. H., *Intermediate Analysis*, New York, Appleton-Century-Crofts, 1956.

38. Olmsted, J. M. H., "Completeness and Parseval's Equation," *American Mathematical Monthly*, Vol. 65 (1958), pp. 343–345.

39. Pontryagin, L. S., *Ordinary Differential Equations*, Reading, Mass., Addison-Wesley Publishing Company, Inc., 1962.

40. Putzer, E. J., "Avoiding the Jordan Canonical Form in the Discussion of Linear Systems with Constant Coefficients," *American Mathematical Monthly*, Vol. 73 (1966), pp. 2–7.

41. Riesz, F., and Sz.-Nagy, B., *Functional Analysis*, New York, Frederick Ungar Publishing Co., 1955.

42. Riordan, J., "Inverse Relations and Combinatorial Identities," *American Mathematical Monthly*, Vol. 7 (1964), pp. 485–489.

43. Rudin, W., *Principles of Mathematical Analysis*, New York, McGraw-Hill Book Company, Inc., 1953.

44. Strauss, A., "Continuous Dependence of Solutions of Ordinary Differential Equations," *American Mathematical Monthly*, Vol. 71 (1964), pp. 649–652.

45. Struble, R. A., *Nonlinear Differential Equations*, New York, McGraw-Hill Book Company, Inc., 1962.

46. Sz.-Nagy, B., *Introduction to Real Functions and Orthogonal Expansions*, New York, Oxford University Press, Inc., 1965.

47. Taylor, A. E., *Introduction to Functional Analysis*, New York, John Wiley & Sons, Inc., 1963.

48. Titchmarsh, E. C., *Eigenfunction Expansions Associated with Second-Order Differential Equations*, Part 1, 2nd ed., Oxford, Clarendon Press, 1962; Part 2, 1958.

49. Tricomi, F. G., *Differential Equations*, Glasgow, Blackie & Son, Ltd., 1961.

50. Wallach, S., "A Simple Derivation of Jordan Canonical Matrices over Arbitrary Fields," *American Mathematical Monthly*, Vol. 72 (1965), pp. 614–618.

51. Yosida, K., *Lectures on Differential and Integral Equations*, New York, Interscience Publisher, Inc., 1960.

Index